BETWEEN
HEAVEN
&
CHARING
CROSS

BETWEEN HEAVEN & CHARING CROSS

A true story

of interworld rescue

by Jules Hillyar

Matador
9 Priory Business Park,
Wistow Road, Kibworth Beauchamp,
Leicestershire. LE8 0RX
Tel: (+44) 116 279 2299
Fax: (+44) 116 279 2277
Email: books@troubador.co.uk
Web: www.troubador.co.uk/matador

ISBN 978 1780884 516

British Library Cataloguing in Publication Data.
A catalogue record for this book is available from the British Library.

Typeset in 12pt Aldine401 BT Roman by Troubador Publishing Ltd, Leicester, UK
Printed and bound in the UK by TJ International, Padstow, Cornwall

Matador is an imprint of Troubador Publishing Ltd

*I dedicate this book to Valerie Mackenzie,
without whose participation, notes
and recordings it would never have
been possible.*

*Front cover picture
specially painted
by Valerie Sadler
of Rusthall*

What man's mind can conceive,
man's character must learn to control.
Then he may go forward into light.

Edison.

CONTENTS

VOLUME ONE

AUTHOR'S INTRODUCTION

The true story I have to tell is unusual even within its own genre. For instance if one accepts that The Seven were discarnate, having survived physical death, then they were certainly not recent arrivals trying to prove their case or report on the afterlife. Nor could they be called channelled teachers or guides. They were a group of young men who as part of their spiritual growth chose to rescue those trapped between their world and ours, and who needed the back-up of a team on earth. "You push and we'll pull!" neatly summarized it. Our recording of that work was intrinsic to their purpose.

But intrinsic for us was our unique adventure with them as individuals, operating one must add through a reluctant medium: the cross-currents of relationship over issues that arose, the doubts and dilemmas, the merging of interests and clash of viewpoints, the multifarious portrait of different worlds thrown strangely together by their coming to a village house in Kent.

Over forty years have passed since the affair first wrought its profound effect on me as a young adult, and still its reverberations filter up to play on my heart and mind. The weight of personal circumstances, plus the cooling-off period required to look back honestly and maturely, have impeded attempts to weave a just narrative. I kept at it however because The Seven's purpose was linked with my own, one which in 1964 had spirited me away from boarding school.

Eight years later that link with their purpose saw me at Ashdene as advisor to the earth team. Quite how a rather distrait, indolent youth came to be so spirited, and on what basis such advice was offered through 1972, curious or careful readers may wish to make preliminary note – for my upbringing supplied no signpost. Father was an executive on Farmer's Weekly and a prolific writer on antiques who labelled himself an agnostic, whilst ex-schoolmistress Mother took pride in her devout atheism. My two elder sisters appeared noncommittal, their baptism and weddings being our sole church attendance. Psychic research was unknown to me, and religion was equated with theology whose picture nullified both. Once, from our driveway, my thought had lifted to the empty sky: "where could any God or afterlife possibly be?"

I was only good at spelling and standard English, now and then drawn to ghost stories in semi-conscious search of something never found in them. My basic education in the three R's was more or less complete by preparatory school, whereupon academic subjects drifted meaninglessly over my head. They dulled the edge of learning, had no vital reality in my experience, and would never be needed in life. Instead I daydreamed of boyish hobbies: guns, soap-box carts, my old car on its orchard track, or of hideouts in the woodland round our Sussex country home. Uninvolved with the family, steering clear of clubs and teams, shirking eleven-plus and common entrance exams, I romped about with my two Labradors heedless of the future, sensitive within my island universe.

But during adolescence at Embley Park, a minor public school near Romsey in Hampshire, the focus dramatically changed. Embley had been Florence Nightingale's mansion wherein tales continued to abound of her ghost walking the dormitories: a marked rustle of Victorian skirts, seated pressure on one boy's bed enough to terrify him witless, and many more beside. For the first time I was facing the concept of such phenomena under the same roof. My mind sprang instantly alive with curiosity. Awe and wonder transfigured classroom dreams, eager for knowledge. If she and others survived, what sort of life were they living – and where?

"Interest", wrote Clarice Toyne, "is the sharpener of all effort, interest and a sense of ardency, joy, high adventure". So excited was I by this unknown territory that lack of result in nightly vigils only strengthened my determination to explore by other means. When no help was found in the school library, old volumes on psychical research were bought cheaply from a local secondhand bookshop. Voracious reading followed. The extensive work of prominent scientists first taxed then exercised my awoken young brain, while their conclusions in favour of survival heartened an intuitive sense of firm ground ahead. Summer O-levels were ignored, deficiency at most of them signing me up to another school year. Autumn term however brought a much relished opportunity. Schoolfriend John Bradshaw had returned from his holiday with the fad of the glass and alphabet seance.

We formed several associates around us in the boot-cellar, mistakenly thought to be a safe haven. Assumed discarnate communicants were rife, each challenged by John to 'kiss the crucifix' – which test meant their moving the glass up against his pendant on the table. Whether the wide range of respondents accepted or not, most nights were shot through with dramatic incident. Unaccounted smashing of the glass, partial materialisations or poltergeist activity made impersonators irrelevant and cheating chums flee. The latter brought back a barrage of persecution which hounded our modest number from cellar to cellar, once turning a hose on us. By then, quieter venues were an extra imperative since communication itself had become more gentle and rarefied – one might say almost reliable.

There was still no sign of Miss Nightingale, a fact I hardly noticed in trying to evaluate signs of anyone else. Strict scientific evidence of the kind I studied was out of the question here, so not being credulous my earnest desire for truth resorted to the country-boy's own gut-feeling within each session. It may have been this which developed into what was later identified as 'clairsentience', for whoever was moving that glass I now began to get the definite sensation of three benign people present, standing behind us like sentinels.

Acute awareness of them, which felt too susceptible to voice, shook me greatly. I remember coming up afresh from our cellar that night, up into the bright main hallway to find myself conceptually in two worlds. Occupying the same space another life coexisted, unseen, unknown, unrecognised by the oblivious faces that passed to and fro. Injustice reared in my heart, a panoramic wrong that I must put right, an ignorance that must be primed by fuller knowledge than school confines allowed.

As sentience and enthusiasm grew apace, so did my secret firmness of purpose. The device of the glass now looked a child's game, ever subject to impish molestation and ridicule which trampled through this private, sacred communion of mine. I yearned for latitude, for scope to learn, explore, experiment, share the tremendous news. A decision was imminent. Unsuspected by friends because unborn in me as yet, it was triggered impromptu one night in November 1964. The glass suddenly spelled out that someone present was about to leave Embley for good.

When mid-term surprise asked who was meant, the thing jerked strongly up to me. At once its wearisome, questionable means – incarnate or discarnate – became of no account. Amorphous aim was precipitated into resolution. From that moment to the furtive packing of sandwiches afterward, nothing is remembered except disclosure of intent to John Bradshaw. The next morning, by moonlight at exactly 4am, my raincoated figure strode out of those school gates ambiguously "for good".

Full of romantic, innocent zeal, I aimed to throw in my lot with the Spiritualist organisation – knowing only them so far out of a vast field. But because on second thoughts they were unlikely to embrace a runaway sixteen-year-old at that or any hour I hitched home to Sussex where the faces of puzzled parents behove me to another, half-true cause for flight. Their remedy of a tutorial college to retake GCE, unperceived hotbed of pot-smoking radicals in Tunbridge Wells, was my offbeat introduction to town life and first base of the actual course in mind. Soon, membership of the local Spiritualist Church brought wider access, through its library of claimed after death material, to my chosen field of study – covertly pursued at the Tutors where also self-experiment with out-of-body states put me on a new "high" far above that of cannabis. By 1965, as mounting insight took rise from comparison of accounts, the education which I had sought – and now inwardly recognised – was taking root.

What initially took root of course was that claimed after death material, and here I must make myself clear in explaining one part of my provenance at Ashdene. It was not based on the platform image of discarnate communication, or on the kind of seances staged by ignorant screenwriters for dramatic effect and which I never came across in life. During the 20th century there emerged a much more serious, well-documented mass of communications via sensitives of high calibre, and on the whole these have remained unknown to the public. Paul Beard played a significant role amongst researchers who examined them closely. He was a member of the Society for Psychical Research for 25 years, and for 16 years a much respected President of the College of Psychic Studies in London with wide experience of the field's many aspects. In his book Living On – a study of altering consciousness after death, he puts my point with greater authority than mine:

"The volume and quality of psychical research carried out over the last hundred years by scientifically qualified minds is not yet generally recognised. It is too easily assumed that material which relates to posthumous communications is largely confined to the ramblings of uneducated mediums, and to listeners whose minds have been disturbed and made credulous by grief with a consequent loss of all critical faculty. This is an erroneous and unrealistic view. The actual situation is otherwise".

When I grew to appreciate the volume and the quality to which he refers it struck me that if world literature had been publicly treated the same way then our great classics would not be generally recognised either. We would only know of pulp literature. Further on, Beard adds: "Post mortem accounts are often considered as no more than rosy wish-fulfilment narratives, as brightly coloured as a travel brochure. Some accounts are of this kind, but quite a different picture emerges when more serious communications are examined".

Realising this early on I still analysed the whole spectrum of published material, not wanting to miss a thing. Various levels of discarnate experience were compared in detail, both among themselves and with out-of-body accounts, near-death glimpses, senior discarnate teaching, and independent clairvoyant observation. Then I discovered that Dr Robert Crookall had done so in a scientifically methodical series of books starting with The Supreme Adventure, and these became my textbooks for a long period. Nor were mediumistic issues overlooked – the complex difficulties of transmission and reception, the issue of evidence, cross-correspondence tests, super ESP, the trance personality, subjective factors, multi-personality, and other matters ably sifted in books like Beard's Survival of Death.

After a year with the Spiritualists I sided instead with the more cautious, incisive angle of the College of Psychic Studies. My other-world fascination had reached the point of discerning, via the accounts, the nature of that self in us which is non-physical *now*, trying to sieve what we are without physical camouflage dimming it down, and what of important relevance most endures out of our earthly values. Spiritualists on the other hand, rather than front themselves with discarnate teachers' view of our evolution and value fulfilment, for me concentrated too much upon so-called proof of Uncle Fred's mundane continuity. I thence laid all blame at their door for perpetrating a shallow, ersatz veneer which screened off public awareness from the true situation.

If unfair of me, it was the kind of oversimplistic, crime-against-humanity stand perhaps forgivable at age 17. My move out of the family home into an attic bedsit at the Tutors, where exam time slipped away unattended beneath psychical study, was the launch pad for years adrift in collation of a broader context. It wasn't any search after life's meaning as such, just the innocent following of my own star. There was I, a callow country lad emotionally young for his years, with little but the next world on his brain, finding himself amid the world's rank scepticism. Aspirants on the spiritual path, which I was not, say that one should keep one's feet firmly on the ground and head well above the clouds, be in the world yet not of it. My sky however was clear. I just felt neither of this world nor truly in it. Concepts of marriage, children, money-making, even of home or personal transport, were not on my agenda – and for all I knew a mortgage could have been a dead greengage.

I had become mainly preoccupied with how discarnate information, and my grasp of its mediumship, matched other sources of inspired knowledge. In particular I wanted to see if these other sources clarified the discarnate view of earth as a "dull reflection" of their non-physical realities. Was this a mere aesthetic view or a cutting-edge handle to the true nature of things? Many a whole night was spent thus immersed. Part time hobo work for my upkeep meant that half the day could also be devoted to copious sifting. Each successive bedsit floor was littered with open books during cross-comparison of their detail. Religious scriptures were examined prior to concentration on esoteric sources such as Gnosticism, Hermeticism, Rosicrucianism, Theosophy, Anthroposophy, Huna, the Bendit-Payne work, the Arcane School teaching, or wherever earthly seers claimed an insight into our psycho-spiritual make-up.

That psi-perception, termed "objective mysticism" by the respect of two English scientists, earned trust from my degree of sentience at school. Its cosmic map hung together and found support from pioneer physics. But I was not merely believing what I wanted to believe. My one concern was with plausibility, corroborativeness, and a feel of inner validity.

These criteria being well met, studies took to the road. Centres here and abroad specialised in esoteric instruction, hitch-hiking travel around which made my life itinerant for long periods. Often left penniless from their cost on top of books, outwardly tramp-like with donkey jacket and shoulder length hair, body and soul were kept together through mundane wayside employment, sleeping rough in cellars, barns and bus shelters. The shared cup of tea was not uncommon, though I was seen as an oddity even among fellow drop-outs – a view preferable to that of religious sectarians whose hatred of my heresy fist-pounded it to the ground outside a bus station and left it unconscious behind the dustbins. In this milieu drug abuse was rife. Junkies were kinder than sectarians, if incredulous that after three stepped-up trips on LSD I should find them boring compared with out-of-body experience.

But earning had slid under stabler auspices by 1969, when psychical data was understood more workably within the broader esoteric context. Amongst a great deal else it had become obvious why discarnates should find earth reality a "dull reflection" of theirs. Perhaps the most lucid rendering is of how infinite dimensions of reality, each with a dimension of ourselves, fill apparent space. Via the "ratchet effect", so named by Professor Tiller of Stanford University, vortices of energy on each dimension act as "transducers", stepping down wavelengths of energy-matter into reflected lower wavelengths and occasionally into physical planets. Verified out in rather exhaustive detail, this subtle anatomy of cosmos and creaturehood at last cemented my grasp of how inner realities cause the physical by reflective action, and set the substructure beneath information shared by me at Ashdene.

Putting flesh on it was a lot easier when I used the spiral principle from those vortices, linking them with the Eastern esoteric tradition of body chakras. Claimed psi-perception like that of Dr Besant and Rev. Leadbeater was synthesised with both Dr Bendit's and Dr Steiner's work by greater use of the spiral. Having no academic pretensions, I would have been startled then to learn that eminent physicists had already advanced the same principle. Increased complexity thereafter had me rely on a consensus of mystical or transcendent experience, often from the collation of physics Professor Raynor Johnson.

Such areas tended to lie outside close definition, or were beyond my unspiritual ken at that stage. Yet part of me had an interior sense of how to smooth out anomalies, where to make links, and what twist was the result of mere cultural conditioning. Thereby a worldwide gamut of evidence describing the subtle anatomy of life was integrated subjectively and objectively to my own satisfaction. Open-ended, it clarified not just those axiomatic factors of our survival, reincarnation, religion, or the whence, why and whither of existence, but ground which its sources had not intended to cover.

That ground was mediumship, from knowledge of the subtle bodies. During my itinerary, continued interest in the kind of source material tied up by Dr Crookall however, was all mistaken by friends for an interest in mediumship per se. Though to me it represented a natural evolutionary faculty that deserved support like an artistic gift, my focus was on the output. And if discarnates were responsible, their fragile, hampered utmost to get through to the few who would listen drew my real support.

What the prima facie teachers among them had to tell us was far more important, I felt, than earth humanity's status quo. My closest source of recognition for this view was at Ashdene, where Valerie knew how spiritual knowledge without discarnate education misses a large chunk of understanding and perspective. So that errand of justice which had arisen in a school boot-cellar did its homework over eight years to be wheeled in by her for service with The Seven, and on.

When afterwards she left our notes and tapes in my care, the promised responsibility of turning them into book form was lone and onerous. I had never written a book before, yet our brief that The Seven's purpose made it crucial was no small incentive. Issues around each session were seen to have fertile value, the plot had a peculiar one-offness worth relating, and Paul Beard, who had heard some of the tapes, encouraged me to "write it down...stand up and be counted". These motivations together lent me nerve against a complete absence of any journalistic training or skill. Not least was the onus that if I didn't try, no one else would.

With little choice therefore but to do my best and be true to my angle inside, I submerged again into the feel of place and period from which facts took shape, letting my memory set their original stage novel-style. Although the latter style is also used to convey nuance or improvise, one suggested idea of turning fact into fiction would have defeated the whole object – which I hope is self-evident to those who accept a discarnate source. Those who find such acceptance difficult, or who are unable to make a willing suspension of disbelief, may enjoy the humanistic ride through our credo in assurance that all sessions physically happened.

An impartial report would have been neither realistic nor faithful to how it was, yet objectivity is not thrust aside. Doubts have their role to play, as they must for any healthy-minded student however at home with the subject. Thus so very often, both then and since, have I reappraised the nature of the communications, allowing for a wholly psychological origin – only to end up in clouds of nebulous hypotheses which didn't altogether fit what was on the ground or sentient experience. The discarnate one did, and our going along with it engendered the story. Physical events can be verified by those, correctly named, who took part, and by the tapes. All else must be left to the reader's own consideration, advisedly after a look through similar literature, using as we did that sense of inner validity for which one is responsible to oneself alone. My level best to portray how it was, in the most thought-provoking, informative and illustrative way I can, hopes to draw that judgement as much from the heart as the head.

The practical need to edit recorded conversations for brevity and clarity has lost nothing of worth. Three tapes lacking sufficient yield have had their valuable sections preserved and soldered on elsewhere. Otherwise the communications are as they were received. Unrecorded exchange between us is a synthesis of vivid memory scraps, participants' notes afterward, and taped highlights from similar occasions. Writing out, at age 60, my behaviour at age 24 has not been comfortable. Temptation often arose, especially while transcribing our rescue attempts, to use poetic licence and pretend I said or did something more intelligent. But then that would not be telling the true story. What follows my Preamble therefore is the most accurate picture I can reconstruct of our adventure, opening at Ashdene on January 10th 1972.

If the example of earthbound cases who didn't want to learn is only instructive to the same number here who may need to learn, then The Seven should be modestly content. If also readers are led through enjoyment of the plot to help with this problem from our advantage on earth, then the book's double aim will have been fulfilled.

Jules Hillyar
Tunbridge Wells 2009

PREAMBLE

ON EARTH It was understood that, between the Wars, two young Army doctors, a fellow officer and an Army nurse were stirred by a book, Thirty Years Among the Dead, relating how the wife of its author Dr Wickland channelled sad earthbound cases who needed his help out of their entanglements and guidance onward. The subject was much debated by those colleagues, especially by two of them at the bookshop in London's Charing Cross Road where they had found the odd account and where they would often chat with proprietor Mr Leggett. Since he knew of no comparable account it remained their sole source of enquiry into what was, both to themselves and the author, a valuable area for medical research. Then, one sunny evening in 1933, the four were travelling out together in an old black Morris when it skidded off the road, down an embankment, and burst into flames. There were no physical survivors.

PASSING OVER But the trauma of their passing over was nothing to the pitiful nether-world scenes of human desolation they now encountered, far more widespread and deep-set than the book had portrayed. Thousands from any walk of life, from any religious persuasion or none were trapped in an earthly fantasy carried over with them, many in ignorant destitution; and these were not the worst. Moreover, too seldom witnessed was the astounding effect of prayer from earth, its power ten times more penetrative than effort from discarnate helpers. Witnessed also was the lack of sincerity and compassion from those still incarnate who knew a little or a lot, yet did nothing. So stunned were the colleagues by their discovery that they made a solemn pact. They would team up in concerted work to reduce the pall of this grey throng affecting earth, and demonstrate through a physical channel the varied spheres of its prevalence with the need for fuller realisation of the cause among us here.

THE PLAN The four moved further on, and found great numbers of helpers engaged in rescue. Among them were their own spiritual kin, their native group soul which specialised in such work. Before long, under wiser direction, a plan was evolved. Two of them, the most psychically flexible, would reincarnate as channels: one for oral rescue, the other for prayer rescue. First to take that plunge was the nurse in 1938 for prayer rescue, followed in 1941 by one of the former doctors for his oral work. He was a capricious character who had elected himself into the job to make up spiritual leeway.

When grown sufficiently in physical life they were to link at different stages with group soul members here to implement the plan. Its three-stage formula would open with stubborn cases tackled orally by an earth team via the channel, seven of the discarnate group in attendance. These seven would then move to a higher sphere, and from there inspire through the channel a Centre of education to prevent such cases. Stage two would see the female channel arrive and let through the rest of the discarnate working group. They would bring less stubborn cases to be rescued by a concentration of thought-power from the earth team plus vocal advice, providing a model for stage three. On that model, and supported by the group's Centre, a wide network of teams would be kindled by a story written of the plan's actual unfoldment.

Its formula took us ten years to discern in full, but what actually unfolded was a drama that began just outside Tunbridge Wells, Kent, in 1972…

CHAPTER ONE

FIRST HINTS

There was nothing paranormal about Langton Green. Set facing a range of tall evergreens, its commonplace shops and terrace cottages hugged the main road. Behind lay Victorian villadom and newer residential building, hints of which the rambler would glimpse through an occasional gap in the trees. He would be more likely however to feel drawn along the single line of shopfronts where village life is upheld despite noisome traffic. Then in gentle contrast he might catch the aroma of freshly baked bread wafting from a doorway, or eye a newsboy preparing his round. And above the patois of rustic commerce float heralding tinkles of creaky shop doors, or the ping of a cash register.

All very quaint and customary he might think. But next he would have met elegant wrought-iron curls with the signboard: ASHDENE GALLERY – PORTRAITS AND PAINTINGS. Mere sight of this triple-fronted lodge, nestling comfily on the roadside, could guess its olde worlde service as a public house. A closer peek at the first of three bow windows in early 1972 is liable to have made him shrink back from potted plant domesticity. Much more cautious approach at the second bow would prove unmerited, for here, shown in grand wooden frames, were oil landscapes of cornfield and bluebell grove. Suitably encouraged, he might pass along the courtyard and gaze into the shop itself, whose plate glass stretches almost to his feet. Propped against some huge urn or easel, vivid portraits languished in a faded velvet decor. Whatever else was discerned in each likeness, the eyes would have struck him. So lit up were they with individual appeal that other features seemed almost superfluous. Away into the shop's dusky interior, where frames leant at random one upon another, men, women and children gleamed through veritable windows of the soul.

And so indeed they were to the artist, whose flair reflected deeper propensities than our companion would have begun to suspect. We allow him to continue his lone path through the village, leaving us at our destination. He would scarcely have noticed, standing at the rear, her brush padding from palette to canvas, the tall, graceful lady in loose smock and long strings of plain beads.

On this January afternoon the shadows were already casting unwelcome hues over her work, so she lifts a bangled wrist to find the hour and returns that brush to its turpentine home. The sound of sliding locks make a small black nose appear from the forward display area, where since lunch it had strained and twitched after passing canine scent. Beneath a mop of long, waxen hair the nose, attached to a Tibetan breed, would stoop to anything between dormant intervals and perk up to the name of Chloe. At the lady's call, Chloe shakes her molt over the nearest painting and pursues a dogged trail, like some tiny clockwork rug, in the direction of her Mistress.

Taken into the next room we find it co-extensive with the shop, reaching back seven metres to a French window. Our artist runs a sentimental scan over the gallery of favourites which adorn its walls as we follow her under the dividing arch into the front part, housing a library, and let her pause before its elegant white fireplace. The sun still streams in here, and those accomplished fingers toss a curl aside to feel winter's thin rays on her brow. She loved the dappled playing of light. To watch it pour through leaves onto a woodland path, or draw the dream from a contemplative face was pure joy. Today its afterglow reveals her own high forehead and cheekbones to have that well-bred look, hard to define. Yet once it had served her as a fashion model, and the worldly-wise might have guessed at such eventful years in her retracing turn and stride to an opposite door.

Chloe meanwhile, by the foot of the French window, had found a view of the garden. Rambling rose and clematis mostly festooned its surround of old whitewashed walls within the L-shape of two barn-like outbuildings. These crumbling pantiled structures spurned half a century of neglect to grant the garden a huge bent arm of protection against North and East winds, whilst all day, and over the neighbouring wall till sunset, light flooded into its open heart. There, in crowning glory amid rosebeds, rockery and herbaceous borders, a majestic young weeping willow caressed the lawn with its fountain of fronds.

Looking back from beneath this tree, Ashdene's rear elevation was of gaunt, comparatively drab appearance, broken up by the central drainpipe whose rusty setting betrayed years of leakage. And because garden ground sloped gently away, an unfortunate wall looked higher. Sash windows ran along the first floor marking the main shop-length bedroom, a bathroom, landing and far left a special room. Two bedrooms at the front of the house were allotted apiece to her teenage daughter and choice guests.

As dusk falls, our attention is drawn down nearest her annexe kitchen to the large ground floor window, for inside a table lamp has been lit. The two of them have passed across a narrow hall into her snug sitting room. Surrounds of soft pink, mossy green, and rich gold harmonise with a symphony of books, pictures, ornaments, rugs and cushions, all pleasantly arrayed as if they had been there forever. Resting upon the mantle of an Edwardian fireplace extends a wide mirror, tracery-framed in gilt. Sprays of dried hops round its upper length are randomly reflected in the glass. So also is the petite table lamp, one of three in scarlet, balanced somewhat precariously on the shelf end. That was how she liked it. Beams would thus rebound with more sensitive creaminess, and anyway her aged furniture would not have withstood a brighter show. An example was the small divan where she now settled close to the fire. Had even *her* slender figure leaned heavily against the arms it might have given creaking complaint. But a thick-weave oriental throw and tapestry cushions covered every flank, expressing strength of character rather than weakness of limb. Besides, she was perched on the seat edge eating out of a saucepan.

Open within reach as usual lay a valued book, tonight significantly unattended. Again and again her concern strayed to the card on the mantelpiece. Neatly made out to "Valerie Mackenzie" it invited her to a party, consent to which she had given days ago without due aforethought. Valerie found parties shallow. Most of her fifty-five years had a cosmopolitan mix to them, and the duller tint of parochial chitchat had less appeal – especially when her artistic habit saw under people's make-up to the low-smouldering discontent in their lives. Her own vale of sorrows through constant ill-health, a stillborn son, then divorce, had stored compassion in plenty for human angst, with the listener's heart for that sad, vulnerable aloneness which adulthood often disguises from itself. So she had already heard in private the home truth of many who would be there.

In fact with some of them she shared a singular line of interest. The book beside her was no novel or art treatise. Its author, Dr Paul Brunton, pointed by title to The Inner Reality, discoverable when mind and emotion are stilled, and from which one may receive a spiritual influx of peace and equilibrium on tap. Few understood how central such ideas were to her life. Those of socio-cultural religion had long ceded to the compound mysticism of Brunton, Joel Goldsmith, Raynor Johnson, Clarice Toyne and other lights whose free-spirited, empirical wisdom she could trust. Having set aside her fourth upper room as a Sanctuary, the place had for years been imbued with the atmospheric flavour of devotion, and tucked away in this retreat she would tape-record to music favourite tracts or prayer which evoked her finer feelings.

Whatever may have been their state as the party hour closed in on her that evening, greater capacity to say no would have helped. She was far from well. Her abdominal trouble had begun to do its worst. Still no exemptive phone call was made.

On the party doorstep she braced herself for an ordeal, yet was softened by her host's welcoming smile. It bore some commiseration because this lady was her spiritual healer, and understood. Although Mickie Bishop did have permanent cures on record, Valerie's ungrumbling sangfroid at failure in her case made do with light relief, and now just settled for their bonhomie – impassive to the offer of quick treatment aside. Perhaps quietism in the Sanctuary beforehand steeled her onward through the hubbub of familiar nodding faces.

If not, then at least her focus swung from personal endurance to one far corner of the lounge. There, alone and forlorn, sat a young man. He had a leg in plaster and his lean, handsome features looked drawn with pain. On impulse she headed across and sat down by him.

Naturally the injured leg gave her an opener. It drew from him that while working on his family's nearby farm he had fallen under the tractor wheel, crushing a limb and part of the ribcage. Weeks of discomfort hobbling in and out of hospital, along with the irksome confinement, had become unacceptable to his outgoing nature. So in desperation he had tried Mickie Bishop's services, gaining improved mobility. At that result Valerie took his intelligent mind to have acknowledged the spiritual element, which mind did no such thing. He had remained a sceptic, and quite adept at defending his position.

The adeptness was mutual. They locked into debate, growing fascinated with each other – she by his waggish, vulnerable charm and he by her obvious sincerity and breadth of vision. She imagined this lanky, well-spoken farmer's son must have stood out amongst the villagers of Chiddingstone where he lived. Neither career-orientated nor studious, his freestyle attitude appeared to have set him adrift from the family – a reputable one – and embittered his father whom he tried to avoid. One rare brush with tradition in marrying a local lass had found her no match for his rakish temperament. Squabbles had stretched the gulf in outlook between them, its only bridge their joy over a son and daughter. While such confidences rolled into Valerie's understanding, debate aside, the love he felt for those children was evident from his proud gleam. But behind it she discerned a hesitance.

Hours had passed, swallowed up in their excited talk. By now the party had run its course, the lounge was desolate under a pall of smoke, and both paused, suddenly conscious of being on their own. Short peals of laughter rang from the hall where stragglers were in conversation with their host. Valerie supposed that by limiting her sociality to the corner hobnob she had appeared rude. He on the other hand was preoccupied internally.

Quite why he felt tempted to tell her a most private secret, he didn't know. Somehow it seemed natural, so again he was talking. Laid bare were the months of intensive conflict over responsibility for the children that had wound him to crisis point. On the eve of his accident, nerves sprung tight, he had been set to wreak mischief against his wife.

Breaking off there, he waited for Valerie's reaction. Many a listener would have felt psyched up to hear the exact nature of his malice aforethought. She however was an impressionable lady whose otherwise capable judgement gave way under stimulus to a vivid sense of the melodramatic, assuming the best, or as at present the very worst.

Probably it was that pause of his, pregnant with visions of the wildest atrocity, which said enough to her, and which she broke with a spellbound gasp of horror. We may never know the truth, for seeing his coup de théâtre thus embraced he chose to enlarge no further in case it proved a comparative disappointment. Fortunately for him, she switched to an appreciation of the passions aroused in mismarriage where children were at stake.

But soon they heard the arrival of his lift home, at which he scribbled down his phone number. Thrusting it into Valerie's lap he grappled his crutches and hove himself upright. She was only half attentive during their exchange of hands and smiles, haunted by an odd, eerie cognition that all along her mind had been trying to stem back. In every other respect he was a stranger, yet the essence of him was already known and recognised – as an actor is seen recast in a new role.

Still entranced by the odd sensation she helped him out through the hall and into his waiting car. Once he was safely inside he rolled down the window, looked at her over its glass, and grinned. The fresh night air tweaked her to realise that she hadn't even asked his name. "Oh it's Peter," he said with uncharacteristic shyness, before being driven away under a starlit sky.

★ ★ ★ ★ ★

Normally the most picturesque morning as then blazed over an artist's pillow would fail to rouse Valerie before 10am. Late nights pushing insomnia compelled slow transition to the new day, and seldom was anything allowed to disturb that vital phase. Tradesmen, customers, bosom pals and relations alike beat their fists upon wooden silence. Her bedside phone might clamour long across the quilted mound and still draw no response, though perhaps if one ran into her room shouting, "Fire!", a languorous finger might have slithered out to indicate the nearest water-source. And since every known artifice would fail to budge the lady from her nest, particularly after a rare night out, one can imagine how exceptional it was to find her today up and around two hours early.

Then again, so was the fillip that had set her astir from first awakening. There seemed to be within her a purposive, single-minded element not her own. Of course last evening's rapport had left such an impression that she intended to ring Peter... sometime. But the urge to start preparing lunch at her home with him the very next day, and before even ringing the presumed-upon guest, was not her style. Nevertheless everything went as expected. When eventually she did phone the invitation it got his enthusiastic response, and on their drive back to Ashdene they regained a mutuality which had lost nothing from the night before.

Not until then however did she recall her odd insight of knowing him well already. That recall should have stayed with her this morning, but had been thrust aside by some curious inner knowledge overruling her. It was as though if she were extra still she would sense what it was.

Would it have her, at fifty five, plummet into the heart of a thirty-one year old? Earlier years might have caught her so; latter ones sought the spirit whatever its bodily form. Yet hadn't she herself provided all its impetus from the start? She had first gone to the party against her better judgement. *She* had been the one to approach him. Now her own invite was bringing him home.

Road markers scurried disconcertingly under the car bonnet till she pulled into Ashdene's forecourt. As her mind became distracted with transferring his plastered leg from car to home, he began to see what he could see of her artist's den. But for the disablement his impulse would have been to skitter about with the enthusiasm of a puppy, nosing into every corner. Instead he resorted to questions, from the gathering up of his crutches to where sitting room comfort diffused him. Any chance of feedback being rare, Valerie slid through to the adjoining kitchen in search of her coffee jar. Still within range of repartee, it proved easier to listen than respond. Let him sing for his supper she thought, entertained by the humorous verve he brought even to domesticism.

If only one could peal away its sheath of trivia his true feelings might show. Were they confounded like hers or casual? What showed during coffee was that their real background lives outside of the party had little reason to touch. After hearing his share of secular milestones she told him about her inner search. He stuck on how unreal he found the notion of a spiritual world far from communion with it, pert against her disarming reply:

"The best way to find the reality of things is surely to experiment for yourself," she tendered. "Why not try one of my meditation tapes?"

Well out of his depth he sought refuge in chaff about being invited to see her "etchings". It implied consent, but she was too numb recoiling from her undue proposal to take much notice. While always eager to fan the flames of spiritual enquiry, she had seen no apparent flicker in him since they met. Even if she had, volunteering instruction was rash by her standards – while these left her more sure of one thing. The influence was from deep within her, not from without. Somewhat relieved, she put their experiment off till that afternoon.

Its rationale was also set aside, with him full of chatty diversion over a light lunch. Next she took him round the garden, in which he showed genuine interest, before helping him up the stairs to her Sanctuary. If he was to become a good friend, she decided, he should at least taste the metacentre of Ashdene. Besides from her point of view, if he experienced true meditation it might engender a lightning reversal of faith. He himself had not quite grasped why she had to haul him up there, though upon reaching the holy summit his view was a first that merited the climb.

Never had he encountered stillness of such magnetic force. Around this cottage room, twelve feet square, gossamer threads of incense hung in unearthly silence – a silence yet alive with vibrant activity. The very air rang in his ears like some huge dynamo, and even furniture stood so peculiarly inert that it seemed to hum in unison. From the opposite wall a sofa beckoned with soft blue cushions where, breathless, he took seat.

As though on cue, something else permeated his senses, an influence unexpectedly tender and benign, soothing away anxiety the moment it arose. If unconditional love could be transmuted into physical effect, he felt, then here was surely an example. Was her brand of meditation the effect of atmosphere and not a tape after all? Or had she doped the coffee? Artists were a funny lot, by his reckoning. Maybe she was doped up herself. His mind strove for credible answers but the very effort soon became engulfed out of his depth in an ethereal peace which, plain enough to him by now, was not drug induced. And the sober matter-of-factness of her raking innocently among tapes fitted nothing save itself. He sank back past caring, for the sensation lightened to a state in which he could look about him.

Across the room an altar table, draped to the floor in aubergine, bore numerous strewn cassettes. Their recorder lay on one side, its twin speakers to the rear, whilst above, and suspended in ornate brass, a long curl of incense wafted lazily into the air. She had drawn heavy curtains over the window, eclipsing what shred of daylight remained. Instead one venerable and tassled table lamp bathed the scene in a warm incandescent glow. Regency wallpaper of evening blue, which lent overall majesty to the environment, gave way to amethyst at the altar.

Upon its worn surface hung portraits of Yukteswar and disciple Yogananda whose serene and saintly countenances beamed down at our friend with shrewd discernment. Gladly his attention slunk off onto strains of Mahler's fifth symphony weaving its slow, ponderous Adagietto amongst a genteel poverty that almost grew from the floor around. After eyeing her ancient bookcase, bent under weighty disarray of contemplative lore, his search ran up and over a picture of Jesus attending a sick child, past obscure Rudolf Steinerish art, to dive down and peer into fusty old cabinet shelving stacked with boxes of granular incense, charcoal, and motley sacred effects.

Peter tried hard to get the gist of this amalgam. He was unsure what he should have expected. Her antique shrine on legs, parked irreverently by the door, to him struck more an attitude of having fallen through from the attic unnoticed than that of strict formalism. The whole set-up suggested a coalition within her of many religious essences which lent them personalised harmony without. Up against the altar table a Mendlesham chair asserted her focus, one ordinary seat alongside, behind which various fireside types here and there edged pink carpeting on the return survey to his plastered leg. Most items, he saw, would be unremarkable if wrenched apart, but bound in their arcane synergy they seemed too sacrosanct to disturb.

At her bid, he moved to sit up beside her at the altar table where she said he was far less liable to fall asleep. But he had scarcely heard a few minutes of her meditation tape before that original sensation grew stronger, now unnerving him with a mild empressment. It had pithiness, in tune with which a subliminal part of him was acquiescing, pulling from deeper than he felt himself to exist. The realisation sent his heart into desperate rhythm, his breath heaving in frenzied grasp for life as the room began to recede away down a whirlwind tunnel of darkness to oblivion.

Valerie's dismay froze to alarm when he blacked out in front of her, his head and shoulders keeling forward with a thump onto the table. She called his name, tapped his hand, shook him. All proved futile. His condition put her in mind of a comatose case seen years ago, unlike which there was no bracelet on him to indicate special illness. Should she phone Dr Hicks anyway, just to be on the safe side? Medical aid, for her reminiscent of drugs and invasive knives granting small change, was not jumped at. Nevertheless, against an unknown quantity it covered the risk. So she gathered herself up, ran one final glance over his slumped, inert figure, and made for the door.

But back at the altar, muscles stirred. She swung round, watchful as his breath, picking up strength, gave a deep sigh equal to hers inside. Soon his head lifted and the eyes of one very befuddled young man opened to stare blankly over surroundings that, not a moment ago it seemed, had abandoned him. Then those inevitable questions scrambled out, questions as much in her mind as his, born of the longest ten minutes she could remember and the shortest in his life.

Their inelegant retreat downstairs was stalled by his need to ensure that she was not withholding any answers: "What was happening to me Valerie? What was going on in there? I've never felt like that before".

Here at least was one answer for her. Evidently he hadn't blacked out during treatment from Mickie Bishop, whom she decided to ring once they were safely in the sitting room with a fresh cup of coffee. In the event, poor Peter started to shake uncontrollably, having to relinquish his cup for fear that the experience would return and that he, this time, would not.

Anticipation pulled him onto his feet, where he felt more secure. Crutch-pacing the room as Valerie spoke over the phone he stopped frequently to glean from her face the trend it might relay. None showed until she put down the receiver and promised that Mickie would come right away to make a healer's assessment, one that picks up data from the aura at close range. The news soothed him enough to be fluent on her arrival with all he could tell.

After Mickie had listened to his account she stepped behind him into hands-on-shoulders contact. Hers was a workaday, sensible, middlebrow air, for him nostalgically redolent of sessions in her lounge when to have fallen under a tractor wheel was the most anomalous debacle that could ever befall a chap, and when the norm would soon be restored. On present showing any norm was long overdue. He was therefore unprepared for her closing diagnosis.

In fact he could hardly believe his ears, and might have dismissed the notion altogether had she not stated it in such unequivocal terms. Him – a medium? Attempts to scoff ran dry as the unruffled counsel spoke sternly:

"What I'm saying Peter, is that prolonged sittings in that Sanctuary's atmosphere can make you subject to trance control, and I advise you not to go in there again."

Valerie of course was all agog. The possibility had crossed her mind earlier, but this serious admonition made it sound tantalising. Knowledge of mediumship being absent from her bookshelves further heightened the scent of intrigue along a trail which seemed unlikely to end here. In the honey-tongued way she had of appearing to go along with well-meant advice, no trace of rebellion passed her lips. Tact came second nature to one whose own sensitiveness tiptoed at times so carefully around people's hearts that they were hard put to know where they, or she, actually stood.

Uncertain himself, Peter grew more concerned to know where he was going to lie down. For with the verdict over and women's talk rife he hankered after that sound sleep which might sieve away wholesale their nonsense about mediumship. A token yawn got leave of the spare room, under whose duvet he made his slumberous escape. Valerie had only to thank their parting guest before she too retired, wondering on her way up creaky stairs and past her dormant protégé what new scenario may spin with the morning.

★ ★ ★ ★ ★

As it turned out, little of note happened for several days. These, by her account, were spent in "endless talking" which included efforts to resolve his marital breakdown – the while she shuttled him home, and from "a worsening situation" there, repeatedly back again. On later visits she met his wife Jean in a friendly manner, if not yet hearing her side of the tale, and between them matured agreement that his leg injury was adding to the complications of an eight year marriage which needed space – time apart from him to convalesce, her to review. Peter brightened at this fresh, easy horizon in which he could see his children as often as he wished, because whereas Valerie's appetite had been whetted by the warning, his sought comparative peace in the commonplace. Thus, with the relief of decision, their final journey taken to his home collected two suitcases of clothes and returned him to what became a new beginning at Ashdene.

They got on well together, despite her inexperience as a nursemaid. He would sit in the studio watching Valerie ply her craft, even tempting from those hands a portrait of himself in oils – executed briskly with her sentiment and skill. On occasion he might embrace the ever-ready crutches to hop round the garden or try light housework, chatting away in his usual voluble style. But every other day obliged their trip to the Kent & Sussex Hospital for his painkilling injections and agonising physiotherapy.

Sometimes they sat in the Sanctuary, having made light of Mickie Bishop's advice that he should not do so. He had slurred over that blackout experience as a one-off, along with her "superstition" about trance control which he thought nonsensical. Also his dislike of being left alone edged him into another try at meditation beside Valerie. He quite enjoyed their togetherness in peace, sensing her devotion, seeing the dreamy expression come into her eyes, tranquilly content and confident. He may not have suspected her secret hope that if atheism could fall such easy prey to trance, then a conscious approach inward might win his faith.

In other respects the arduous discipline rankled him, and kept consciousness to a shallow veneer which was wary of its depth. As a result the first session passed without incident, allowing the second to follow with looser rein. It was the third that took Valerie by surprise.

After meditation she had felt venturously inclined to have a try herself at spiritual healing on his painful knee, and was hit by a strong smell of anaesthetic over the spot. Bending to trace its possible source in the plaster she found none. Instead, to her consternation, his leg began to quiver and the knee struck up definite undulating movements as if worked invisibly beneath her palm. Their circular motion was one which, had he been able to use the muscle at all, would have required rare dexterity indeed. Furthermore his face no longer showed discomfort or tension. It had in fact become calm, eyes smiling open to declare a total cessation of pain not experienced in months.

Both were jubilant, the wheels of their relationship oiled with triumph – albeit on Valerie's side a touch wobbly. Whilst she accepted his gratitude in release, underneath lurked doubt as to having played any vital part. Was someone discarnate behind it? She knew that many healers claimed to have an invisible therapist at their elbow, or considered themselves a mere channel for psychic energy, yet the degree of sensed apartness from these manipulations arrested her. Did that apartness always feel so acute? Or was Nature displaying the kind of stunt where healed sceptic turns healer, roused after miraculous cure to dispense treatment worldwide? On second thought the infirmity was not grand enough for theatricals. Nor for that matter was the cure.

Peter's casualness toward his knee movements as a quirk of the mystique that was healing, and her private query, had seen them continue through four sessions when the day came for his plaster to be removed. She left him that morning bright and hopeful in the care of his therapists. But on her return at 2pm he was sitting in a wheelchair, still armed with the crutches, and looking grey with pain. Morphine injections to the knee having rendered him incapable of standing, he now presented a dismal, leaden figure, burdened under the prognosis that several weeks must elapse before he could walk unaided.

Valerie's heart sank. Her mind swirled in their fog of disappointment, fraught with the nightmarish struggle to load him aboard her Morris Estate. They travelled the three miles in broody silence, each a prisoner of melancholy, till at Ashdene the battle resumed – lifeless limb jostling aluminium frame out of her car and up winding stairs to his bed, where Peter fell in utter exhaustion.

Empathy stirred in her, and though the afternoon dimmed into evening's shadow she never once left his side.

Even when a village lamp had long spread amber fingers across the coverlet, with him fast asleep, she railed at feeling useless however. Presumably the doctors knew what they were about, ineffectual as their tactics may appear, or stultified as she may feel at the capsizing of her own. Yet it left the bare facts clear to see. After spiritual healing she had found him painless and exuberant. After medicine he was worse than ever.

So tentatively, in this eleventh hour, she stretched a hand over his knee. Time seemed to slow down. Intermittent traffic whooshed by under the window, empowering the silences between. His slackness of jowl, throaty breaths coming from the back of an open mouth, minded her to relax more, adjusting her sidesaddle position on the bed's edge. Whilst aware of a strange pitch to the air around, she had not so far sensed the onset of treatment and thoughts roamed listless. Then, in that unguarded moment, realisation struck that his leg was moving. Not in its previous circulatory fashion, nor in the fidget of sleep, but stiffly upwards – as if being hoisted by an invisible winch.

They would have cut a droll spectacle, Peter snoring away with one leg raised and Valerie looking on like a gobsmacked conjuror's assistant. She pinched herself against illusion in the semi-dark, though to solid gaze the leg stayed at a forty-five degree angle for almost thirty seconds before sinking mysteriously to rest. As it did so she noticed the air-pitch turn off, along with a change of atmosphere that made some former vitality conspicuous by its sudden withdrawal.

Still, time having reached midnight from such a day she was in no mood to think further. It was enough to pull herself upright, head for the door, and doubt if any solution could alter where in heaven's name all this was leading.

CHAPTER TWO

THE OVERTURE

"Valerie! Valerie! Come quickly! Come and see!"

Woken by these morning cries at her bedroom door the party in question asserts that she "leapt" out of bed. Difficult as it is to imagine Valerie leaping anywhere, let alone from her bed, one may grant at least that she slithered from her cocoon with more haste than usual. The sight that met her eyes however would have merited a quantum leap. There, incredibly, was Peter in full stride around the landing, quite unsupported, and wide-eyed with delight.

"Look Val,"said he, "I can walk without my crutches! Isn't it great? I can walk!"

And so he could, to her bleary astonishment.

"Try the stairs," came its uncertain challenge.

"I already have. Watch!"

Valerie craned intently over the bannister. Apart from a minor wobble here and there she had to admit the transformation was impressive, though maybe he "shouldn't rush things".

Peter laughed.

"Get dressed and I'll make us breakfast!"

So saying he was off, happiness the energy of the day all over his face. Exhortations to "be careful now Peter please!" floated after him in vain. She might as well have spoken to a bird gleefully released from its cage into the open sky.

Throughout that morning Valerie boggled at the change in him.

She had read of such healings but not known one at first hand. There were surprised faces in the village too, which after witnessing yesterday's traumatic scramble from the car now saw him strolling gaily round their supermarket collecting a celebratory beanfeast. Back indoors his reborn fleetness of foot came under steadier observation. Asked if there was not the slightest twinge of pain he conceded to some, on and off in the knee, but nothing that bothered him. Nor did it show, and the odd sight of Peter moving freely for the first time in their relationship left her stunned. Congratulations seemed meagrely inappropriate for a "miracle", the term that best fitted it from her vocabulary. He reluctantly could think of none better, lenient because his freedom by any name was sweet.

Over the next few weeks' sustained improvement, when for fear of another letdown Valerie was bent on finishing touches to that knee, her sense of latency deepened. Not due to the ongoing "miracle" itself – which perplexed his physiotherapists so much that they refused to take back the crutches – but on account of her newfound power to produce strikingly visible effects. Each time she made healing contact the entire limb began a further series of motions that included stretching, twisting and bending in a consistent, apparently methodical sequence. The sequence was one factor which secured her belief in its extraneous source, apart from his bewilderment that it was happening at all. Another factor was discovered by trial and error as being indispensable to the whole process, lying in the need of his limb to be relaxed and pliant – thus lessening the ability of self-propulsion. His attitude under spiritual healing anyway was one of passive succumbing to attention, while sittings in the Sanctuary without trouble had loosened his guard to a semi-conscious state which at times sparked Valerie's concern. But her clincher came on their subsequent visit to the hospital, where she watched his therapist then change to the very same manipulative sequence, and on every visit thereafter follow with uncanny precision an adjustment made the previous night.

On its own this development would not have fired her much. On top of everything else it brought curiosity to boiling point, for meditation supplied no answers. The recourse she chose was of a kind which needed the cooperation of someone who had become an ally over the years, and whose integrity she trusted.

Demure in character, fellow artist Betty Longhurst kept her measure of psychism private outside Ashdene. She worked among volunteer catering staff at the nearby College of Psychotherapeutics, a holistic healing centre where she first met Valerie. Their parity of gender, age, aesthetic and philosophic interest had dovetailed, although as personalities they were quite different. On a prearranged weekday afternoon Valerie would be more or less ready by the fire, floral smock and trinket bound, her hair swept casually back into flowing waves, pensively scraping the last remnant of lunch from a saucepan – that loner's dodge to minimise washing up. Never in a month of Sundays however would such a tack have been employed by the lady about to enter. The sound of a motor purring quietly to rest outside, the woody rattle of a door left expectantly off its latch, heralded Betty's tallish but mild figure in neat skirt and cardigan, every inch the middle-class norm, with winning, sincere smiles for her emancipated chum. In talk they invariably made toward esoteric studies, a newly discovered book, or luminary, or forthcoming lecture.

Whether, on their afternoon of March 9th 1972, they debated Valerie's enigmatic situation is not known. But after half an hour both rose to follow their set route upstairs. At the Sanctuary's altar table they took seats abreast of each other and relaxed, peeling away superficial thought.

A button was pressed at Valerie's side. Chorales of the Requiem de Duruflé spired and fell, interspersed with her voice in prayer. On the music's eventual fade-out they still sat motionless, cushioned from within or imbibing the replenishment gained. Then slowly, her senses lightened from their sojourn, Valerie opened her eyes and reached under the altar cloth. Out came a massive art pad, which she spread on the table in front of them. Thumbing through its pages of laboured scrawl she arrived at a clean space. Betty meanwhile, fresh from her own devotions, looked on as if they were about to indulge in some normal activity like arranging a vase of flowers. Taking up a biro between thumb and forefinger of her right hand, she caused it to hover over the page until Valerie's left hand clasped its upper stem. Loosely conjoined, they laid their alliance into writing position and waited.

The practice of automatic or directed writing, both terms for its independence of the writer's conscious volition, is standard among mediumistic forms and the procedure varies greatly. Some practitioners feel an invisible hand guiding theirs, whilst others note degrees of overshadowing via the central nervous system. In a few cases the medium's mind can roam free as reams of paper are covered, frequently in distinctive hand-writing, sometimes at abnormal speed or in languages unknown to the recipient. Directed writers themselves tend to hail from every age-group, persuasion and walk of life. In fact engineers, housewives, medical men, clergy, all share a practice mostly carried on alone and outside psychic circles.

Results cover a wide spectrum too, ranging from the quasi-intelligible level to works of high spiritual or literary merit. Though the bulk of material tends to fall between these, some schools of opinion believe that a portion of the world's religious scriptures were thus produced. Latter-day channels ascribe its source either to the inner self or a discarnate communicator, bearing in mind that the inner self can provide equal revelatory value and that discarnates say they must use the channel's subconscious to transmit anything at all. Psychical research has it well documented.

Neither Valerie nor Betty had any knowledge of this research. What they did have was a staunch conviction, driven home through years of hands-on experience, that their writing originated from a source independent of themselves. Experimentally they had trodden a well-worn track. Progressing from a planchette with wheels and alphabet on to placing a pencil in its apex, and eventually discarding the contrivance for their present mode, had given acceleration to their question-answer routine. Communicators usually made the opening gambit, thence proving patient, humorous and sympathetic in response to questions – sometimes heavily underlining points of spiritual discernment, or referring to texts which the two had never read but turned out later to be correct. At any point Betty might receive vivid pictures symbolising detail too laborious for script, and there were occasions like today when they seemed quite literal.

As our two sat poised for the first kinetic current to endow their pen with life, Betty's inner lens blurred away physical perception to show a mist-filled room where several people were moving about, busily intent on some shrouded enterprise. She recalled that their previous contacts had been a fraternity of Wykehamists, though these men had withdrawn weeks ago and were unlikely to have returned. So was the picture purely symbolic or an actual glimpse of newcomers taking over? She peered at them until too soon the spectacle faded, report of it being given to her unsuspecting companion.

The wait had been longer than usual, leaving Valerie in no mood for metaphors. All of her unknowing now got focused into a simple appeal about a nebulous vision: "Please, whoever you are, can you explain what your picture means?"

At once the pen threaded its spidery way across the page, startling even these old hands with its vitality and strength:

a preparation for coming events

"So far so good," she muttered to Betty. Then out loud: "Is that all you're going to tell us?"

Both sensed pressure welling up in the atmosphere about them. A warm, percolating current ran down their fingers ere the pen crept forth again:

now you see through a glass darkly
but then face to face. Time is running out
and there is much to be done
help the world with prayer and love

Intrigued by its cryptic style Valerie pressed on to the topic of Peter's leg.

"Can you give your identity, or at least say who is doing the healing?"

The answer rolled into motion as she spoke:

the young man was a medical practitioner on earth before
we his colleagues have come to help him

While that went home a clear, dynamic image whirled into Betty's view. It looked like a Victorian child's toy top, though spinning a glorious array of colours.

"Is the top significant?" asked Valerie, determined to elicit all she could.

a symbol of healing energies for the spirit
we are with you always in love

Touched by this last tender valentine the companions were slow to realise therein the author's signing off. Now they stared over still enclasped fingertips at a contact from which the energy had ebbed, putting every phrase at a premium.

On face value their brief dialogue had given hints which both clarified and deepened the mystery. It did seem feasible that Peter's former-life colleagues should surge round him in his hour of need. But a "preparation for coming events" in which there was "much to be done" sounded ominous to Valerie. Was she to be an instrument for extended healing work? The thought of cripples in an unending series struggling loquaciously up and down her stairs sent apprehension into whether her health could stand the strain. And as to these "colleagues" of Peter's, how reliable or forthcoming would they be? Earlier communicants had always introduced themselves and written openly, whereas the present crew were quite taciturn in style.

Yet she reminded herself, while stowing these first meagre fruits of enquiry beneath the altar table, of a distinct impression that had persisted throughout the script's progress. Almost dimming the import of mere words on a page, it was of a presence which had settled, fraternal in flavour, right beside her as if by way of emphasis, with a kinship she found hard to ascribe.

Betty corroborated the impression unbidden, her more acute sensitivity admitting that the strength of contact was unprecedented in their experience. Together they had the feeling that a wholly new and different era of involvement was born.

Suddenly the sound of Peter's latch key rasping in its lock down below made Valerie twinge with anticipation. She felt unsure about sharing the content of their afternoon in case he turned it to ridicule, and particularly from a mood of indulging the earthly whims of his children. Her decided option – since few could guarantee to get a word in edgeways – was to play it by ear, for already he had swung open the sitting room door.

"Val, if you could have seen ... Val?... "

Her voice from aloft returned him to the hall.

"Oh you're up there," he sighed.

Nonetheless, passion to recount all led him into the Sanctuary, where his prey readied herself.

Sight of Betty diverted him into unctuous greeting, critical moments when their host was hopeful of luring the conversation to less hallowed ground. But Peter strayed chattily onto her settee, first plumbing the depths or otherwise of Betty's private life, then amusing them with the predicament of his lost ignition key and the reaction on his children's faces as they were teased over the prospect of having to live in the woods forever.

It was at some point during the narrative that she began to notice faltering in his speech. Every so often he would pause for breath. If she was not best pleased at his overstretching himself in the period of convalescence, worried looks from Betty as he teetered precariously on the settee made her approach more sympathetic.

"Are you sure you're alright Pete?"

"No... I'll be okay," he croaked . "I just... feel a bit... strange... " whereupon of a sudden his head fell back onto the cushion.

They sat somewhat nonplussed.

"I think we should get help," said Betty.

"No wait!" Valerie's attention was on his lips, from which there now broke a whisper:

"It's Joseph... "

Valerie was struck dumb, but as the situation came clear she responded ad hoc:

"Joseph?" she echoed. "Who are you? I mean, what did you do on earth?"

"Oh I used to grow strawberries," came the desolate little voice. "But please Miss, it's all dark here. Please help me. I feel so alone!"

"How can I help?" she begged, frustration mounting.

"You know I'm here now," said he, the sigh of relief and its significance going unnoticed.

"I will pray for you Joseph. What else can I do?"

But his answer glowed with gratitude:

"You've done it Miss. You've listened to me."

A tender pathos had come through the gloom, and she realised how his dark, lone concept of death had been dissolved by her kind attention.

It also struck her that such an available method of contact might be used to cast the net further. For if Joseph could communicate, why not the anonymous writer from among those colleagues? He or she may be the sort of personal guide mentioned in her literature, supposedly near enough to keep an eye on Peter's inner welfare and whose aid might not only salvage him but clear up many residual questions – in particular about his proneness to trance.

This gamble would have had much less appeal without Betty's trusted support, and a sense of rightness overlooked because of its inherent presence. So because there was no sign or feel of Peter returning, his body's present occupant must be gently let go.

"Joseph, I must ask you to leave the medium now if you will. Alright? You can come again, I promise, and you don't have to feel alone any more. I'll be here."

While she was wondering if the promise had been a bit rash, his docile submission made her feel worse.

"I'd like that Miss. I'd like to come again. "Well goodbye, and thank you." The breath rose, then sank into quiescence.

Neither said a word, touched by the humility of his withdrawal. Peter's back lay slumped against a corner of the settee, one arm hanging limply over the side. She retrieved this and felt his pulse. It was uncommonly slow, pressing her initiative:

"Can we speak to Peter's guide please? Is he here?"

A gust of March rain spattered the window panes at her elbow, token of nature's indifference to personal whim. Betty checked her watch, tilting it toward the lamplight. Fifteen minutes had passed since he fell there, net result a needy stray. Was their venture ill-judged? Her unease hung upon the risk they ran with so inexperienced a medium. Moreover, a fresh development rose to confront them.

Starting with tremors, his body began to shake all over, and Valerie began to fear that she must call the doctor. With Betty she had drawn her chair in front of him, portable cassette recorder on lap, becoming steadily more concerned, until within a minute the shakes subsided into an almost breathless calm.

Yet something about him had changed. Something different from the Peter she knew loomed large, rather inscrutable. Here certainly was the auric presence she had felt during their writing. Could this mean that the one she sought was in control? Irresolute, she fiddled with her bracelet and checked the recorder was running. Then, in those tardy seconds, a sudden voice spoke out:

"COME ALONG VALERIE!"

It was an encounter more potent than sound alone. Somewhat taken aback she stared wide-eyed.

"Oh… I-I'm sorry. I wasn't sure you were here. Is this Peter's guide now?"

"It is. Good afternoon."

Tones sharp at first were now like those of a benign schoolmaster.

"And was it you doing the writing?"

"Not I, but Orlando. He is the most adept of us in that medium. I was present however, and would ask your forbearance. Time is indeed short, but much has to be perfected before we can make ourselves clear" – words which swerved to pitying lament as another paroxysm of shudders swept Peter's body – "Oh this poor boy… goodness me… this poor, poor boy" – thence to resume in stronger tones when the ferment had passed: "I want you to be careful with him Valerie."

She felt guilty: "Not to let others in you mean?"

"There we certainly have a problem. But above all I don't want to lose him you see. Hanky-panky is the word that springs to mind. We have a serious job to do, and the Channel is inclined to take it rather lightly. He's going to leave, you know, and forget all this unless we keep him… "

" – On the path?" she identified.

"In a way. But you mustn't stress this Valerie."

"He doesn't really want it does he?"

"He is not sure whether he wants it or not."

"So what would you like him to do from now on? I mean, do you want to make use of his obvious ability as a medium?"

"I should think so Valerie, after all the trouble we took to get him here! Besides, it is the nucleus of our arrangement with him. Meanwhile I'd be grateful if you could give me more warning in future. I've been rushed back here by that unfortunate fellow."

"You mean Joseph?"

"Yes, this is partly why I'm having trouble. It's rather like being thrust on a cloudy rostrum… "

"And not knowing why?"

"Exactly. If I could have a thought-beam first, then I am notified. I feel that you are ready. After that, given half an hour, or an hour, I can ensure that conditions are clear. And it's not going to hurt this boy to sit here for… well, a tolerable length of time. Until I feel you want to speak to me, or there is an intrusion, I have no prior knowledge. You understand?"

"So you'd like us to spend some time warming up?"

"Well phone me, my dear! Need I elaborate? Just a private beam before you let him sit here again. Then we can try to explain the situation more fully. There is so much resistance now. I cannot stay long."

That was becoming all too apparent. Their dialogue had been beset since it began not merely by recurrent seizures, but by invisible sources whose attempts to intervene, she was plainly told, could not be held off for much longer.

"In fact the boy must be returned very soon Valerie."

"But what is it you want to accomplish through him? Can you tell us that before you go?"

"Oh it's a team of course."

"What, a permanent partnership between you?"

"That would be my wish, and others'."

"And is this to give healing?"

"No, knowledge… of a kind… to an intermediary level of your plane which many people miss entirely. I think perhaps even you Valerie have missed this, along with your friend."

"With Betty?"

"Yes. We feel terribly strongly, as many do on our side, that you are leaping ahead of yourselves. It's like getting to the top of a mountain and wondering why you're there. To find the Kingdom of God you must climb and fall back, climb and fall back. Do you understand me?"

"Yes we're too precipitate, though aren't we climbing and falling the whole time anyway?"

"A little perhaps. But there are those who don't at all. You see, it seems to us that there are so many on earth who know nothing, others who *think* they know a great deal, very few between."

"So this is the level you're interested in?"

"Very much. Does it help anyone if the knowledge of your top people stays at the top? They are the intellectual first-nighters of your world Valerie. There are very few people going to the matinées, and these are in more need. Too much knowledge is ignoring the populace, whereas to avoid the main pitfall in passing over for instance, a little knowledge is better than none. Do you see?"

"Well we'd like to help people, although spiritual development is still very important isn't it?"

"But of course my dear. That is the ultimate aim."

Reassuring terms. Moreover the steadiness with which they were uttered spoke to her of probity, of oakhearted commitment in one whose full measure remained unknown, and whose now obvious discomfort left hardly a moment for the asking.

"Will you say which plane or sphere you are from?"

"Certainly. I am at the stage of moving through the Gate to the Garden as we say… and that will… be better… for us all. Valerie… perhaps we could… discuss this… another… time."

"Sorry, yes. Would you just tell me your name?"

"You may call me Philip. Now I must go. We shall be… speaking to you again shortly. Do please remember… what I have said. May God bless and keep you both."

By the end his tone had worn slender as a thread. One last convulsion shook the limbs, then died away.

What might, however, have been an empty wait until Peter returned, for Valerie was aglow with the impact of her encounter – how uncannily secure she had come to feel in Philip's presence. Such an ally she would willingly serve, alone if needs must, though the prospect of doing so under cross-fire from that "Channel" who manifestly – if thankfully – was drifting back again led into a thought less sublime.

When so much left unresolved may later crop up to feed his doubt, just how far could she carry him along with her? But then nothing was so liable to shake anyone out of their questions as Peter emerging into his own.

Time had almost stood still for him since the curtain fell. His way was full of queer moving lights, muffled voices. There was a rushing sound, the sensation of falling, until Valerie's voice was heard telling him to wake – be comforted – he needn't be afraid – it was all over. His eyes opened slowly, finding himself the centre of attention.

They had turned on the main light and were blinking at him, force-laughing because nervous of any backwash. He felt indignant:

"I can't think what you find so funny! That was really weird. And my head hurts."

"Come downstairs Pete. There's some aspirin."

Postponing the main pill he had to swallow, they guided his stumbling figure out of the Sanctuary to safer environs below. Halfway down unfortunately, he checked his wristwatch and in startled dismay brought the little caravan colliding to a halt.

"My God – look at the time Val! I must have been up there a whole hour. Couldn't you have woken me?"

"Er... no. Come on down and we'll talk about it."

He moved forward, eyeing her suspiciously.

"About what? What's been going on then?"

Betty felt sorry for him, worried for her, both in their own ways having sewn themselves into a corner. He had lolled upstairs recklessly against advice, and she had used his default to glean information from the guide before trance control was expedient or safe. If left to the colleagues it might have been resolved by inner contact. Were they counting on Valerie now to assuage his stirred-up fears and take upon herself a diplomacy that ought to have rested with them? The idea made Betty glad to busy with refreshments once the two were seated, facing each other uneasily across the fireplace. She had a soul above nursery rhymes, or she might have thought of the parlour in which a spider entertained a fly.

"Well?" challenged the fly, agape with expectation.

For all her worth Valerie tried to look assertive as she placed the recorder between them on the coffee table, but only succeeded in looking surreptitious. His eyes followed her movement, lingered on the machine, then swung to her again, scenting some sort of confession to come. And when it did, he listened more intently than usual to an account which to him sounded as if she herself was speaking from another world.

His emotions locked in a battle where disbelief was winning.

"Hold on a minute Val! You're seriously trying to tell me that beings from outer space actually spoke with my voice? What did they say then?"

"Not from outer space Peter. They're from... well... another dimension. Anyway you can hear for yourself. I managed to record it".

He had suspected this fact of course, but got caught unawares by a creepy feeling at the sound of his own voice in talk which he knew didn't belong to him, like hearing a play on the radio.

What did it all mean? The play went on. Curious as he was, he longed to listen, but to do so became impossible with all the thoughts whirling round his head. Was it conceivable that someone else could actually speak through him? He stared over at Valerie, who met his gaze with benevolent eyes. She switched off the recorder, seeing him about to rise in self-assertiveness.

There was a moment's pause while he lit a cigarette, the better to present that assertiveness in as cool a guise as possible. Betty set down two mugs of coffee, then retreated before an avalanche of questions less playful than they seemed.

"So you want me to pass out every day and let you have cosy chats with another dimension? Do you really believe that's what you were in touch with? I mean, how can you be sure I wasn't sleep-talking or in some hypnotic delirium?"

"By using my intelligence and knowing it couldn't be either. We have the real thing here Pete. I feel it in my bones. It's vitally important that you sit for them. You're a natural medium like Mickie said."

"But I thought she warned against all this?"

"Of course she did, not realising it was meant you see. The whole thing's been spiritually planned, and you're the great link!"

"But why me?" he protested. That's what I don't understand. Couldn't your spirits or whatever they are have found someone who's already involved in psychic matters? Why not Mickie herself for instance?"

"Good heavens no, darl'. She's a healer not a trance medium. Besides, you're the one who was born ready with the gift, which has to develop sooner or later, perhaps coming as a bit of a shock at first till you get used to the idea. A gift like yours can appear quite late in life when the conditions are right for unfoldment, and hardly ever in the way one imagines."

"Frankly I don't know what to imagine, except that the way you're going on anyone would think I had an incurable disease. Where's it all going to lead then? And what am I supposed to do in the meantime?"

For answer she drew herself meaningfully forward on the settee:

"Pete… you remember our first lunch together, when we discussed the spiritual life – the value of self-exploration, attunement with inner levels to find one's source of fulfilment – and you said how unreal the whole idea felt to you?"

He nodded, struck by her new impetus.

"… And I pointed out," she said, "that to know the reality of anything you have to experiment yourself?"

In recognition of her drift Peter took a long breath but made no reply. She continued in kind-sounding tones.

"Well here's our chance to really explore together what's going on, whether these people are real or imaginary, whether or not the healing was a freak one-off. At the party you granted me those alternatives – true or false – and I think you understood which would have greater significance. Right from the start you'd gone to Mickie Bishop for help, allowing the possibility that some unknown, invisible element might bring about change for the good. And it did, we both agree. We're happy here, you're almost healed, yet instead of dying away that element is actually beginning to show up, explain itself, perhaps leading us on to greater happiness or perhaps not. But we won't find out with a negative attitude that treats it like a disease to be suppressed, swept under the carpet. There'll always be a lump which we'll keep stumbling over unless we positively take it up and see just where it leads, give it an opportunity to unfold – without letting the trance practice go on longer than you want, I mean. If we don't do that, and we decide that what has happened so far is the limit of its fulfilment in our lives, then we'll never know what we missed, deciding on that alone as truth and stopping there in a ridiculous attempt to protect whatever we think we've already found."

She paused to assess her audience, which had been very still and remained so because he could see little worth disputing. He let her round off without comment.

"So we must persevere with a few sessions at least darl', if you can possibly bear it. I'll ask my friend Jules over, who's au fait with these things, we can get his opinion, then decide where to go from there. But I feel certain it'll work out for the good. Please try and believe that."

Since the issue clearly meant a great deal to her, he resigned himself with caution.

"Okay, we'll see how it goes."

Valerie sank back in relief, while Betty felt this a propitious moment to leave. Gathering up her handbag she stood and turned to him.

"I'm sorry you had such a rotten experience," she soothed. "Problems tend to look bigger when they first come up. This one will look less in time. See you again soon, and be gentle with your gift."

Peter nodded blandly. He rose, shook her hand, and watched the pair of them move chatting into the hall. Maybe his acceptance had been too rash, for the prospect of being known among his friends as a medium filled him with misgiving. Half aware of Valerie's return, her arm round his shoulder, he stared in front of him feeling ill at ease. It was then that she hit upon the need of action to mitigate his worry.

"Tell you what. Let's drop it away for now, have a crack at that famous recipe of yours for supper, and from tomorrow you can take over the garden. How's that?"

Such an idea at least helped to relax him, and once they were settled with a meal on their laps watching television, he had a chance to observe her. For even though it baffled him that anyone could get so fired up about otherworld beings, his sensitivity realised that somehow this passion suited her more than the figure he now saw. She was nestling into a corner of the opposite settee, fork poised disinterestedly over her food, her impassive face turned from him toward drama on the screen, and looked oddly miscast.

When later they retired to bed he found it hard to read beneath her manner as with swift affection she touched his arm and trailed off down the corridor. How could she be feeling so certain of this whole business? Against the silence of his bedroom he flung question after question until, safe at last between the sheets, weariness with it sent him fast asleep.

But in the next room Valerie lay awake, her mind on the message not the medium, playing over an advent that it seemed she had awaited half her life. Truth to tell, over her fairly wide experience of communication it was the tug of relatedness to this particular source and its future which had touched her heart. A new ardour was alive within, yet she had expressed only the outermost tip of it in terms he would understand. Beneath lay the felt reality, savouring of heroic service even though unclear as to form. The inner sense of it melted first into prayer for him, then lulled her into restful sleep – whereupon Ashdene, having witnessed two very different steps into its future, hushed down to stillness of night.

CHAPTER THREE

A CURTAIN RISES

At the time of Valerie's call I had settled comfortably into a garden flat on the outskirts of nearby Tunbridge Wells. Ten minutes stride down the hill each morning would bring me to The Pantiles, its Chalybeate Spring for which this provincial spa town was once famous, and my adjacent place of work – a quality modern furnishers. After heaving our shop mat out onto its step, I would check my fob-watch against the neighbouring clocktower, pop it away into the waistcoat of my cheap bespoke suit, and retreat among Scandinavian glass, woodware, lighting, furniture, carpets and fabrics in pursuit of those tasks appropriate to an only salesman.

Outside business hours my raison d'etre was divided into study, teaching groups, and healing a tad awkwardly to oblige the same Spiritualist Church whose angle I had decried in youth. Yet it was at one of their services, in 1965, that Valerie's attention had first been drawn by my being a long-haired teenage healer among veterans. On her approach afterward we seemed to connect, talking half the night at Ashdene. Our mutual respect deepened through varied circles and seminars, she commending my discarnate studies and myself becoming impressed by her spiritual ideals. If in her case such respect mistook psychical knowledge to imply spiritual aspiration, I may then have been guilty of quite the reverse.

Nonetheless my ability was much overrated by her, viz. notes where she has me down as "an extraordinarily gifted physic". No more than she could spell was I even "psychic", in popular parlance, unless one counts that sentient faculty awoken at school and useable to explore discarnate sources of knowledge or as a healer. By now, at age 24, my healing work was perfunctory while the main focus had swung to incarnate sources like Jiddu Krishnamurti and Dr Kaushik.

On the day her persuasive tones came over the phone I was therefore not only loath to break a respite from psychic affairs, but also wary of her placing complete trust in a sentience not equal to the job.

"I may be too rusty for it Val. You'd do better to check him out with a decent professional."

"Oh, that would take ages Julie-boy! Besides, I've told Peter all about your marvellous work and he can't wait to meet you. Come over for a meal with us anyway. Such a lot's been happening, and right up your street. Pick you up in about half an hour okay?"

I had forgotten how in Valerie's ears my doubt would merely be construed as the kind of humility she might expect from her mystical image of me. A smile set in upon hearing that plummy pet name again, and I agreed at the prospect of her good company plus a needed meal.

But hunger got left behind once her car had turned within an inch of my herbaceous border and whisked us off along the Langton Road. For what had been sketchy over the phone now spread into graphic detail, with quotes that glistened in the light of her intrigue.

"One thing still bothers me though darl'," she said, outmanoeuvring a final bend before the village. "Do you know what's meant by – going through the Gate to the Garden?"

"It's a phrase sometimes used by senior discarnates to symbolise the second death, when entering the first mental plane. Why, did Philip use it?"

But already her face had cleared.

"Well I never! Sounded so airy-fairy. Yes I see."

Caught up in review she failed to elaborate, which was probably just as well since we were poised amid traffic for a dash into Ashdene's courtyard. Meantime my own thoughts went to the possibility, if her contact was above par as she claimed, that such a homely footing might help Peter feel at ease and thus encourage the high standard of information achieved elsewhere.

Having drawn up outside and entered those familiar portals however, I came face to face with the challenge of a medium who desired least of all to be our champion. At the halloo of voices he had rambled in from newfound exploits in the garden, his manner trying like mine to veil that country boy's suspicion of the stranger in environs we had both come to regard as a spiritual home. Indeed throughout our ensuing conversation across her coffee table he was sizing me up for some mark of the crank to confirm his letout clause.

He had not sized up long when, by the change in his face, my line of questioning sounded preposterous enough. After the run–through of his trance experience and symptoms there was enquiry into his reaction to basic colours, metals, atmospheres and locations, then into the nature of his dreams, archetypal heroes and beliefs – during which one could hardly blame the fellow for a number of stiff, evasive answers which just escaped the awkwardness of refusal. But constraining him was not so much the invasion of privacy as the need to screen any trace of what might be taken for psychism in his make-up, thereby hopefully being excused that empirical trial which loomed large and indistinct somewhere ahead of him.

"What do you reckon then Jules?" he ventured at last.

"Well you show the hallmarks of a sensitive."

"Meaning what exactly?"

"Meaning in this context that you could be classed among a wide range of people who are subject to psychic influence of various kinds."

He looked incredulous. "So you actually believe I was taken over by a supernatural being the other day?"

"Ah no, that's much more difficult to establish I'm afraid, because psychic influence isn't necessarily of the discarnate kind. We all have within us the same rudimentary psychic organism you see, which varies with individual nature and expresses itself in many different forms. It's the organism through which we unknowingly act and react upon each other all the time, and I was merely saying that yours, being more developed perhaps than most, is therefore sensitive to a whole spectrum of influences from the world you know – never mind the one you don't."

"I see," he murmured, casting an imperious glance at Valerie as if wondering if his trial might now be called off for lack of evidence. "Does that do away with the trance business altogether then?"

"No that's one of the variables," said I. "In fact it seems quite likely to me. I won't bore you with the details, but basic to this organism I'm talking about are seven major vortices of energy, each at their own degree of unfoldment which determines how the nature of your sensitivity can be expressed and its extent. Now from the symptoms and reactions you've described, those very two vortices that are said to energise for trance appear in your case to be far the most active."

He was not taken with this, but I persevered:

"And there isn't anything supernatural as you call it because everything has to be in accord with natural laws, whether known or unknown you see, to exist at all. So if we assume a basis of genuine trance we've got the perennial problem of who or what caused it."

"Oh, I thought we'd never get there!" Valerie boiled over mildly from the heat of her suspense. "Aren't we ignoring the whole thing of Philip and what he told us?"

"We had to initially Val. I understand it was the important outcome, but to Peter the mediumship of it must have been very disconcerting. He needs to feel safe in that experience, reassured about its being not supernatural or paranormal but as organic as his body, part of a healthy, recognised pattern shared by many others who find it's a natural function of the psyche. Don't you think?"

"Yes absolutely… of course. So maybe we shouldn't have a sitting this afternoon? Only I've got it all ready upstairs, put the fire on and… everything."

Peter glared at her as if she were a cracked sewer pipe, without even realising how "everything" had gone to include that preparatory beam requested by Philip. She lowered her gaze in the manner of one who receives a rebuke. I was unsure for whom I felt more sympathy.

"It's up to you Peter," came my stab at arbitration. "I didn't mean we shouldn't try. Any opinion I'd offer would need that acid test in the end. Do you want to?"

He knew at once from our upturned, expectant faces that the trial was unavoidable. Yet he was by no means alone in feeling outmastered by this critical decision. Not until his muttered allowance to Valerie of the deal they had made found us climbing her staircase did I note that my ethics would never normally have encouraged a reluctant sensitive into trance – leastways not such a beginner as he. Somehow I was swept along, sympathetic to his mood though dreamily detached from the psychological risk threatening our entire purpose.

There was anyway little time to retract, for the state in which he entered the Sanctuary – nervous, restless, scarcely able to keep still on the settee – was soon yielding to its special anodyne calm. While Valerie played an Adagio tape over his mind, I swept magnetic passes over his body.

"What are you doing?" he asked blearily.

"Just helping you relax Peter. Sit your spine well into the seat, breathe deeply, and rest with the music. You're quite safe. Everything's fine."

"Sounds so far away… I can't… "

But in the same breath he was gone. The head rolled back, his jaw hanging open with long stertorous gasps. We took up our respective positions, Valerie on a low seat in front of him, myself on an old dining chair to his right. Even the microphone seemed poised in silent readiness as noises from the street came faintly, the electric fire burned low, and the room grew dark around our opening prayer.

We had not long to wait, though in like a thief of the night slipped that unknown quantity which always threatens to disturb one's calculations.

"GOD!… "

Suddenly hissed through his parted lips it broke the even tenor of our thought in an instant, and in case we were still wondering what lurked within, a second and third cry made matters clear:

"God help me... God help me!"

"Alright we can. Say more of how you feel." My wish to soothe hoped also to understand. "Let it all out. We're with you. Tell us how you feel."

"Red!... RED!" The body squirmed as if cowering.

"Is that a colour you see?"

"Yes... EVERYWHERE!"

"You don't like it?"

"No!"

"It can be a beautiful colour."

"No!" screamed the voice again.

"Okay don't worry. We'll help you out of it."

"GOD HELP ME!"

"We'll pray for you," assured Valerie.

"NO!... NO!"

"Don't you want us to help?" I pressed. "Don't you want to get out of the hell you're in?"

"Yes," came the frail response. "But not like *him*."

"No definitely not like him." Having scant idea to whom this referred my immediate priority was to hold the sufferer's attention, which began ebbing away as Valerie strove hot on the scent:

"Who's that you're talking about? Who is him?"

Too late. The body had crumpled and our incursor gone, leaving an eerie silence.

I felt shameful enough to have encouraged a reluctant novice into trance, but the incursor let in could have been one much worse than that poor earthbound with mind effects; and we hadn't even helped. So my thoughts of closing the apparently ill-timed session were uppermost. At the point of their being put into motion however, an extraordinary lift of consciousness overtook my personal world.

With an ease that surprised me, customary parameters sunk into the shade as it were, of a brighter, enlarged level of being where together we were acutely more than ourselves. In fact one did feel from that perspective larger than life, part of a peculiar elemental knowing. Our natures knew their work in happy, trustful unison, acting out through the lower shadowy environment our separate roles in steadfast, confident participation with a single Will or Design. To give this invisible Thing capital letters neither deifies it nor reflects the true awe and humility, the trust in Oneness that I experienced. Nothing could divide us because in a way difficult to describe we were inseparable from It and one another, yet at the same time distinctly individual like burgeoning shoots from a tree in Spring.

I felt profoundly secure, back home among kindred, brimming with the exuberance of that union in a commitment to fulfil – whose nature was lost as my rational mind tried to ground it. Then I started to lose grip altogether, like falling from a treetop glimpse of one's homeland into the dense undergrowth below. Right there anyway, Valerie's vigilance had sprung alert to another sort of communion that neither of us would forget.

The muscular spasms with which it began told me that her account earlier had not been exaggerated, and even an insensitive person would have noticed the remarkable lightness, as of charged air, presently surrounding us. Impressed, but a bit palmy from my surprise interlude I bent to take the limp hands in mine, lending what boost I could muster.

Within the space of a minute we watched the fervour crumble away under laboured indrawings of breath, from which someone in that risen, less huddled figure gave utterance husky and difficult:

"Fighting!… "

"You mean you're fighting to speak?" I checked

"Yes… " answered the voice, seemingly preoccupied.

"Do you think you can manage it?"

"I *must!*"

For me, the feel of a senior discarnate in situ was unmistakable. The strong hunch also that its timbre spelt Philip hurried my vocal support.

"We're with your effort Philip. Thanks for coming."

"Thank you … for being here… this time my friend."

"Have you anything to say about the problem with your channel – because obviously he has to be clear for any work you've got in mind?"

"Much… clearer… than this," choked the answer.

"His marital problems need sorting too I think."

"Only he… can do that. You however… can be his earth guides. There are seven of us here… and we will all help. You see… he's doing the opposite… to what we… planned with him… before."

"Before he came back to this earth life you mean?"

"Yes!" he gasped. "Deliberately doing the opposite!"

Hooked by the frustration of it Valerie edged forward in her chair, but left the key question for me:

"And what exactly did you plan with him Philip?"

He spoke more fluently now in a low, restrained voice that quivered with raw feeling:

"Oh we were young… we were young! We came over here together you see… with the aspirations of young men. He had been a not terribly good doctor in the Army. We… decided then… before he went with his Golden One… that he would return to your plane and work… in liaison with us here… telling people about the many and varied spheres that surround them. He swore to be good… pure… and kind. Of course… it would have been difficult for him… never having been pure… in his life! And from the… moment of reason… he has… as usual… done exactly the opposite of that which was expected of him!"

"So he's been letting you all down?" deduced Valerie.

"He has been behaving true to form! Now… the game… must stop. We have waited… too long."

"And when was it that you were last on earth?"

"We came over in 1933."

"So Peter came back in 1941 to do this mediumship, but at some stage after his youth didn't link up with you as agreed. Was his tractor accident meant then?"

"No. That was entirely… of his own… creation."

"But after it something could be done?"

"Immediately. Now he has you. If only... in turn... he would accept us... his life would change."

"Do you think it was good for him Philip," I asked, "to move away from his wife and children?"

"Oh yes indeed my friend."

"Good for him, or good for what *you* want?"

"*So* good for him! He knew her... here... you see. But he is repeating himself... falling into... the same trap... again. It's the very opposite to what he should... be doing."

"What about the children though?" returned Valerie. "Isn't that rather a problem?"

"They both chose, knowing," he answered.

"Oh I see, they already knew about this plan before incarnating did they?"

"Of course."

"He's very tense at the moment," she thought aloud, "worried about them and the future I think."

"He *needn't*. It's all arranged for him! Oh he *fights* me so!"

Evidently Peter's subconscious was still throwing up its opposition, token to Valerie of the whole snag:

"The most important thing is to know how we can help in this situation. Is there anything we can do?"

"The power... of your prayer... would serve him best. His senses are open. Only his mind is closed. He must relax more... learn to look within... and remember. Urge upon him meanwhile... the name of Leggett's bookshop... in the Charing Cross Road. In a quieter moment this... may open a door... through which will come... recognition... of me."

There was a pause as we assimilated his counsel.

"Well Philip," said I, confident of our unanimity, "we'll do everything within our power to help."

"I rely on you! Would you like... to meet one of... the others? John... is with me."

"Fine. We'd like that very much. You'll go out and let him use the body then, will you?"

41

But already his grasp had slackened, his surrender abrupt and decisive. The transition too was swift – from a body unleashed, drooping like a marionette bereft of its strings, to one whose diminutive pulse quickened at the ingress of this new stranger.

A face which was by nature lean became steadily and subtly inlaid with another's sharper, more chiselled outlines until, after eagerly growing animation, we were delivered a full, boyish, nasal greeting.

"Hullo!"

"And you're John are you?" I presumed.

"That's right," said he with relish. "I must say it's great being able to speak with you both at last!"

His cheery demeanour loosened my first thought:

"What's it like for you sitting in there?"

"I always thought he was a bit rotten inside!" the fellow grinned playfully. "He's shaping up well though, all things considered."

"Have you done this before, John?"

"Only once. Some silly bitch in Brighton!"

"Oh dear yes, one can imagine," I chuckled.

"You would. You've seen her!"

"Really? Well we won't go into that. What have you got to say to us John? Anything you want us to do?"

"Yes. Tell him what a silly sod he's been!"

The retort made us giggle, but a hint of anxiety crossed Valerie's face.

"Will he regret it when he passes back then?"

"If I get my hands on him he will!"

Another flurry of laughter ensued, hers this time in politeness before returning to essentials:

"We gather that you all arranged to work through him in this capacity, that he was a medium from the start?"

"Yes, oh yes! He decided to return as one, although I wasn't there originally. He was the most adaptable at the time I think. But he hasn't prepared you see."

"Which means we've a lot to catch up on," I muttered.

"We have actually yes… What?… Oh alright… Yes I know, I'm just coming."

"Who's calling you?" asked Valerie

"Oh, it's just… Look we'll speak again." He sounded fractious and crestfallen. "I've got to go I'm afraid."

Obviously reluctant to tear himself away at what we took to be Philip's urgent beckoning from the wings, he did so with good grace, keen on a longer talk sometime.

No sooner had he left the body loose and tenantless than quivering signs of a re-entry by Philip uncoiled again, jerking back into life with such vehemence that Valerie had cause to whisper in my ear.

"Why was John finding it so much easier?"

"Because he'd done it before, and he also sounds nearer to earth. But the main reason could be that his mind didn't pose the same embarrassment to Peter's subconscious as Philip's, with whom the compact was originally made. Ah, here we go… "

I guided our august friend into place, a process of fits and starts while his stature filled out the body to its former gentlemanlike impress. His eventual mastery commented on John as would an elder brother:

"I hope he behaved himself. He's a pleasant lad, if a little brazen at times."

"Says what he thinks doesn't he!" I grinned.

"Always! You can see the problem of sending *him* back!"

"What role does he play in your group?"

"He works at the Centre… Oh-Ohh!"

A stab of torment drew Valerie's sympathy:

"Is this painful for you?"

"More for him!" grieved Philip. He's fighting me *all the time*!" The words shuddered with conflict, but after deep inhalation and outbreath he got a tenuous hold over it. "Now… we have a few moments left. Is there anything else you wish to ask?"

"You said something about a Centre," she prodded.

"Yes, we all work in a kind of rehabilitation centre… helping those who are lost. We have two Golden Ones with us who… "

" – Those are what we'd call Angels aren't they?"

"… If you wish," said he, as though disdainful of that earthly term. "They help us anyway in the work."

"Philip, how do you plan, through Peter as channel," I asked, "to reach an audience with your knowledge?"

"John thinks he should go to the park."

"Good heavens! And stand on a soap-box?"

"That's typical of him isn't it?" ribbed Philip.

"But it wouldn't be any good," said Valerie, heart on sleeve, "just in a crowd like that."

"Of course not. Something much more subtle is in the offing… and of that we will speak at the right time. Meanwhile our Channel must preserve his energies… and I must leave you dear friends. Jules… I'm sorry… It's going to be a rough exit."

Indeed it was, for such strength as he had left gave out at once like a snapped fiddle string. Nerve-energy rushed from under his loosened grip, its backlash jolting every sinew into a cathartic fury whose scale drew Peter nearer to consciousness, and finally hurled him headlong into my arms, his face white, his eyes dilated in terror.

"Oh Christ what's happening to me? It was all so horrible!" he wailed, trembling.

"Rest easy old chap. You're back with us now."

A hard stifled sob tore its way through his throat and his shoulders shook. Over them I could see Valerie, her eyes full with that eager mothering tenderness which womankind feels for man at his most vulnerable. She stretched to him so that the tips of her fingers rested on his knee.

"It must have been absolutely awful for you darl'. Can you forgive me?"

He mumbled something inaudible and took the glass of water I proffered, drinking greedily. Whatever he had undergone kept him silent however, wrapped in a sombre dream through our closing prayer, then on down between us in faltering steps to the sitting room where, to the tune of Valerie's kitchen preparations, I gave him some healing before the fire.

In that interim he sat passive, without paying any outward heed, staring numbly at the dancing flares of light. Nothing was said by any of us until, when the treatment came to a close, it occurred to me that a stranger like myself might more readily draw him out, especially in surroundings which were second nature.

"Now, do you fancy a stroll in the garden? The fresh air will do you good."

With a gesture half hopeless, half appealing, he nodded his assent and rose to follow me through the kitchen, unable there to face the lady who turned to watch him with so kindly a confidence. Over her quiet garden the night had fallen soft and still. The moon was invisible but its presence was near, for the sky was clear and bright, and the roofs around us gleamed in sharp outline. We stood for a few moments breathing the moist air.

I remained silent, giving him time to recover his self-control. Soon, as we sauntered forth down the brick path, my chief thought broke out:

"Do you want to talk about it?"

The question came as no surprise. He didn't even turn his head. But his mind seemed to struggle up from some profound depth where it had lain insensible, feebly and disjointedly fumbling for words:

"I don't know what to say. I feel so confused. It's like I don't know what's real and what isn't anymore."

"Were you ever that sure?"

His glance flashed over my face, searching and cold.

"Don't play games with me Jules. It isn't funny."

"No it isn't. Certain subjective experience taken seriously can transform your life for the better."

We had stopped in a nondescript corner by the greenhouse. Hands in pockets he scuffed the ground.

"Okay then, tell me this. Does something have to be real for it to be frightening?"

"Obviously not," I replied, "but if you've made up your mind that physical perception alone is real, then anything else is going to seem either unreal and therefore unworthy, or a challenge and frightening isn't it?"

His attention rose to the panoply of stars over us.

"I suppose you'll say they're an illusion next."

"Only if you think their reality is limited to what you see. A deeper perception would open up their deeper reality. Trouble is, we erect barriers where none exist, and you've just taken a header right through yours – so you naturally feel shaken and scared. Accept that fair reaction, because anybody in your shoes would feel the same, but for God's sake don't let it smother the basic experience. Bring that out into the fresh air too, and see how it stands up under the heavens. Can you pinpoint what bothered you most?"

"I'm not sure. I remember being drawn up through a kind of funnel, and then floating like before in that horrible inky blackness. I couldn't seem to get upright this time. It was so awful, Jules – I thought I'd died. Then I started hearing my own voice first hand, not just on Val's tape."

"Did you hear what it said?"

"In bits, which kept fading and coming back again, but none of it made any sense. Was that a spirit?"

"Hold on. Were you aware of anyone else?"

"I could hear your voice and Valerie's sometimes, sort of muffled in the background. I didn't see those faces again. If you mean did I see the spirit, no I didn't thank God. Maybe I'd have flipped if I had. I thought *you* were meant to be figuring all that out."

My figuring out at the time was actually concerned with how much "that" would survive his incredulity in the telling, a decision which resolved itself as he lit a cigarette. For in its glare one could see that his expression had set tight, apprehensive of what he dare not comprehend. I motioned us to continue along the path, his response to which angled more toward a seedbed en route than to the theme in hand.

"So what happened then?" he added curtly, as though it were of no special moment to him. It was a moment nevertheless which required special care.

"Perhaps you'd be in a better position to make up your own mind about that," I proposed, "if we first dispense with that word, spirit, you used just now. You sound like you're misleading and scaring yourself by slapping the image of a wraith or spectre on human beings who as far as I know are simply discarnate."

"Doesn't it amount to the same thing?"

"Not in your head it doesn't, I bet. Otherwise, why think you'd have flipped if you'd seen one? You've borrowed a derogatory image from other people's fears of death which you react to without thinking, a superstition that goes on projecting fearful imagery as if it were true. Do you want to live with that in your head – the product of herd-mind thinking? Or do you want to suss things out yourself for a change?"

His not unmindful silence let me continue.

"Given for instance that you're normally aware of yourself as incarnate, or in a body of physical flesh, if then you temporarily experienced that same awareness outside your body – in a subtler one – did you suddenly become in those minutes a nonhuman wraith? Or were you merely discarnate for a while, with your human selfhood perfectly intact? During that experience, you didn't doubt it did you? Work it out yourself. Maybe that's all you lose at death – just a physical garment. And if that's all that happens to everyone, maybe some people who've already shed their physical garments have come back to heal you, then to borrow yours once in a while to share their further experience or show us a certain way of helping others. That, in answer to your question, is what appears to me to have happened, which isn't particularly unusual. You mustn't regard yourself as some kind of screwball because of this Peter. Dozens of practical, healthy-minded sensitives have been through the same and more, allowing it to open in them a greater awareness of life and losing only the delusions that have held them in unnecessary fear. So relax, give your mind the benefit of the doubt. Put those thoughts in your pocket for now and we'll discuss them another time – maybe hear the tape when you feel ready. Meanwhile enjoy physical things, like the garden here, and this meal of ours if it hasn't gone cold!"

Perhaps because my words, which had taken us back to the kitchen door, offered him a handy way of escape he didn't try to argue or enquire about our session. Instead he turned to face me with grim simplicity:

"Will I have to do it again?"

"Not if you don't want to. It's your decision. I suggest you wait and see what develops, remembering that you're ultimately in control and can stop it with an effort of will if you prefer. Allowing and resisting at the same time sets up the friction which hurts. Be your own master, and allow your faculty just enough rein to see for yourself what's happening. But above all try to be patient, because the first steps in anything are bound to involve tumbles. Val and I will give you all the support we can, though she's got a heart big enough to manage on her own – as much for you, I might add, as for the mediumship."

At this last remark Peter eye-fixed me keenly for a moment, met only my expression of coaxing hopefulness, and went on inside. The meal awaited, but under Valerie's quizzical stare I was glad that his prior dash to the loo gave time for a quick dissuasion against her playing the tape. We agreed to spare him its challenge until the residue of his shock had died down, enabling the next couple of hours to flow smoothly. On lighter topics his vein of humour soon joined our attempts to keep a situation afloat which might have run aground.

That it also drained him of tension was obvious from his peaceable kilter by the time he took off early to bed, as Valerie remarked once he was out of earshot.

"He's much better, isn't he?"

I just nodded, for the time of joint reckoning had arrived and we knew it.

"Well?" she purred, tucking slim legs beneath her. "How do you think it's going to turn out, and will he be able to cope?"

"I think he has the ability to cope very well," said my caution. "How it turns out will depend on whether he uses that ability, which depends on how much he comes to accept them."

"You mean he might never accept them enough?"

"I don't know Val. He's not the prime candidate for looking within and remembering at *that* depth is he?"

"How many of us are?"

"Okay, but most of us have no cause to do so. From what Philip and John said I assume his psychic sensitivity was meant, a couple of years ago maybe, to tune him into them and remember their compact. But his ego by then had pulled him under earth conditioning which cut off the inner will for it, so now he just reacts to this wake-up call of theirs like an average punter. I've tried to give him a punter's picture of my opinion so far, though he needs more than that to chime in."

"Philip said the power of our prayer would serve him best didn't he?"

"Yes, which could include us visualising him attuned to his inner self. It sounds like that's the life Peter had decided on before rebirth. Ordinarily, soul-influx time is supposed to be within the age-range of 28 to 33, and he's 31. Philip says they've waited too long, but in any case they may have planned his psychic attunement to inner self and colleagues at one stroke. That's my take on it, if he's doing exactly the opposite as we're told."

"Oh no doubt in my mind there. "

"Right. I was only thinking that to help reversal by prayer alone is a bit steep. He might need an outer endorsement of them which he can believe more than he does mine, someone he doesn't see as being so involved but who can clairvoyantly pick up on them without any prompting."

"Like Marcus Grainger for instance?"

He was an Eastbourne palmist she had befriended. I meant another species entirely.

"No we need one from the main qualitative sphere in London, someone of calibre at the College of Psychic Studies or the S.A.G.B."

"But won't dragging him solemnly up to town on the train make him feel even more out of his element?"

She was right, I had to admit. The formal pressure it might convey was the very effect we should avoid."

"I know!" she exclaimed. "How about Mary Rogers?"

Still shades off the calibre envisaged, here nonetheless was not just a healer of renown but quite a gifted lady. Having myself noted the testimonials of Harley Street specialists recommending her clairvoyant diagnostic ability, seen her win over distrustful Anglican priests and cynical TV journalists, and listened to her husband, twenty five years an MP, campaign sincerely on her behalf at Westminster Hall, I felt inclined to give an otherwise ordinary, fortyish, silver-blonde, buxom mother of two consideration for the job. Her existing relationship with Valerie moreover, coupled with her country apartment being only half an hour's drive south, won my casting vote.

"Okay. I suggest we leave it a week, let him immerse himself in earthy pursuits with plenty of fresh air and sunshine if possible, then motor down there on a casual chat basis and see what she picks up without prompting. Even if she can't distinguish between live beings and thought-forms he might simply presume confirmation, or at least infer that he's not going potty."

Valerie agreed, leading our discussion over issues of spiritual protection, wholesome diet, and how to be "earth guides" with allowance for his choice, until at midnight we adjourned to the Sanctuary for a spot of prayer. I then took her daughter Mary-Ann's bedroom opposite Peter's in case he should awaken disturbed from such an evening. His, unlike ours, had after all been spent devoid of any belief-structure to reconcile the idea of invisible people in control of his body. Neither was he aware of the disclosures they brought, nor imbued thereby with the sense of mission that now lightened our footsteps past his door.

Alone for the first time myself in the shadow of these deficits I lay abed pondering the whole affair. My prompt conviction of its authenticity and import had surprised Valerie because of what she knew as "the normal pussyfoot stealth" in me over appraisal of any mediumistic produce. But then she was not aware of my uplift in consciousness just before Philip came, which had left me with a recondite sense that accepted him and John more swiftly than I would otherwise have done. I felt self-conscious about it, though a fair judgement anyway required provisional trust in the case they had presented. Whether Mary Rogers would actually endorse their existence was to me the immediate crux. If she didn't, Valerie's belief in them might weaken and Peter might refuse to sit, though that was small fry compared to the tussle seen ahead if she did.

For granting them bona fides, had they also got a strategy to pull this gifted but green and reluctant novice into proper working order? "He hasn't prepared you see," John had said, which I took to mean that in not accessing the psychic level of himself as pledged, Peter had not smoothed out the distortions of nascent mediumship – work needful with any gift till practice matures it. Maybe his focus on the lower emotions too had lowered the frequency of his psychic state, attracting those earthbound characters into control. "There we certainly have a problem," Philip remarked. Were they geared to surmount all that? I imagined they thought so, having bothered to establish themselves with us. Or was Peter's memory of Philip expected to shine through and save the day?

My overview, however, pointed to Valerie and I being as much part of the plan as he, so perhaps we ourselves were answerable for our state of readiness. The decade we had spent in metaphysical homework might have arisen from an inner directive toward our "earth guide" roles, though prone to error of course. Had we done our own homework properly enough to cope? All in all I came to conclude that if we were heading for a debacle it would likely be one which the years had prepared and not the moment.

★ ★ ★ ★ ★

Spring advanced in Langton Green, and in Valerie's heart, while she and Peter drove down to Mary Rogers' Sussex home, there was an open, trustful, delicious feeling. Such sentiments had been alive in her since those latest unveilings from Philip. Pent up against Peter's almost total lack of interest she had found outlet in phone calls to my flat, when it was decided that the purpose of our mission to Mary was better served by a tape recorder than my presence – which might weigh too heavily on what was supposed to seem a light jaunt.

The grounds for inviting Peter were left to her, but are not hard to conceive. Restitution never took long in their amicable relationship, and the snug enfold of permanence felt at Ashdene had overlaid his anxieties for a time, rooting creativity in the garden. Indoors, because her fondness for a wide circle of acquaintances was very much his scene, he may have accepted today's trip as just another on the social round.

"Let's go and see Mary Rogers!" – would have been enough to throw him blithely and capably at her wheel, bringing them among the petite meadows and pine woods of Wivelsfield Green sooner than she expected. As Peter slowed along Hundred Acre Lane for the driveway of High Pines they were well ahead of the 6pm venue which her trustfulness had covertly beamed at Philip beforehand. That same mood had omitted to give any advance warning of their visit, so an initial glimpse of the popular healer in jeans and headwrap peering disconcertedly over the bonnet of a furniture van should not have surprised them. She was having new upholstery delivered, though upon recognition of Valerie welcomed them both into her home for a quick beverage.

Hers was one of three apartments into which the great gabled house was divided, with sufficient space like at Ashdene to include a sanctuary. Unlike that of Ashdene its white walls and red carpeting surrounded a large, central hassock for the use of her patients. Pride of place above the altar was given to an illuminated oil portrait which Valerie had undertaken to paint based on a spontaneous vision of Mary's, said to have lasted about twenty minutes and believed to be of The Nazarene. Its having surpassed either's best hope kept up their conversation rooms away where they sat around her hearth. But at the point of Valerie's artful steering to enlist her present-day vision, the healer suddenly signalled for quiet. Peter, she noticed, had fallen into trance.

Immediate ken of the symptoms drew Mary to take up his hands in support. They were cold and limp. His breathing was less tumultuous than before, as though itself being taken up by someone whom she obviously felt to be on the verge of control.

"Come through friend… Come right through."

Moments of heaving respiration passed, then:

"Good evening," emerged a mild voice, whose hint of duress led Valerie to assume it was Philip's.

"Oh good evening! You managed to come then! Did you get my message this morning? I'm trying to do what you said – send you a… a beam."

"Yes of course we did Valerie," was half whispered.

"And are conditions better today?"

There was no response. Mary took over again:

"What is your name?"

"King… " trickled out, this time with effort.

"Are you a King, or is your name King?"

"David King," enunciated the voice softly. "Do you feel the pressure?" Adding to his discomfort, one of her dogs started to bark from the conservatory.

"No, there's no pressure," she averred. "Don't worry about the dog. Nothing will harm you or move you. Don't leave the body suddenly. Just do it very gently and use my power. You can stay a little while and then leave very gently because you'll have all the power which is around me, you see."

"Yes," said the compliant David.

"Don't make it hard. Just slip out of the… "

" – But why is it so difficult to come through?"

"Well, the medium's subconscious is fighting you. It won't be difficult in time. What did you do, David?"

"I was a soldier. Why… is there… ?"

"Why are you shaking the leg do you mean? Did you have an injury in your leg? Were you shot in the leg? Where were you – Tobruk?"

"No I died in '33. My brother crashed the Morris."

"Yes, you're experiencing the pains you had then. Quite often David, when souls come back to me I sense the asthma which they had. They seem, on returning to earth, to re-experience their old earthly conditions. But with practice you'll find you don't need to do this. You've now been through it, so release these earthly pains."

Whilst re-experience is indeed common for novice users of a channel, the leg shakes here might have been Peter's own – triggered again by stress. If David had been briefed about what to expect it could explain his puzzlement, sending Mary into her standard explanation because she was probably unaware of Peter's injury.

"You're doing very well David," she sailed on. "If you have another medium like myself, you see, you can use the extra power to… "

"That's why I'm here. John advised me to come."

"So are you one of The Seven," Valerie chipped in, "with he and Philip?"

"Yes but this is my first time. They'd already tried it through someone else."

"That's right, John said he had. Were you with them the other night when they spoke to Jules and I?"

"No I wasn't there."

"I knew he wasn't!" crowed Mary. "He told me before he spoke through here – telepathically."

Valerie continued to elicit what she could:

"Is there anything you want to say David?"

"No, except that I'm going to come through more often now… and help. But because of… the pressures… John said to come first with this lady."

"Yes, fine," perked up the lady again. "You just slip in and out of the body. Now, tell me which part of the medium you entered. Was it at the back of the head or the top?"

"At the back," said he, with forbearance.

"Right. Now you take it very gently, and when you leave, do so the same way and withdraw very slowly as though your body were oil. Just slip out through the aura without jerking or shaking. My power will help you move back, and the next time you come I'll tell the medium to breathe more deeply and you'll come in more easily."

"Very well," said David, taking the hint. "Goodbye."

"We do send our love to you friend."

"And send my love to the others too," Valerie added.

"Bless you," were his parting words.

As the head tilted peaceably downwards she conceived his release from the pressure of physical density to be like that of a deep-sea diver leaving the ocean bed and slipping up through murky waters to a brighter, more real world above. Then she thought of his being the third member of The Seven to have plunged here, while Mary gave off little bubbles of soi-disant clairvoyance – one of which quickly got burst:

"Have we got some Air Force boys?"

"No they're Army I think."

"I see them in uniform. He was twenty-eight when he left, you'll find. Now, no tremors. There's no need for it. Slip out very gently. Goodbye David. Deeply breathing remember. Come and see me sometime. Was he an officer? I can see the belt and the cross-belt. We'll let Peter come back now. He's coming."

"Don't tell him about it yet, please!"

"Umm?... No."

"He'll be alright will he?"

"Oh yes dear. Look!"

Certainly there were drowsy signs of a return. In the narrow lull his frame had hung slack and immobile, but now eyelids were fluttering open dopily.

"Uhh-sorry Mrs... um," he snuffled. "Didn't mean to drop off. You must think I'm terribly rude."

"Not at all Peter. You've had a refreshing nap."

"God it's dark in here. Is there a power cut?"

Twilight had stolen upon them unawares, and when they left High Pines half an hour later the stars were twinkling through its branches. Even then Peter was still blissfully ignorant of the event from which they drove away. Ensconced in idle chatter beside her turn at the wheel, his humour lifted her despite the irresolution churning within – the unhappy choice of whether to tell him on the spot, or at home, or never.

Never telling him could hardly be imagined let alone borne. Doing so at home brooked a delay whose every minute threatened to undermine his trust. Having avoided an uncomfortable scene at High Pines why not tell him here, while their wheels were in motion, the going soft? She met his laughing eyes for an instant to reassure herself, then looked back to the road.

"Pete… I simply have to tell you. Someone came again while you were asleep."

His smile disappeared into a moment of bewildered curiosity.

"You mean… one of your spirits?"

"His name's David actually."

"But how? It wasn't like the last time was it?"

"No he's new," she said, connecting unrelated facts. "You don't have to worry though, because Mary helped."

"How embarassing! Is she into all that?"

"Oh yes, she's a medium herself you see, and clairvoyant too. She saw them in the service uniforms they wore at the time of the crash, with Sam Brown belt."

"What crash?"

"Well David said that his brother crashed the Morris. I suppose it's how they and Philip must have passed over in '33. Anyway that's why I took the portable – rather sneakily I'm afraid, in case she saw something I could record. You don't mind, do you?"

A jerk of the shoulders and a sigh was all he gave her. She glanced round at him briefly, but his quiet face told her nothing. It had frozen into hard, unyielding lines, fixed on the road in front of him. There fell a dead silence broken at length by her sense of guilt:

"Are you angry with me?"

"… No," he said hesitantly. It's just that… if these people are in fact real, as you seem to think, and have actually survived the grave, I still don't see why they have to home in on *me*. I don't want to end my days as a cranky medium in a Bayswater bedsit. Why can't I just be me, and live an ordinary, uncomplicated, free life like everyone else?"

"But Pete, crankiness comes from a person not from mediumship! You'd have to be a crank in the first place to end up as one. Most mediums I've come across aren't in the least like that. They're just average people who try to steer clear of cranky sects, and whatever you think of Mary she isn't a prime example – although they're also practical housewives as she is, business executives, university lecturers, priests, even J.P.s. Some of them, like Eileen Garrett for instance, work with physicians and psychologists, and keep an open mind about the people who talk through them. Or take Ruth White, the medium for Gildas. She's Headmistress of a primary school, and you have to be down to earth for that. In fact I'm sure any of them will tell you that to do the job properly at all, not only do you have to be very well balanced, but it's an absolute must to live an ordinary, uncomplicated life like everyone else."

She cast an imploring look at him that didn't meet his eyes. He was staring heavily at the floor.

"Maybe," he said with slight disdain. "But you haven't answered my question. Why *me*?"

"I was coming to that." She began quickly, pulling out the heart of the matter, dreading his response to it. "Actually I thought Jules had told you, but the thing is … they say you agreed to be their medium before coming to earth."

"Good God Valerie! Into reincarnation now are we?"

Such a possibility sounded too foreign for him.

"And what's more," said she, standing her ground, "they say you worked alongside them as a Doctor in your last life, and are asking you to remember Leggett's."

"Leggett's? What the devil's that?"

"It was a bookshop in the Charing Cross Road. You used to go there with Philip I think."

She found it impossible to meet his look any longer, though she made an effort to do so. Peter uttered not a word. He was as one turned to stone. His eyes, with hers, became once again fastened on the road, but his stare this time was wide and intense.

Whilst the nature of their ensuing pause was not hard to fathom, its extent made Valerie soften up.

"You had to know sooner or later darl'. It must sound rather ridiculous I suppose. Not that you're expected to believe everything right away of course, but somewhere deep within we... we have these memories, like we do from childhood... unconsciously reacting to them or... resisting them sometimes, and there was just a chance the name might ring a bell. It doesn't then, presumably?"

He shook his head in silence, not looking at her.

"No... well Philip did say you'd have to relax and look within first," she reflected, "though I shouldn't think they'll want to make an issue of it. They're only trying to jog your memory a bit in the hope that you'll come to accept them. And none of us, least of all me, would want any of this to become a burden to you, because there's absolutely no need. We can keep it to a very close and private circle of friends who understand, if you like. After all, if it's going to be as easy as this evening there's hardly anything to worry about is there? You can still be you, living life to the full, and Jules says that mediumistic development can actually enhance your appreciation of things you enjoy."

Peter stirred, raising his eyebrows as if to throw an ironical rejoinder. But he restrained it. She herself hesitated, then continued with the utmost gentleness:

"It's quite true you know Pete. I've heard them say the same in lectures. There also has to be fulfilment and security in one's material life apparently, to keep a proper balance. So as you're ready and able to stand on your own feet again now – in fact very much need to – what I thought was... if we could start some enterprise, like a small garden shop for instance, which you could really feel happily involved in, and perhaps earn enough money to support yourself and Jean… it might be the best answer, mightn't it?"

His drawn face unclouded magically. Having tried this once with a friend and failed however, he knew the sterling problem all too well.

"But a shop lease costs thousands Val! Then there's fixtures and fittings, outgoings – you name it. What am I expected to use for money, shirt buttons?"

They had passed through the fringes of Langton when she thus found herself in the hot seat. She had no answer for him, though the notion had flashed upon her with a curious vividness, swift and sure as an arrow. It hung in the air while they trundled into Ashdene's forecourt and both emerged broodily.

Over the village an evening mist had fallen, through which her elegant little shop façade with it's low-plunging window inclined Peter to dawdle.

"I had that sort of frontage on my flower shop in London," said he wistfully. "They're quite rare now."

"Well why don't we use it?" Valerie had sidled up behind him, a note of proud resolution in her voice. "I can paint anywhere there's light, you see. Besides, my work doesn't depend on passing trade like a flower shop does, and my fixtures might suit you too."

"I'd pay you a proper rent though," he insisted, not yet believing his ears.

"Oh that can keep till you're up and going."

He had been taken off guard, and it showed as his quick eyes sought hers:

"You really don't mind giving up your studio?"

"Of course I don't, if you mean business!" Her head was thrown slightly backward, half-laughing in a tender, mocking way. "Let's go and discuss it over supper."

So excitedly they laid their plans, in the heat of which nothing more was said of the earlier occurrence. Her advice about it had not gone unheeded, but during those last hours of March 30th 1972 Valerie first grew aware that already in his young head such considerations, far from being used as a key to balance, were instead being absorbed into rationale along the lines of his ambition – where time would tell that she had not a shadow of influence.

CHAPTER FOUR

THE GATHERING OF THE CAST

Gatherings at Ashdene, when not for metaphysical aim, usually came about by coincidence. From week to week, temporary incumbents would rub shoulders with regular habituees in a sporadic, often incongruous manner which left one never quite knowing with whom one would next be sharing a settee. Not that the company was ever less than intelligent and gracious, but Valerie's catalytic nature had a way of drawing unlikely people together, and her mixed harvest at tea-time the following Friday was deceptive because it was usual.

Since a 4:30pm summons Betty had waited on one of the settees, clad in plain, spruce and seemly attire, handbag tucked well at heel, listening with courteous interest to some harum-scarum exploits of college life from across the coffee table. Their narrator was the bouncy and vivacious Mary-Ann, home after another bout of studies and who, on approaching her 18th birthday, effused all the quick-witted energy of youth in liberal if not decidedly bohemian spirit.

Curled up cat-like amongst the cushions, dabbing king-size cigarettes into a bulbous glass bowl, her denim and pullover style characterised for us a happily tomboyish journey to womanhood, while others took the view that she had amply arrived. The latter would dance attendance by phone or on foot, and whenever I answered the doorbell they would hover, blinking at me with the expression of someone looking for a pint of milk. Pint-sized she may have been, but milk she was certainly not – most candidates fizzling out under her strong, proud, though popular leonine disposition. For whether Mr Right turned out to be a fusty seer, a seven stone weakling, or a handsome knight, he had to have that touch of resonance.

Somewhat comparable was her reach toward things of the spirit, fuelled through a close relationship with her mother. Although too absorbed in secular affairs as yet to venture beyond the shallows, her keen, alert mind was always quick to sense practicality or meaning, which sense lent sufficient enthusiasm at one stage to buy several copies of T.E. Lawrence's poignant after-death narrative and distribute them as a challenge among her friends.

If from myself, currently foraging for a stray book along the shelf behind her, Mary-Ann engendered the kind of fondness one might feel for a younger sister, this would have been untrue of the young man who lounged in an easy chair nearby – not least because he was around her own age. Having something of youth's leggy charm besides its awkwardness, John Maynard was a bit of a ladies' man in his quiet way, though well outside the social circles in which she herself revolved. Moreover their background values were so disparate that, in asking him along as the top seed of young intuitives from my meditation class, the possibility of these two having the slightest element in common never occurred to me.

His long-haired, angular frame in faded jeans, manbag and sandals moved in that nomadic folk-world of guitars, music festivals, vegetarian food et al, and with large feet planted firmly on mother earth such influences as Tolkien, Castenada, and Kahlil Gibran when allied through a pale, sensitive face bespoke the mild natured stargazer. Valerie likened him to a shy Afghan pup, at which caricature I had to smile. That is, until in turn being compared to one of those plodding labrador guide dogs.

At present, with an ear to her daughter's badinage wafting over Betty's head, she stirred sanative broth in the kitchen. It was her most neutral domain, for aptitude had long bid her mind upstairs and the ailing stomach had whittled epicurean fancy down to a Walnut Whip. The snag of this chocolate delicacy was that it happened also to be the relished prey of certain other household gannets, from whom even half-eaten morsels had to be hidden in odd, out-of-the-way corners.

I had just chanced upon an early example carefully secreted behind a pile of books, and was trying to determine its rough age, when the front door rattled and footsteps sounded in the hall. The fact that all eyes turned except Valerie's made me wonder for whom else she had left off the latch, suspecting already that more was astir out there than her medicinal gruel.

Mary-Ann's turn of enquiry meanwhile had been caught by the item I held up between two fingers, which roused a cry of playful exasperation:

"Mummy you are wicked! You said there weren't any chocs! Oh Robert! Look what we've found in the bookcase. Isn't she naughty?"

Sure enough, in the doorway towered Robert Riddell. Except for a Teutonic strain in his 31 year-old makeup, Robert's dignified bearing was in every other respect that of an Englishman. Solid, well-to-do, fit for any requirement this world can make, he was so suggestive a figure that it scarcely needed the artist in Valerie to deck him with images. Another time and circumstance might have found him in straw boater, white flannels and blazer, manfully punting some twenties belle and a picnic hamper along the Thames at Oxford. But tonight, on his way home from the offices of The Sunday Times, we were offered the formal weekday accoutrements of a finely tailored blue suit, neatly pinned tie curling into his waistcoat, and highly polished black shoes in which, after a glance of bemused indifference at the trifling tidbit in my hand, he strode forward to greet his host with the air of a diplomat who had just been on the phone with most of Europe's Foreign Ministers.

Had he actually managed to do so, I doubt that any of us would have been surprised. For Robert's public relations department reportedly had a hotline to governmental sources of information throughout the world. The kind of man too who could organise committees, conferences, and talk of the latest art form or advance by science naturally reinforced his esteem in the eyes of others. Such an esteem, exaggerated or not, may have led to his being sufficiently instrumental in shaping the Tutenkhamun exhibition that year as to find him, months later, among the Queen's touring entourage. Nor did this greatly surprise us at the time, knowing him to be an alphabet of all the proprieties.

He also had plenty of imagination. His bachelor cottage in the South Downs village of Jevington was rigged up with an expedient whereby the evening meal was cooked to a fine turn exactly upon his arrival home each night. Then, having satisfied his gourmet appetite, he would pore through rugged accounts of the world's great explorers which were stacked in voluminous precision beside his favourite armchair. From earthly pioneers, whose privation and stamina had on occasion thrust them to the brink of mystical experience, it had been a small step to those explorers of the multidimensional universe when his best friend's mother happened to be Valerie. Her son Nigel and daughter-in-law Sue lived near The Hungry Monk, their fashionable restaurant which was yards from Robert's cottage.

Over their shoulders the link with Valerie cleared his view of religion and triggered profounder interest. It brought him testimony he had never known existed, including the celebrated works of Dr Brunton. Later in 1972 something of a milestone for him was to spring up with Professor Raynor Johnson's The Spiritual Path. Apart from answers to vital queries of his own he found within it such an ideal orchestration of Eastern-Western approach for the beginner that, with imperative ardour typical of Robert in those days, he purchased Foyle's entire stock of copies and mailed them to "deserving" friends.

It made the only parallel I ever observed between he and Mary-Ann, whom after moving her legs to allow him room on the settee took on the appearance of a whisp beside a colossus.

"Not interrupting anything I trust?" He looked about him, then met my assurance from behind:

"Nothing much Robert. Have you heard the tapes?"

To my knowledge he had been sent duplicates.

"Yes, this is why I'm here," said he, surveying my shop-soiled suit disparagingly.

"It's why you're *all* here!" Valerie announced, as she came to take her seat beside Betty. "I thought we might discuss them. What did you think of our latest one?"

The question was addressed to Robert, because she had found me dismayed with the result. Not with that of David King coming through, which in my chagrin I hadn't even bothered to hear, but with how little of substance Mary had claimed afterwards to divine. There was almost nothing she couldn't have surmised by inference. This flop being obvious to our friend, his reply was only about the dialogue via trance.

"A corroboration perhaps Fugs," he placated, using her Jevington nickname. "It seems rather a pity that the Rogers woman didn't let David have more of a say. What he did manage to get out was at least consistent with Philip and John, but I'm not sure how one assesses these things. Maybe old Jules here could tell us, and while he's about it explain why for a start no one has asked for each of their backgrounds to check against earth records."

"Because it's a pretty useless exercise," I upheld, thrown onto the horns of a dilemma far older than me, "when in getting that information one may well be just tapping into the medium's subconscious memory. It is especially so if the medium is undeveloped, as in our case. Until he is developed and the controls attain full control, re earth data in particular they can find themselves speaking involuntarily from his subconscious – or even the sitter's. Then there's the old theory of super ESP which parapsychologists like to brandish when they're stumped. They think that the medium might be clairvoyantly selecting material from afar if it isn't known to the sitter, though they fail to account for how this is done. I'm not saying that we've just got subconscious material, or that counter-theories apply here. But as long as these problems exist, among a few others I could mention, the test you're suggesting wouldn't prove or disprove anything."

"So how does one assess it?"

"Well behind your outer senses are the equivalent inner senses which are more appropriate for the job. If you can't use those, you've got your intelligence and the nous you would use as a juror in court when presented with human testimony, the material's quality, consistency, integrity and so forth. Those are the kind of evidences I believe are worth waiting for."

His brow furrowed. "But by your analogy of the courtroom surely a test of credentials would be on a par with some forensic evidence?"

"No, not in testing their validity as discarnates, because the very source of your exhibit is in question from the start. Psychism's mobile nature won't equate to the reductionism of forensic science. On another, higher level we have what you might call a metaphysical rule of thumb, for instance that senior discarnate talk has its own hallmark like a Ming vase, and I personally find psychic research knowledge helpful. But none of this will reduce down to the sort of credence you're looking for. It doesn't boil down to faith on the other hand, because you have behaviour and material to go by. I just mean that playing about with names and dates and places will bring in too many imponderables for assessment at a physical level."

Robert assessed the day's bristle on his chin as I ventured to take his premise a stage further.

"You see, even if you were fortunate enough to get all your given data confirmed by earth records, and by an extraordinary feat of imagination were able to overcome doubts as to whether it had been, unconsciously or indirectly, acquired by the medium from the very same place you found it, do you really think you'd be satisfied? I bet you in particular wouldn't. The general evidence for discarnates is overwhelming, much more than they have for the existence of black holes in so-called space. But irrefutable proof of what appears to be the case is another matter. Scientists of high rank have struggled since 1882 to find a watertight formula that proves discarnate contact, still without success because of the unknown, immeasurable, psychic element. And supposing your data wasn't confirmed, or was inconclusive, how would you interpret such a result? Multi-personality? Outright fraud? Subconscious stuff? Faulty transmission? Imposters on the line? Maybe even clerical error at the record office?"

"You're posing too many questions Jules." He shook his head gravely. "I can't be expected to answer them just like that."

"My point is that you'd be hard put to answer them at all with much confidence. So why bother? Why not use the right hemisphere of your brain instead of the left, listening out for the same ring of truth you got from Brunton and which you said altered your outlook?"

"Yes… quite," said he. "Obviously one must examine the material as a matter of course. I take your point, but I still think it might be interesting, watertight or not, to follow up references so to speak."

"Well we daren't risk that sort of testing anyway at the moment Robert," I cautioned, "because it's a delicate situation. As you know, our medium isn't only a tender novice. He's a reluctant one, sensitive to whatever he can infer as doubt from us, and will jump at the excuse not to sit at all. With Philip and Co. unpractised at control too, both sides need settling into the partnership first if you want reliable data on that level. So I'd rather you wait, otherwise it may kill the goose that lays the golden eggs. Meantime you can get the best reference from what they say, not their C.V."

"Absolutely!" Valerie broke in. "I thought we were going to discuss what they said. Is there no interest in that?"

Robert was then at pains to assure her of how, on the contrary, his intrigue with the stamp of things so far had occupied him for days. Much of it had centred over those two earthbound personalities of Joseph and the one surrounded by red, whose plight stirred up high debate among us. How such people had arrived in their states of isolation and terror was one area of enquiry. Another was why they had been allowed to remain so.

I offered input from the mainstream of after-death accounts, which of course was hampered by only knowing the pattern rather than the specific cases. As Valerie remarked, "an ordinance survey map isn't much good to a landscape artist." Many questions raised during the next half hour fell similarly under the hammer of speculation, for they needed The Seven's on-scene knowledge. At length our weariness with ifs and probables begged the most tempting question from Robert:

"Do you think he'd sit for us?"

Valerie and I exchanged solicitous glances, though from hers it looked like the evening was going to plan. She knew Robert would take the initiative, and also be tactful with Peter.

"Why not ask him?" she said. "You know where he is."

Anyone entering Ashdene at that period couldn't help but be aware of Peter's flower shop, which had sprung up almost overnight, bulging colourfully from one end of the forecourt. Moreover anyone attracted through its festooned portals would have found him most happily and feverishly in his element, eager to please with a potted bargain. The idea of Robert being thus accosted after his purposeful stride through the library brought glints of amusement. We pricked up our ears.

"You want me to come *now*?" rang out the voice of a slightly flustered florist, at a proposal we hadn't heard despite doors left ajar. The diplomatic undertones continued in earnest. Then: "Alright. Give me a minute. I'm locking up anyway."

It transpired that he had taken Robert's proposal in the form of an invitation not to sit for us but to "join us" in the Sanctuary, where in point of fact we would often transfer after a gathering. Peter's awareness of this custom was probably why he appeared quite unconcerned, moments later, on showing himself at the sitting room door in half-hearted attendance before all seven of us trooped upstairs.

That impression, strengthened by an idle comment he made en route, was certainly why I didn't attempt to reassure him beforehand, and why, once we were settled into a loose circle, I deferred the magnetic passes. It felt safe enough for him to sit accompanied by half a dozen familiar people of goodwill.

Our censing of the altar and Valerie's selection of a contemplative tape led the way. My position, again on the dining chair close at Peter's right side, found me every so often mindful of his repeated efforts to sustain consciousness – uphill work when tonight's tape happened to include the image of a serene, silent river meandering effortlessly down its course. He persevered for twenty minutes, in the belief perhaps that it was expected of him, while others drifted within or kept a weather eye open.

When at last his head nodded down to rest I leaned across to examine the somnolent form, conscious of wider interest flickering alive from the others, but conscious also of that indefinable sense of presence which marks trance control. Distinct from Peter's own as rose scent from lavender, its relatively innocuous warmth swelled up, amidst long dilations of breath, to a scale less suggestive of an intruder than the gentlemen we sought. Everyone became watchful, not sure under whose impulse the head rose with deliberation, until its occupier opened up like a shy violet:

"Good evening. It's me, David."

Valerie recognised the soft-hued inflection.

"You came through the other night didn't you?"

"Yes," said he modestly.

"Not quite so difficult this time perhaps?"

"No, much better thank you."

Four extra sitters helped, no doubt.

"What do you do in the group David?" was my coax.

"I work with Philip and John at the Centre."

"And who is Orlando?" returned Valerie, inquisitive about the writer who gave those first cryptic messages.

"He is one of us."

"So of The Seven," she tallied, "we know Philip, yourself, John and Orlando. Who are the others then?"

"There's Brian."

I figured maybe his reticence awaited practicality:

"David, may I ask what the plan of action is?"

"I hope to work with you."

"In what way?"

"We propose to continue on your plane the work I do at the Centre with Philip, because some won't accept us and we can only get through to them after they have re-contacted earthly surroundings."

Taut seconds of silence followed this bombshell, at which even Valerie was tongue-tied. It reduced me to verifying what was obvious:

"Er… their recontact being via the channel so that we can talk to them, yes?"

"Yes," he replied, "and then perhaps you will guide them? It's very important for their progress."

There was shuffling unease among the others.

"You appear very confident in us," I said meekly.

"We know you better than you think, Now I cannot stay unfortunately, because I'm due at a concert."

Somehow his plain, unobtrusive manner in putting the proposal, combined with a certain trustfulness, left me at that stage with little else to ask.

"What sort of a concert is it?"

"It is of very beautiful music."

"A cut above ours I imagine. Anyway thanks for coming to explain David."

He nodded. "Bless you friends."

Bit by bit his loosening relinquished the channel to its former tumbledown repose, and I sat back among our flurry of stirrings, stretchings and whisperings. Within that time however, close monitoring began to show someone's fast and conspicuous approach. Its whole demeanour, gathering momentum with a buoyant, infectious energy even behind closed lids, alchemised the face into cheery, bold relief.

"I know who this is," Valerie smiled.

"Hallo all!" came tones strikingly familiar.

"It's John isn't it?"

"Yes!" he resounded. "How are you?"

"All the better for hearing you John," said I, "and we're virtually able to see you as well."

"Good. Trying hard! Jules you have something to ask me don't you?"

I couldn't think what he meant other than queries about the mediumship.

"Well there are channel issues, but it sounds as if you already know the question you're referring to."

"Yes I do. It's a very good idea, and I think we can put it into practice very soon. You won't have any trouble with him."

Suddenly I realised that he must be talking about Peter, and the notion I had privately entertained at work, days before, of inviting him to sit with my study group one evening. It had risen and sunk again quite quickly in my mind as discussion-fodder for the group without particular form. John meanwhile was continuing in most optimistic vein:

"Let us know the day, and if you could ask which one of us you want to speak... It had better be me!" he teased. "But no seriously, you must make your choice and then we'll help you."

"Okay thanks very much John." My self-consciousness swung to what was more pertinent. "And what have you been up to since we last spoke, helping at the Centre?"

"Oh yes, we're very busy."

"A lot of rescue cases are there?"

"In ours, yes. It's how we met David actually. He came to us that way and we helped him. He's such a good person."

"Quiet sort of fellow isn't he?" I remarked.

"That's probably why I don't see much of him!" said John, raising a chuckle. "I think he's a bit frightened of me! He's no need to be mind you, but I think he is. He was a painter before going into the Army, you see. Lived in Bristol. Still, can't say too much with so many around, Jules!"

"And yet we gather you'd like to have your say via the channel in a public park here?"

"Well I think it's a good idea but Philip's not keen."

"Perhaps it would be easier for us to persuade those already on your side, don't you think?"

"That's what Philip and David want," he admitted, a note of concern creeping into his voice, "but I'd rather talk to some people who are there with you, before they come over. I haven't got much knowledge but I'd like to try, because a lot of problems could be avoided if they knew beforehand what to expect. So now I've got through to you at last, and have my chance, I want to make the most of it you see."

"You can give quality rather than quantity then?"

"Well, hope so!" he grinned wistfully. "But what I want to know is… what *you* want to know. It's difficult for me to pick out."

"Oh no trouble there," I assured him. "We've got plenty of questions. Maybe the most crucial one before I step aside is whether you're just hoping the Channel will carry on as he is, gradually getting used to the trance faculty, or whether steps are being taken to improve his fitness for the kind of work David has now outlined."

"Both actually," said he with fellow feeling. "It'll get much easier for him as it goes on, although his aura's very depressed. I mean there is depression in it, you understand, which takes a lot to put right, and if he'll ever get free of it in the time we have I don't know. But what I do know is that these things are all taken into account on a far higher level than I'm on Jules. Much more I can't really say, except that if you knew what it felt like even to have one of those Higher Ones brush past you, you'd trust like I do that everything's well looked after. It's also being sorted out when he comes over here in his sleep life, and Brian or Philip would tell you about that I expect."

"Right, thanks John. Now there's interest from us in someone who came through just before you and Philip last time." I turned to find heads nodding. "This character was reacting with horror to the sight of red all around. Val and I tried to help but he or she went out again. I'm beginning to wonder if the case was allowed in as practice for us."

"Philip might have," he said, "but I didn't. It must have been before I arrived. This red condition though is quite common down there and varies greatly with the person. I think it's caused by low emotion like greed or hate through earth life. There are very many colours. Some we see when we go down on rescue missions are horrifying in their intensity – you've no idea. I've seen the red myself on occasions, and believe me, red is a very ordinary word for a very frightening experience. But what I want to make clear is that people create it themselves. If they knew that fact, you see, if they had the slightest knowledge, they might realise we're friendly and come back up with us. Very often they won't come though. They're in such a sorry state, surrounded by such frightening experiences, that they regard us as part of the environment they're in. I find I can't do anything with people like that. I tend to get impatient! Philip's more understanding, but even he's not always so fortunate as to get those types as far as our hospital. They're too frightened you see. I think he'll talk to you about that tonight. I *am* getting better, but it's very frustrating. That's why I want to talk to people on your plane who have no knowledge. But I don't know how you're going to get them to you Jules. I have enough trouble getting them to come when they're here!"

An accelerated level of group interest took in the problem while Valerie offered a vestige of hope:

"There's always the odd person on earth whom one can tell though, isn't there?"

"Hullo Valerie!" he exclaimed. "I wondered when you were going to speak up."

"Hullo John. I mean even if it's only one person, that's better than none isn't it?"

"Hmm... so Philip's always telling me. I don't really think it is."

"You don't?"

"Well you probably will, one day, see what we have to do. And I think you'll find it isn't good enough thinking like that Valerie, because there are so many who have nothing, no preparation at all. So of course it's good to get through to one person, but we've got to make it many, many more."

"Oh I'd like to make it as many as possible," she insisted. "What I meant was that out of any number we talk to, only one or two will pick up the message."

"Yes but don't you see that if, having listened, they don't understand or are cynical about it, when they finally get here, and I go to them, they'll think: Ah, she wasn't so wrong after all!"

"Oh well, yes."

"Because many people here who I've seen," he went on, "have

no idea at all about what's happening to them. They're more frightened of *me*! They'd rather stay where they are. But if they knew it was their own creation, or had read one book, they'd immediately respond wouldn't they? Then they'd come with us and see how everything really is further on. Because it *is* wonderful Valerie, and it's so tragic that so many people know nothing about it you see."

"Oh I'm sure John. I think it's why one must never miss an opportunity of telling anybody one meets."

An unsure Robert put his question in her ear:

"Could you ask where John got his own knowledge?"

"Yes, well this is Robert talking now," she came back, "whom I expect you realise is with us."

"Good evening," said John. "Sorry, I didn't hear."

"John, yes. Good evening," redressed the methodical timbre. "My question is: How did you yourself obtain your knowledge? Did you go through anything like the kind of experience which our friends here came across in each lost soul?"

"No I didn't, because my Uncle was a vicar and I always thought that the afterlife was Heaven. I know now of course that it isn't like he thought, but when I passed over I suppose it helped me to realise what had happened, and I started looking round to see what was really there. I met two others who helped me a great deal, and eventually we stayed together... I'm just having a small problem."

He paused a moment, presumably to fend off the intrusion from his right side which I had already deflected twice. It had withdrawn somewhat by the time he resumed:

"Passing over is not an unpleasant experience, but I imagine it would be much worse if one had no idea at all. After a short rest you find yourself with two or three people you recognise. Now I can't tell you how I recognised them, because they weren't from earth, but I did somehow know the two who were with me. They took me to their house and I stayed there for a while. I don't know how long. Then we started working together. I was quite young when I died."

74

"Was Peter with you then?" asked Valerie. "Because you said he was the most adaptable to come back."

"No he wasn't with us then. He came afterwards."

"Around 1933?"

"Yes I suppose it must have been."

Mary-Ann popped a question. "John, is prayer more effective from your side or ours?"

"From your side definitely. And if the people we go to rescue have good friends who pray for them they soon become manageable. I don't know how. I think you should ask Philip. He knows much more about this than I do. Sometimes I'm not sure what I'm doing here at all! It's very strange, because we don't rely on names like you do, and people don't have to talk to us." He broke into a giggle. "Well I'm not sure about me! But they don't talk to any of the others. We know what they want, you see. What's also very strange is the time element, because although it must be a long time since I came here, it seems only a short time to me."

"Yet it isn't all that long," contended Valerie, "if it was just before 1933. It's only 1972 now."

"No, but a lifetime I should think for some people, and it doesn't seem like a lifetime for me you see."

The theme had Robert enquire longer term. "Do you hope to come back to earth in the foreseeable future John, or are you happy enough where you are?"

"I'm very happy here. I didn't have a very happy earth life and... I'm not keen to repeat the experience. But many want to go immediately. Our hospital is full of them. We don't of course dissuade them, but there's nothing we can do because they all have to find their own soul here. When they adjoin, thinking is much clearer and they can decide what they're going to do. I should think that one day I'll be drawn back, because I know it's important. I'm not sure how important, or why. Again, Philip would tell you. He's always going to consult Them. But I'm very happy here."

"By Them, you mean the Golden Ones?" I guessed.

"Oh yes. Where I work you see, there are Two who help us generally. Then there's One above Them, and we have to go via Them to Him. He comes through Them – not in the same way as I come through this channel – but He comes through Them to help us in our development. He seems to be part of us Jules. He knows all of us, and in some way He links up with us. I've been with Him twice, and it's more difficult to get with Him than it is to use this channel. I have to go somehow *into* Him. No that's not right. I can't explain. Anyway He's part of me and somehow part of the others too, and He knows what's happening Jules."

"I understand. It must be frustratingly difficult to put these things into physical language."

"Because we don't use it! It's like you trying to describe something on earth, and before you've finished your sentence the person you're speaking to says: I know what you mean. I don't have to say it to any of us because they already know. So we don't use it."

"No indeed. Now I have to ask, are any of you at present using another channel apart from the writing?"

"No we're not."

"Fine. It's just that claims tend to arise of the same discarnates popping up elsewhere, though I find the majority tend to stick with their group channel."

"And we had to wait a long time for ours, as you know. It's something that has to be decided. Most people returning to earth decide in a group. I met someone recently who is in fact going back there, and he was one of five – going back to be their channel. I'm not sure where he's going or how he's going to do it, but he had to wait ages before everything was decided and worked out even. Look Jules, I have to make way for Philip now. Do remember my promise won't you?"

"I will John. It's been good to have you with us."

After valedictions he left as nimbly as he had done before. In sight of a figure which had again slumped, our wait for Philip was quiet and thoughtful. No one moved or spoke. Only Valerie's tape recorder whirred away on her lap somewhere down to my right. Peter's pulse and respiration were not too far below normal. How long his body was left in limbo – while unusually subject to interference – hinged now on the senior control himself who should be in close touch with the situation. For Valerie an immediate worry was the physical jerks his advent might rekindle.

But our concerns were shortlived when with ease and fixity of purpose Philip moved into place. He would be described years later as having been on earth a tall man with brown close-cropped hair, finely shaped head, and military bearing, all of which at present remained invisible and unknown to us. Yet there was no denying, for those nearest his entrance, the lambent quality he had about him. Not of the kind that mere anticipation brings, but something deep-seated in equilibrium, raying out as if from detached, dignified stillness a lustre that made one feel warm and shimmery inside.

"Good evening," he murmured. "Have you waited long?"

"Just a few minutes," said I. "What have you got to say to us?"

"What have *you* to say to *me*?" was the rejoinder.

Actually that was the more pertinent question since we were now challenged with rescue work, but along with Valerie we overlooked his point:

"I'd like to check with you Philip – the conditions within Peter have obviously improved haven't they?"

"Yes, much."

"And he's beginning to turn to you isn't he?"

"Yes, he speaks to us and I'm pleased about that."

"Is this while he's in the physical?" I piped up.

"While he's in the physical," confirmed Philip.

"He said yesterday," she added triumphantly, "that he felt you were holding his hands."

"It's the only way I can contact this part of him."

Such reformation was news to me, and queried:

"Do you think he's inwardly happy about it though?"

"I think he's inwardly happy. He also has a very strong will. There is little that any of us can do. I try to help him when he comes here."

At this point a section of the tape seems to have been erased, as it often was when Valerie fingered the microphone switch by accident, or when female prudence judged their advice too intimate for general consumption. There were times also when we were specifically asked to withhold certain information from Peter, quote: "until he is better able to appreciate our position". It might have numbered among these, because missing are the several minutes in which I took Philip up rather testily on detail concerning undeveloped mediumship and rescue through it.

Being of import, the gist of what he said has stayed with me – notably his view of Peter as a wayward brother who would reap no more risk or danger than he had already sown for himself in error, nor any challenge which he hadn't already set for purposes of his own spiritual growth and that of the group whose inner life he shared. I began to feel parochial, left with a stout impression of the patience, intricate depth of knowledge and shrewd understanding with which he quieted my scruples, not least rearoused my curiosity as we emerged:

"So were Joseph and the fellow who saw red meant as a sort of rehearsal for us?"

"Not quite in the way you imagine my friend. More an inevitable blueprint if you like. However, it is hoped that the plight of these two demonstrated a great need."

Our return to familiar ground brought Valerie back: "The despair they must feel came home to me."

"That is good," he nodded toward her. "Others were listening yet only two responded I'm afraid, one of whom you were not aware."

"Did Joseph respond?" she asked.

"Yes immediately."

"But not the one who saw red?"

"No, he doesn't want me to help him at all."

"Perhaps we can have another try with him sometime?"

"Yes perhaps, because he is so desperately anxious to prove to himself that he's not dead."

"Surely though Philip," I reasoned, thinking of Dr Wickland's rescues through trance, "if he comes into the body and uses the eyes he could look down and see it isn't his own?"

"Yes but for somebody like him that is even more terrifying. He wants to believe he is alive on earth, as most of them do. Now the rest of you must have questions?"

Robert obliged. "I'd like to ask if I may Philip, about these lost souls who come through to us. Are they in that condition simply because of ignorance? Or is it partly also due to their deeds, or lack of deeds, when on earth?"

"What you must bear in mind," he began slowly, "is that those two are not even a proportion of the untold thousands we find there, each of whom has created their own afterlife in the sense that the particular attitude in which they have lived on your plane faces them mirror-fashion when they pass over. Often we have people who are in that state largely because of some deed on earth. Then again we have people who are lost simply because they had no prior knowledge. We also have people who are lost because they have too much knowledge and are too anxious to put it immediately into practice. This is less common, but confusing for them because their ego has told them during their earth life that they must be destined for better things and yet by thought and deed they have proved they are not. Therefore we have to combine the two and help them that way."

"Just a little extra point," said Robert. "If a person is particularly good in a humanitarian sense but for some reason is ignorant of his own spiritual nature and of survival, would he in that case create an unfavourable condition for himself?"

"No, because he would recognise good wouldn't he?"

"Ah but he may still not understand his condition."

"The kind of person to whom you refer," elaborated Philip, "would not understand his condition because he is ignorant of any life afterwards, but once approached by us would undoubtedly recognise good wanting to help. The people we have most trouble with are those who, from lack of both knowledge and moral fibre, are lost and frightened. On being approached they shun us. They can only be helped through renewed contact with your plane, because in fact they are nearer you than us."

"Yes that figures. May I take you up on the word you used just now – knowledge? Perhaps it needs a bit of clarification. Would I be right in thinking that what you mean by knowledge is not just understanding of truth in an intellectual way, but also of fully understanding it to the spiritual degree where one has transcended the mind, and has reached a stage where we *know* and we *are* that which before we have merely intellectually surmised? So by knowledge do you mean the two together, or would you confine it just to the intellect?"

"Again it depends upon the people, for as you must realise, there are many who have no knowledge gleaned from books because of various inabilities to comprehend such. Then of course there are those who have knowledge only in an academic way. Either may possess redeeming qualities which the other may lack. However they all reach us. As to your main point, this depends greatly upon the amount of time and energy given to such realisation. Having reached a certain stage on passing over you will then be of great assistance, not only to your personal self, but to that portion of you which is forever with us."

"Can you tell us about our sleep-life?" asked John Maynard, whom I shall call J.M. "We leave our bodies at night do we not? So do we actually pass over in a temporal way to your side and become conscious of you?"

"It depends on your emotional state as you prepare for sleep. Those who are relaxed and desirous do come with us and help, not according to their professions on earth but according to the work they had already begun before their return to your plane. This is furthermore how many people work out past mistakes. It is not of course relevant to everyone."

Underneath his words Philip could have been aware of what felt to me like the same pressing influence as had tried to impose over our conversation with John, and which I was mentally struggling to keep from intrusion on himself. The advances were increasing in persistence when he added:

"I think you must hurry this up."

"Perhaps you'd like to end it now?" offered Valerie.

"No I'll hold on for the moment."

My signal for a speedier tempo to tighten the force-field around us returned J.M:

"Could you tell us about our guides? How close are they in our everyday actions, and how much do they actually guide us?"

"Quite simply my dear friend, they are to you what you want them to be. I'm going to enlarge on that but I'm fighting off something. Do you feel it Jules?"

"Yes I do."

"As you reach out to them," suggested Betty, "they are able to help you more?"

"Absolutely. But they are much more aware of your follies than perhaps you are yourself. I cannot think of a situation, but an action which is foreseen to lead down any sort of disastrous path could be prevented by them. Of course if one is aware of their presence... I'm sorry."

"What is it you're fighting off?" asked Valerie, "Peter's subconscious?"

"No, it's another person isn't it Jules?"

"Yes," I answered, deciding to try vocal command:

"Now leave him alone please! We can help you in due course. Move right back from the medium's light and wait your turn!"

They did so. After a pause he spoke again:

"I think it's better Jules. You see this is an example of what I have been talking about. Not the matter of guides to your friend, but the fact that many are so anxious to return that they are trying desperately to... "

That instant the body toppled out of control, then swayed and fell with heaving gasps onto the backrest. Philip had either been hopelessly undermined by the pull between medium and intruder or had moved aside to allow the latter an inevitable and much needed outlet. Whichever the case, for safety's sake I had no option but to see it through:

"Alright then, be gentle. Who are you?"

"Rose!" was the mournful cry.

"That's a pretty name. What's your problem?"

"All the water," she moaned.

"A lot of water around you is there?"

"Yes my brother's in it."

"You're not in it too are you?"

"I want to be."

"Why do you want to be in the water with him?"

"To get him out!" shrieked Rose frustratedly.

"We'll get him out," said Valerie in an attempt to calm her. "Don't worry."

"I *do* worry about him! I pushed him in!"

How she had become discarnate was far from clear. It flashed across my mind that if her brother had in fact passed over from drowning then she herself may have just left the body from shock. If so, she was not the first such case to use a channel. But off the cuff I thought it easier to treat her as discarnate.

"Anyway what's done is done Rose. You can help him most by easing your mind and listening to us. We can try to clear it up for you both, okay?"

"Who are you?" she queried suddenly, as one waking from a bad dream.

"I'm Jules, on the earth plane," which she might have thought a strange thing to say.

"Am I with you?"

"In a way. You've entered someone else's body on the earth here. But you're not on earth any more and no longer have a physical body. What you have is an exact duplicate of it making your whole life much more free. So you must realise that you're in a new world now, where your brother is probably waiting."

Yet these tidings filled her with new anxiety:

"I'll stay here. Then I won't have to go and see him."

"Well no one's going to force you. See him when you want. In the meantime so much else awaits you there of great beauty and pleasure. It'll be quite a surprise."

"No I can't go anywhere".

"Yes you can. You'll find the ability to travel wherever you like, hundreds of places, just by willing yourself there," I persisted, though after labouring this theme with no apparent effect to a point where I would have welcomed the same facility myself, Valerie's whisper about a little help from our friends changed my tune: "Just relax and allow the helpers to guide you. There are good souls standing near, ready and waiting to light your way."

And hopefully so they were, for she left at once. Perhaps the recontact with earth had indeed helped her orientate out of dreamland, opening her, in Philip's words, to "recognition of good wanting to help". No one ventured to ask him what became of her, but such a stark reminder of my inexperience at rescue feared complete failure. It smoothed my brow therefore, as with a freshening of ambience he re-ennobled the limp form and gave me a nod of approval.

"Well done Jules. Alright? Now these are the sort of people you must pray for. Would you like to know anything else?"

Robert wanted to know more of this man-in-charge:

"Could you talk a little about yourself Philip, how you progressed since leaving earth?"

"Yes certainly. On passing over I recognised myself immediately, and consciousness then came of activities set in motion prior to my return." He paused again in an effort to repel more boarders. "I'm having considerable trouble here."

Even my straining senses could feel the competition, which had multiplied since Rose's successful barge-in, and his perseverance surprised me.

"Quite a few crowding you aren't there Philip?"

"A great many. Could your friend… keep talking?"

Robert cleared his throat volubly for the task.

"Yes of course. Well we asked John this question earlier and it was most interesting to hear him recount his personal experiences. You see I feel that people here can identify more easily with case histories to begin with, because it helps them to understand how one moves from one stage to another. Now we touched on the stages of knowledge, and you've just said that when you passed over, certain things which you set in motion on earth enabled you immediately to find your fuller self. I imagine this was of great help."

"Yes it was," recovered Philip. "They were not, however, set in motion on earth but previous to my return there."

"I see. So this was a remembrance of your last post-mortem life in fact?"

"Yes."

"Now the people who find themselves in a position such as Rose, does it take a very long time for them to be helped by your group or other groups up to the hospital? And what happens then?"

"For some it can be almost instantaneous. Like a starving man who is whipped every time he goes for bread, the time when he isn't whipped he will take it. Yet for most it is not so straightforward because having eaten the bread they do not then wish to follow the hand that feeds. Recognising that hand is their first step. From there on it is just a question of healing and guidance. The next step for them is to leave our Centre, our hospital – call it what you will – and make contact with their guide, or guides. Having done so they may then determine their future place and role. Intensive training and teaching is necessary to make up for what they lacked when they came here. They can then see the point of going on to better things, and one way they can do this is by returning to your earth. Of course there are always exceptions. Natural curiosity takes many people to many places."

"Are there a lot in your hospital?" asked Mary-Ann.

"Indeed there are. Do you want numbers?"

"No it's okay, I can believe it."

Robert had begun to ponder a question much shared.

"Philip, you said that you yourself are moving on to a higher level.

Have you any inklings as to what this might entail? And will you still be in contact with your group and us?"

"I will be able to contact you through this channel and the group through their two Golden Ones. To you it may seem unusual that one such as myself must go on. It is not of course because of knowledge, but because of a special need which must be fulfilled. In a sense my work with the group has, if you like, earned some sort of small promotion. Therefore I am going on. It will be quite soon when our Chief One calls, and he will take me to the next stage. This will be interesting for you, useful for me, being set to help more advanced ones who are also lost. It is what I meant when saying that often, people with knowledge also have their problems. Does that answer your question?"

"Yes very clearly thank you. Would such a stage mean then, that you have actually broken out of the karmic cycle, so to speak, and that you will now remain in the higher worlds?"

The answer came simply and without pride.

"I feel, and indeed have been told, that my karmic cycle as you call it is cleared... because of my work here, and my work when last on earth. Now having been told I can move on, there seems little point in moving back... does there?"

"Goodness, I'm almost prompted to congratulate you!" Robert exclaimed after a momentary hush. "It seems a tremendous step because we on earth here, when we begin to understand about this, feel a certain frustration in that, during the cycle of experience we're all working on I suppose, we come back to this earth again and again, and only perhaps when we've left each time realise that we've failed once more in the objectives we've returned to pursue. And when one examines this in the light of what knowledge we have here, it appears a most dismal prospect for some, who feel unable to grasp the reasons for which they have returned – in terms of personality faults – and only have the opportunity of awakening to these when they've left this dimension."

"You have a remarkable ability to answer your own questions my friend," twinkled Philip. "This is exactly the work I shall be doing further on. As you say, these people, expecting a great deal of themselves, sometimes achieve precious little. Opportunity for the realisation of which you speak is always there within however, just ignored by the ego which reigns for a time respecting only its outer world. As to congratulations, my calling is by no means rare. Three people, who indeed worked with me, have progressed thus, due to a combination of rescue work and working with their powers to the full. Please ask me to elaborate if you don't understand."

"No, again that's very clear."

"One short question now please."

"Could you tell us," Betty asked, "whether the same guide is retained all through one's earth life, or are they changed as one evolves?"

"What before I had hoped to make clear is that your true guide is your self."

"By which," checked Robert, "you mean the soul?"

"Yes. Intermediaries there are however, who remain close through many lives, some of whom change as you grow, like your outer friends."

"I'd just like a bit of guidance please," sprung back Robert, "on another extremely fundamental issue."

"Very quickly then," he urged.

"Yes right. What can we say to someone who is so anxious about Christianity that he insists on Jesus being the only saviour of the world, that he is the only son of God, and that the Holy Trinity is the only one to be recognised? Our group here tends to believe in a totally nonsectarian approach toward the whole issue of personalities such as Buddha, Krishna, Jesus and so forth. What can we say to try and broaden that person's mind?"

"Mind is only broadened by experience my friend. But if you deal with a person such as this you may explain that to the Great God of All, every soul is literally a son and potentially as Divine. Those few among us who have already grown so high as to let the Light of His

Spirit flood through them, radiate such Oneness that Each seems a unique and only saviour to the many sons who yet have far to grow. It may then be understood that the Trinity to which you refer is one of Spirit, soul, and personality – key steps of self-realisation within us all. They therefore who have achieved the same steps and realised the same Spirit within through their own areas of discipline, of course deserve the same recognition as Jesus does in ours."

"Thank you Philip." My acknowledgment of a pivotal session was backed up round the room, though it alerted Valerie to when he last left the channel:

"Now will you be able to go easily tonight?"

"Yes thank you very much. God bless you all."

His exit this time was comparatively smooth, after a short delay ensuring Peter's readiness to take back control. Even as their interchange became complete a breathless quiet remained over the scene, everyone rooted to the spot in what had been the longest, most informative session so far. It felt like coming out of an epic film at the cinema, one's focus abandoned to the furniture around – the opaque toyland textures, forms, props of physical appearance into which Peter eventually earthed himself, heavy-lidded, fitful, and a mite suspicious of us.

He guessed the outcome straightaway from our replete faces, but he bore little sign of the change credited to him earlier. Except for a desire to learn whether anything had happened or been said which might prove embarrassing, his main concern was the unconscionable length of time it had taken us, all the while commissions awaited him in the shop – bouquets to be prepared for a wedding the next day, we were piquedly told. So no one could deny his tiptop return to normal from the effect, as at Mary Rogers' flat, of another refreshing sleep.

No one either acquainted him with the proposal of rescue which we would shortly need to consider, aware that his own especial need after channelling was to get physical again. The beeline he made downstairs for his handiwork in the shop therefore chanced to provide a healthier and fitting alternative than to sit through our deliberations.

Mine were uncomfortably brewing as I watched the others follow him out. Valerie alone, who was the last of them to leave, understood why.

Formerly I had doubted that The Seven could ever coax Peter into pulling his weight in whatever "partnership" he had originally agreed with them. Tonight, further to our being told its ominous nature, we learned he had at least come to accept Philip – borne out perhaps by an obvious lack of resistance to him. Philip had also quieted my doubt that a reluctant, undeveloped medium could channel rescue safely. But now, I was torn by acknowledging my own reluctance and undevelopment for the role seen ahead of me. Earthbound rescue of this kind was regarded by professionals in psychic work as heavily demanding and dangerous. They shrunk from it. I did too, though for somewhat different reasons.

Valerie understood how she had drawn me away from avid concentration on Krishnamurti's talks with the lure of a new discarnate knowledge output. She never suspected it would land me instead at the other end of the spectrum with discarnate ignorance. Theoretically I knew the area we would be dealing with, but was no hands-on practitioner down there and nor did I care to be. From that mere theoretical knowledge I would have to safeguard Peter and the others as well as myself. Sooner or later he would have to be informed of the situation, yet this didn't bother me so much as our joint fallowness.

Despite David's implied confidence, none of us had any psychological training or experience conducive to the task and, apart from myself, no one had grounding in the safeguards of even routine discarnate communications never mind those of a rescue circle, which must of necessity be more stringent. One is, after all, creating an open door not for the bulk of posthumous humanity but its unfortunate dregs, a door which most Spiritualists do their best to keep firmly shut.

Their history had long shown them the physical and mental havoc wrought by cases where rapacious passion, terror, torment, depression, and sometimes hostility were allowed to discharge themselves through unwary mediums onto sitters. My front-line placement in our team would make me the first target. Thought of it brought to mind the tall order that those attributes of sound physical and mental health as are required in an ordinary circle must in rescue be supplemented by dedication, inner fortitude, compassion and self-discipline. Had I ever met such a person?

The idea of wrestling with Peter's waywardness in a programme of rescue was singularly unattractive too. His urge always to be doing something or going somewhere never saw him sit down long enough to engage in any serious reading, so our sole resort was to offer verbal conciliation on the move as it were. My being also seven years younger than he, and a bit reserved, didn't have the weight that an older, maturer man might carry. Philip wasn't kidding, I thought, when he said of Peter in an earlier session: "We have a serious job to do, and the Channel is inclined to take it rather lightly." On balance there was my promise to him before knowing the proposal, and there was Valerie at present regarding me from the Sanctuary doorway: "I know that look," she avowed. "You don't want to do it, do you? Please help us Julie-boy. We need you." At a pinch only *she* could ever have won me round, my boyish heart not knowing why.

Conscious however that I couldn't bear her to be in the fray of it without my support and protection, a mute nod from me saw her go downstairs while I continued to ponder out of the Sanctuary window. Tension grew that our appraisal might include the delicate one of each person's capacity for the work, and that any choice of a team must also demand high standards from myself. In no position to put the question mark over fellow heads I decided that the best measure was to wait until they had a picture of what they might be in for and let them put it there themselves – if possible without imposing doom and gloom from the start.

In the event things turned out somewhat differently. No sooner had I picked my way around assorted legs to a niche held for me beside Valerie than the range of their mood was sounded. Most were still heady from the primal impact of the session, exchanging sentiments and comparisons, observations on the tenor of each communicant – but with sparse reference to the proposal laid in front of us. When touched upon it appeared to have got an edgy though gratuitous compliance, as if part of the scene. An issue over which Philip had made the effort to come through and answer queries looked out-dazzled here by the novelty of having had an interworld chitchat.

Because rescue now proved to be The Seven's direct aim, their need of our cooperation had become fuddled with an automatic obligation or ability to do the job.

At its root may have lurked that notorious tendency of ascribing undue warrant to discarnates purely on account of their exotic state. This understandable view led me to recall that not always had tonight's questions been geared to the issue. They were often of mere curiosity value, as if assuming our fitness to do rescue with the motion carried – which was fair enough except that the answers given were introductory not instructive. But for fear of assuming too much myself I held fire and awaited the cannonade of questions ready to spring from Robert.

We had cleared the small table for coffee after a risotto, Peter had come and gone with a second helping, and Valerie was fiddling with her recorder as he leaned across to me earnestly.

"There are one or two items I'd like to get straight in my mind Jules, if I may?"

"Go ahead," I accepted gingerly over the microphone in Valerie's hand. He smiled at it then took the floor with everyone turning to listen.

"Right well first of all, about these unfortunate characters we're being asked to help. Now I appreciate that they must be nearer us in terms of frequency rate let's say, than to Philip or John, who might appear to them like ghosts or be shunned generally. What I don't quite grasp is how, if they're nearer earth, they fail both to realise that they are dead and that they're using the medium's body. Is this really so usual?"

"Yes, because it's their very nearness to earth which makes all seem as before. They don't notice the subtle but crucial difference that physical matter isn't on the same frequency. They think they're looking at physical matter still, whereas in fact it's invisible to them. They're just seeing their own subjective picture of it projected onto the atmosphere like a photo-slide on a screen, and that doesn't include the medium's physical body or ours. They'd only see our astral bodies with their idea projected on those too, and the medium's physical body is just space where they feel rather more stable and comfortable."

"A space left by his astral body which has gone?"

"Right. Take Rose for instance, and remember that all through her life she would have been building her thoughts and emotions in the astral body she would use when the physical layer comes off at death. So when it does come off, like a lampshade off a bulb, those same thoughts and emotions are not only experienced with a frightening acuteness in her case, but they also ray out onto the subtle, malleable atmosphere around. Her astral body and the astral environment seem as solid though, because they're on the same frequency."

"Comparable then, with the illusion here on earth that our physical bodies and environment only appear solid because their atoms are vibrating at a similar rate?" he suggested.

"That's it. Which is why many people caught up in panic over the death process are completely unaware of having changed frequency. They may have seen death as an extinction, or a transformation, or placed it far off into the future and hardly relevant to their life now. So when it actually takes place without apparent change or going anywhere they don't recognise it, and just continue their private drama – overlooking any minor irregularity because to their senses everything appears roughly as tangible as before."

"What I didn't follow," queried Mary-Ann, "is that if she pushed her brother in the water, how did she die herself?"

The simplest of my surmises was offered.

"On reflection I think she probably died later from another cause, having long regretted the day she hadn't jumped in to save her non-swimming brother after she pushed him overboard during a quarrel between them. It explains why she accepted straightaway that she wasn't on earth. However bound up she had got in her drama, and confused, she knew vaguely that she had died and was more concerned about having to face him."

"In any case," Robert summarised, "the guilt-cum-remorse held her in an earthbound condition."

"Plus ignorance of that condition," I hastened to add, "which may have kept her in the etheric double."

"And what's that?"

"It's a matrix or force-field between our astral and physical bodies, but not important for us here Robert. I was just thinking aloud."

"Thinking of it though as a possible handicap?"

"Yes. You see, for most of us going through an average, natural death, once the cord is broken and our physical is shed, its etheric part remains on the astral body as a sort of cocoon-like film over three or four days of fluctuating, sleepy consciousness."

"Is one aware of this cocoon?"

"Not as such, because it takes the form which mental habits dictate – your clothes for example."

"Thank God for that!" he joked.

"We can rather, having used it continually as our inner self-image. Anyway what remains of it should as a rule shed itself and disintegrate with the physical. We're then free in the astral form with those habits of clothing and image most clung to, and are usually greeted, as John said, by one or two people we recognise. But attachment to some physical event or to the physical body itself, particularly when the transition is sudden, can put off that shedding of the double for a long time. They mooch about in a dreamy haze which is semi-aware of our world when not being assailed by their own thought-pictures. Then they're even more bewildered to find that no one here is aware of them."

"I should think they are," Robert commented. "Was Rose in this state?"

"Possibly. Her asking if she was with us made me suspect it because she wouldn't be sure. Much of the time, guilt over pushing him in might have held her in action replays of the event. To her they'd be like an acute, recurring nightmare without being able to wake up in the physical as we can. That's why her use of the medium's physical to wake up is more important by far than which degree of earthbound she is."

"And it's why The Seven need us," said Mary-Ann, "to help give guidance when people like her *do* wake up."

"Guidance they might not dare to believe," I mooted, and this'll be our main challenge perhaps. A lot of them by all accounts remain ego-bound, like children, with their replica of earth life projected around them – instead of adjusting to their astral self in its own astral environment."

"Is that what John meant," she asked, "when he said they have to find their own soul there?"

"It's what I took him to mean. Finding their soul in the sense of becoming who they are, which is more astral self than ego, although I suppose he could have meant what Brunton calls the Overself."

"It's still spiritual growth though isn't it?" spoke up Valerie. "I mean, finding who we are behind who we *thought* we were. One wonders how many of us do grow very much in an earth life."

The thought suspended me, causing a break while Betty slid off home, Mary-Ann poured fresh coffee, J.M. went to the loo, and Valerie turned the cassette over in her recorder. Robert was pensive, watching this process of hers beside me, then rallied to the fore:

"Jules I think we have a problem. How do we direct our rescuees to the helpers if, as John said, helpers are somehow seen to be part of the earth-life mirage? After you directed Rose to their help I thought she'd gone with them, but now that seems open to question."

"I quite agree."

"For instance why, if she saw us as astral selves, didn't she spot Philip here too? Because he, being an astral self, was at that time within the etheric and physical like we are."

"That's very astute of you old chap!" I grinned. "Yes, the set-up is of course similar in that we're astral selves using the etheric-physical as a medium. But there's a big difference between our having grown in with our own bodies here and him just using Peter's. Our constitutions are tightly knit, born into the job as it were, whereas a senior discarnate's interaction with the medium is tenuous. They stay discarnate, only linking up to a degree, and even though tuned down to the medium they may still seem part of the earthbound mirage. It also makes them easier to dislodge."

"And Rose wouldn't know what she was doing?"

"I shouldn't think so, beyond shifting an obstacle of unknown origin. But that's a guesstimate without knowing her exact state. I do know she'd been there for some time, at the head of many others who are all attracted by a kind of luminosity from the medium's aura. John sat tight, though Philip had to give way because his link was looser. When he did, she fell into the sudden freeness assuming it to be empty, and was unaware that her every expression was then being reproduced through a medium. Anyway, I do accept that we have a problem with their recognising the hand that feeds, as Philip put it."

"Well in the first place," he took stock, "many of them apparently don't know they're dead, and you say they don't know they're using another's physical body either. On top of that, if half the time they can't recognise helpers from their side, and we ourselves can't see them or their situation at all, how in God's name are we going to rescue the poor blighters?"

The seat of consultant into which I had fallen got rather warm. I was also noting that his whole approach pivoted not on whether we should agree to The Seven's proposal of rescue work but on how we should carry it out. A rough arsenal of theory had to be mustered:

"By explanation and suggestion," I threw him, "plus initiative hopefully. If our explanation is believed it might raise their consciousness enough to see the helpers, who I assume will be standing near us. Bear in mind too that our medium is in a suggestible state, which to an extent must include anybody using it. Our physical voices also should sound more penetratingly real than any in their dream world. Reawakening in the physical might stabilise them for us to get their full attention, and that's what the helpers can't get."

94

"Alright," he ceded, "it seems we're in with a fair chance. On the other hand those three attempts to date have had the same advantages. Strawberry-grower Joseph was most attentive from the start because he was lonely, and one almost couldn't fail with him. The case who saw red had a short attention-span and beetled off. Rose appeared to wake up but we're not sure where she went, if anywhere. The score so far then, even though we may have extra pulling power, doesn't make our mission look much easier does it?"

"Oh I was just giving you the bright side Robert!" I grinned. "Obviously our advantages are only as good as our use of them. We'll have to learn as we go along by trial and error, and it must be understood right away that I don't have any practical experience at rescue bar the red case and Rose. Hands-on I'm as green as the rest of us. I even forgot to guide Rose to the helpers till Val reminded me, you see."

"Yes I do see," he yielded. "That should level us up for an interesting time. What did you learn?"

"Mainly that having got their attention one needs to use initiative pretty damn quick to maintain it while guidance is given. Otherwise they'll retreat."

"We need to know their condition too, don't forget."

"Yes, as far as it gives us a lever to get them out. But we already have, or at least I've tried to explain, a rough idea of the kind of nightmare they're known to find themselves in, and we know they must be persuaded to trust the helpers. It's getting them to do so, I'd say, which will be difficult. How we'd manage it I don't know. We'll have to put our thinking caps on."

"Point taken. We must have another talk with Philip before we start then. Is that possible?"

He looked at Valerie, but instead of direct assent her wariness came across keenly. The security aspect, particularly against violence, bothered her most.

"You'll think me awful," she said, "but I'm worried about how easily someone even as innocuous as Rose could barge in over Philip like that."

"Mummy, her brother was drowning for pity's sake!" cried Mary-Ann.

"Yes I know darl'. Plainly the poor child was in desperate straits and had to be helped straightaway. I'm only saying that the takeover was accidental, and for all we know it could have been a violent person barging through instead. Isn't a special doorkeeper on their side meant to be in control of who uses the medium and when? I would have thought John or someone was staying around to keep order. If they actually decided that Rose was more urgent I could understand. It's the haphazardness of these cases who blunder in, this time right over Philip, that I find worrying."

She swung to me for response, which was given.

"I'm certain Philip was well aware of the type he had to let in Val, and at this stage he can't afford the impact on us of anyone harmful – especially not on you. If we ever get volatile types you'll have us three male six-footers to deal with them. It's partly why I sit so close to the channel you see. There's a psychic weakness in Peter which is making him vulnerable. Back at the first session remember, Philip did admit to having a problem with people encroaching on control."

"And come to think of it," joined Mary-Ann, "didn't John mention tonight a weakness they have to correct?"

"Latent depression was given. I suspect it's what causes leakage of vital energy and a thinning of his natural defense system. He also puts up a *degree* of subliminal resistance still, I mean to *them* rather than the earthbound, which slightly compounds the problem. But I think that'll decrease as he gets used to them. Meanwhile they're trying to heal the weakness, temporarily at least."

Valerie's frown was lessening. "Was that the other thing you checked with Philip? I only understood the first one where he talked about Peter veering from his own plan of achievement."

"Yes but the veering has accentuated his weakness."

"Oh I see."

"We've probably no idea," supposed Mary-Ann, "of the grim frustrations John and Co. are up against as doorkeepers, and they're out of their own element too aren't they Jules, in coming lower to work with us?"

"Absolutely. They have a certain amount of power with them, like oxygen below sea, and can only stay so long. They must use that power both to stay and to counteract interference, which is a hefty demand because what seems nebulous and subjective here on earth becomes very objective and tangible to them. Thoughts are things in any world, but outside physical camouflage they're seen as the highly vigorous forces they are, taking a multitude of shapes, colours, and sounds either positive or negative. On The Seven's own plane these are stable, organised by minds there, but on lower planes they're much less so from earthly people who don't realise the effect is self-created."

"How do they cope at all then?" queried J.M.

"By concentrating mind power where possible. Around Peter's mediumship though, they have more to cope with. He brings a lot more earthbound pressing on the reins of control than at times they can handle, and if we're going to join their work I think we should understand this clearly. Anyone with his psychic attribute is a beacon in the dark to any earthbound, and that added weakness of his will make it easier for the weaker of them to get control. He hasn't prepared himself with the self-discipline necessary for balanced management, which leaves The Seven having to do their makeshift best. So to answer your original question Val, this isn't an average, neat little set-up where the medium is properly primed and committed and the doorkeeper fulfils his humdrum role. If it were, I'd have asked the same thing. It's going to be a risky business, because what we have here instead, as far as I can see, is a staunch band of rescue workers whose purpose-born, very flexible Channel has neglected the pact he made with them and allowed his considerable energies to become tainted with disuse."

"Or mis-use!" supplemented J.M.

"Well alright, he's probably no worse than the rest of us. I'm just stating our apparent position, which in its immediate effect on us means that Philip or John would be hard put to keep off intrusions magnetically attracted by the condition of Peter's psychism."

"Like keeping wasps off a picnic?" Robert suggested.

"Something like that, only bigger in size! It must have been pretty frustrating for them I imagine, and it's why they seem staunch to me... dedicated too."

"Good gracious!" breathed Valerie. "I've never heard you praise the guides before."

A slight flush crept up under my skin. "Credit where credit's due," I shrugged.

She gave a knowing chuckle then waxed serious again:

"And yet if it's so difficult for them, won't asking us to plunge into rescue make things worse?"

This was a cardinal point, and I felt hesitant:

"In the short term, yes. It's half what led me to query the mediumship with Philip this evening, and I wish now I'd asked him to elaborate. Since then it's dawned on me, you see, that when he originally said, right back in the first session, that they wanted to give knowledge of a kind, he didn't mean talks as we think of them – though we may get those as well. He meant they're planning to use the actual rescue cases, via your record of them, to get their message across to people on earth, develop spiritual muscle in everyone through the challenge, and fulfill their mission that way. The dangers are taken for granted, built-in. They're why he made himself available for questioning."

"And why he put such stress," she twigged, "on Peter having inwardly agreed to be channel?"

I nodded. "Inwardly being the operative word. His ego alone wouldn't give it enough weight. Mind you, they'd never have embarked on a scheme like this without calculating the risks entailed, their own capabilities, limitations to the psychic force-field which Peter set for himself and how much can safely be achieved in its present state. Of course we don't know that rescue wasn't part of the whole deal anyway, tying in with that liaison plan mentioned. But because the condition Peter's got into is going to make their work more of a challenge for spiritual growth, I imagine they're now steeling themselves to give it all they've got."

"Grasping the nettle. Yes I see."

Right then she may have been about to ask the nature of said dangers or risks. Other than those for Peter, one danger on the cards for us was psychic attack, its insidious varieties reputed to enter the subconscious and wreak mental havoc in some form. I was unsure if she knew of it, but Robert next complained of "so much speculation on too little fact" – calling for reply:

"Well this is just my handle on the facts that we have Robert, although because I'm using known criteria the current President of the College of Psychic Studies is very likely to agree with me. People far more qualified than us attempting earthbound rescue have found it's not for the fainthearted – and that's without a dodgy medium, which as facts go is not little. Nor is the fact of our being raw novices like Peter is. And for what it's worth, another fact is that I wouldn't dream of taking part unless I believed we had the support of senior discarnates with higher guidance, high motives, and a fair amount of hardy experience under their belt. From known criteria again the points they make suggest they've got all three, which we need to offset our lack. But being human they're quite liable to human error – especially when unused to a channel – and this sort of work can get tough. So given these most basic facts, maybe we should each consider how much we really want or feel able to become involved."

At that moment however, Peter came thudding through from the shop. Such unworldly talk, vaporous to him, seldom outlasted his appearance. Besides, he wouldn't feel ready to hear our source material for a day or so.

"Still nattering away then?" His chirpy yet tired-looking demeanour cut across our patchwork of thought, and in a trice he spotted Valerie's recorder. "Oh I see you've been listening to your tape," he presumed, with the hollow add-on: "Must be awfully interesting."

Valerie switched it off, no one bothering to explain as we stirred ourselves to accommodate him. Even when tired he was a tonic for us, his infectious sense of piquant fun – too circumstantial to relate –

filling the room with laughter. One could read between its lines how swiftly and surely he had built his world at Ashdene, by taking up new causes and projects which had fast become absorbed into his everyday round.

His approachable, magnetic personality had soon made him an attractive figure in the village, drawing custom for floral display at weddings and funerals. He had not been idle, either in the garden or in the wait for his shop to earn goodwill, but had instinctively looked around to see what he could do on a tiny budget to increase their productiveness and wellbeing. Small-scale measures though they were, his success with them was obvious, his brisk achievement characteristic of him.

Equally Peterlike was the trait he had of catching folk up into the whirlwind of his enthusiasm – only to do a sudden bunk and leave them emotionally stranded while he scuttled off to pursue some further novelty or iron in the fire. Our evening's end, if not a prime example, bore his hallmark when having wound us up to a climax of mirth he promptly yawned and went to bed.

In his wake we blinked at each other till the vacuum took effect. Three of us got on our feet, agreeing to digest all our food for thought, and the party was over. Robert gave J.M. and myself a lift back to our flats in Tunbridge Wells – a journey for the most part spare of comment, dismembered as we felt from talk of rescue work. Our frail try at conversation kept it under wraps as if too sacred to indulge out there in the brash, breezy world of a Volkswagen Beetle with one window missing. But through that porthole, once J.M. had been dropped and I stood in my driveway watching Robert turn the sky-blue buggy, he threw me words of resolve before he sailed away down to his coastal retreat.

"We must form a team Jules. I might ring you midweek, although I'll be there next Friday anyway."

My parting assent knew that at least Valerie would ring me in the morning with her after-impressions, and Peter's if he had heard the tape. Yet the prospect of hers alone had so come to absorb me that tonight's full moon was the only light by which I hunched on the edge of my armchair, brooding before the empty gate. For an element in her manner toward these particular communicants had seemed to disclose her unspoken glint of recognition alongside mine. It felt that, way beneath the issues raised, we knew what we had to do, the same spark perhaps having been kindled in us both.

★ ★ ★ ★ ★

Before we got our team ready, Valerie was to secure a private talk with Philip. Meantime she had indeed rung me the next morning, albeit keener to hear of my after-impressions than tell me of her own, but chiefly to make a lunch date at Binns Restaurant on The Pantiles.

We met up by the old Chalybeate Spring near my workplace and threaded our way along the Colonnade to this most English haunt of hers, in whose chic wood-panelled quaintness she had booked a window table. Its outlook gave onto Linden Park Road, habitat of The Tutors from where eight years earlier I had launched my lone quest – never once conceiving any notion of rescue. Today, sunlight poured down that road over our silverware and onto the classic ladies and gents about us. I thought how foreign to their conversation our topic would seem if they knew it, outré even to one which Valerie had shared at the same table with Helen Greaves, writer in our sphere. Maybe a lonesome time lay ahead of us.

Accompanied for now by the friendly tinkle of china we felt it was expedient to keep Friday the main session night and vital, to offset our unpreparedness for rescue, that a firm bond be cultivated between us and The Seven. I had urged we do so by dialogue with them when possible and attunement when not, both of which sat well with her of course. She wanted to check with Philip for instance whether Mary-Ann and Betty were perhaps too vulnerable to engage the earthbound. I gathered this was simply maternal protectiveness of her daughter and heed over a tendency in Betty to depression.

Another question concerned the apparent influence overriding her normal behaviour up until preliminary contact was made. Although mid-term she had come to feel sure of its origin within herself, since these talks with Philip her belief had grown that he must have been the influence all along – which fired her curiosity as to how he could exercise such sway. His subsequent answer would prove significant, being the first verbal intimation of our unity in a group soul.

Peter's response to the playback of her tape over breakfast was not auspicious. He had heard it as far as the proposal of rescue then took exception, querying why our work should be necessary and why he should be medium for it. From his point of view after all, he had only agreed with her to continue sitting on a short trial basis. "Philip and the other two," he admitted, were "probably real" and he didn't mind them at present – especially if they could give him more healing for his leg which had become a bit painful again. Any further agenda however would have to be aired when he had the time. At that point apparently his interest had waned on such a busy morn for his shop. But he did give over-the-shoulder consent to join us every Friday, "in the way," she said, "that a secular guest consents to join the religious family at prayer."

Despite this ongoing stand of his, not wondrous to hear across Binns ice cream, I noted her confidence that everything would turn out right. It may have been why she felt no need to exploit his request for healing in the Sanctuary, which she knew could lead to her sought-after session with Philip. Instead, believing herself nudged by the latter to treat him elsewhere, she opted for the library – upon which minor resolve our confab ended. So how she obtained her talk session upstairs the next evening is unclear.

Her notebook says that she sent Philip the requisite "beam" during an afternoon meditation with Betty, and awaited him once the good lady had gone home. Perhaps she had already asked Peter to sit for her. Or else, because he had no present hang-up about the Sanctuary, he was not unknown to pass along the landing, pop in casually to confer on something domestic, then linger chatting until his heavy head began to sink and the sensation of trance to overwhelm him. In a flash she would have grabbed the ever-ready portable and list of questions, her eyes, grave and concerned, bent on him, wondering if it presaged a response to her appeal and prayerful in case some drifter was about to emerge from the almost breathless form.

Such was the look of things that 6pm., by whatever means they had arrived. And as she sat there a storm raged against the window-panes, one of those sudden pelting showers that descend from April thunderclouds – brief but drenching. It plunged the Sanctuary into gloom, with nothing save a dull, rubescent blush from within the lamp base colouring the altar behind her. She barely noticed the downpour, every whit intent on the subject at hand which by patient, unhurried stages was heightening into the port and presence she knew.

"Now this is Philip isn't it?" she ensured.

"Yes. Good evening Valerie."

"Oh it's lovely to talk to you again." She picked up her list with relief. "I've been hoping to ask you a few questions on our own."

"Please do," came the dispassionate tones.

"Well, umm… one question is about this work we're going to start on Friday evenings. Are you happy with the number of people there, and do you feel everybody is alright?"

He paused before answering:

"All except two actually."

"Which are Betty and Mary-Ann?"

"Yes."

"I thought so," she said, and her thinking fished instead about Renée Newbon, blonde young American co-owner of Pilgrim's health food restaurant in Tunbridge Wells and avid student at the nearby College of Psychotherapeutics. "Now what about asking Renée? I don't know whether you're aware of her, but she's an extremely strong soul and I think she'd be a tremendous help."

"Yes, as you will. Be careful that you don't have people with emotional problems. I feel that the person to whom you refer is not quite ready because of her emotional state."

"Well we needn't ask her then."

"Uhh… Ohh!" His breath quivered suddenly, was cut short, and caught in a gasp. Evocative of earlier occasions it had Valerie once more feeling at a loss:

"Is it the same difficulty again? Although Peter's much better isn't he? Or is someone trying to get in?"

"Many are," he muttered. "It's rather a fight."

"Well we'll go on because my talking may help. I wanted to know if by any chance you are the Philip who wrote through Dr Alice Gilbert."

"I have never used any other channel."

"It was just that this afternoon Betty and I wondered if you could be the same Philip."

"I am sorry to disappoint you," he said. "Do you have a light on?"

"Yes it's a little pencil light I'm using to see my questions and keep an eye on the recording. Does it worry you?"

"It makes the colours in his mind… "

"Brighter, does it?" she supplied.

"No… " The answer groaned into silence.

"Never mind. Another question is about when Peter and I were with Mary Rogers the other evening. She claimed that Rameses II wished to use Peter. Now is that at all true, or is it pure fantasy?"

"Mary Rogers," he recovered himself, "is well known here because of the lower entities whom she attracts. Consequently, her vision of gold, plus her very active imagination… Do you see?"

"Absolutely. We'll disregard it then."

"In fact the vision of gold was one of our Ones."

"Ah, well I must say one did feel it was part her and part the truth. So we'll take no notice of that."

"But by all means take notice of the lady."

"Not always though obviously. I mean she's quite… "

"You are certainly intelligent enough to know that which is of reason and that which is not. However, if she should speak with my Channel I will endeavour to enlighten her."

"Oh that might be interesting. I think someday we will go over there again. Anyway we're all set to help the lost ones, and I remember your saying about all the thousands there, so maybe if we can break through and bring light to these people their lives would have more purpose and they would gradually understand the… "

"Crumbs to the crowd," mused Philip.

"Pardon?… I'm sorry, what did you say?"

"Crumbs to the crowd."

She echoed the words uncomprehendingly till he said:

"I will elaborate another time."

"Alright." Her thoughts hastened on. "I've been meaning to ask you Philip, about how you've been able to influence us. Because a great deal that has happened over recent weeks does seem to have been due to you. I mean the way you managed to get Peter here, and all the extraordinary turns of event since I met him. How is it that we can be so influenced?"

"When I talk to you," he replied with care, "I must use the first person singular. Consequently you are always relating information to the first person."

"And it doesn't actually relate just to you?"

"Indeed not. If you slice into a cake, does that portion lose its connection with the remainder?"

"No, I'm beginning to see now."

"Your earth personalities are only the icing on your portion of Our Cake. The greater part of you lies beneath, linked with Us. I may impress you all therefore by simply impressing that part of me which is connected with each of you individually."

"Because we're all parts of the same Whole?"

"Exactly. And we remain so even after the last crumb is split, for if you have ten portions in your cake each will remain as much a part of the Whole as if you had only three. When you have grown up through the many layers of your being into your true self, your portion of Our Whole – when there is no further aspect needing to incarnate, all potential being fulfilled – then you will of course have attained the Oneness. In turn, when all the individual portions of Our Whole have fulfilled every aspect of themselves outwardly, and become fully conscious of the true self, then Our Group Whole attains Oneness with the Universal Whole."

"And what of the Golden Ones? Are they involved?"

"Certainly. We and the two Golden Ones are part of such a Group Whole under the One. That one stands, if you like, at the apex of a triangle reaching down to the two Golden Ones at each side of its base. These in turn stand at each side of an individual at the apex of another triangle below. But even our One at the top stands between a Higher Two at the base of a triangle above Him."

"Fascinating! And are some of us easier to impress than others?"

"The easiest to impress are those who truly seek, for they are open. You need not ask such questions however in readiness to help the lost ones because you know that, were they easy to impress, your task would not be necessary would it?"

"No… quite. But it must have been a tremendous thing for you to bring about, especially with Peter."

"Although he did not seek as such on your plane, the part of him that is with Us did in fact prearrange his welfare so that his seeking help allowed impress."

"Oh. So is it better that he remains outwardly free from knowledge of these things?"

"Whereas before he had not grasped the essence of our relationship, I am now able to talk with him while his body sleeps. Consequently it is easier to work through him, for when he is like this he fights me not."

"I do talk to him about the tapes now after we've listened to one."

"That is good." He paused, waiting for her, then: "Do you have another question, or do you feel that you do not have sufficient answers?"

"Oh no, you've answered marvellously Philip. It's just that I'm not sure how long you can afford to be here. You must have lots of important things to do."

"My role is a busy one," he acknowledged, "but at this stage I can direct my thoughts to serving my colleagues at the Centre without a presence being needed. On Friday we plan to speak with you all. We will then explain to you what you are about to become involved in and how best you may help. Please do not forget that the emotional state of those in your group should be settled. Do not therefore invite those whom you, and you alone, feel are not thus suited. Your friend Jules has much important work to do."

"You're happy about him then aren't you?"

"You could not have made us more happy. You could not have made me more happy."

"Oh good. Are you happy about Robert Riddell? He's a nice, strong person isn't he?"

"He is going to benefit a great deal."

"And John Maynard (J.M.) is alright too is he?"

"He also has much important work to do, and he will link up with his guide who of course is John. This however will take place at a later time. Is there a question which is more personal to yourself? I know you have one that is not written."

"Yes in a way." She sounded reluctant. "I wonder if you can tell me whether I'm making any progress spiritually. I seem to be making so many mistakes."

He spoke earnestly, voice now close upon a whisper.

"Child, you are going to join us in our work. For you, there will be no indecision. You will link and continue the task that you were doing with us before you decided to return. May I help you in another way?"

"Please, anything you can say would help."

"Take little notice of the people who are about to surround you, for although you are going to have a rough passage in the next few weeks, the work you are doing will be invaluable. You realise of course that I mean the rescue work."

"Yes I do realise that. Thank you very much Philip. Is it possible for you to communicate with me through my mind, or do I have to talk to you like this?"

"My dear child," he said with the utmost gentleness, "if you should need comfort at any time, please come to this place of light and wait for me. Where words are needed however, you will find it easier to talk to me as you are doing now, because often your subconscious is stronger than that of my channel."

"Yes I understand. Was I right yesterday that you didn't want Peter to come up here for healing, or was I just imagining it?"

"We are healing him. Now I do not mean to be abrupt with you, but I am going very shortly."

"Will you be able to go without any trouble?"

"You must not make any sharp movement until I have gone. Remember that we are always close."

"Thank you again ever so much Philip. Goodnight."

As he withdrew, slowly and surely, she realised it was the protective brotherliness about him which she found comforting.

Otherwise, like the rest of the team-to-be when Philip's explanation of "influence" was played back on tape, the nature of "Us" had at once too macrocosmic and personal a bearing to absorb by ear. His picture did seem to confirm my unison glimpse, but even this for the time being remained hard to assimilate let alone express, so raw and precious was it to me still. Its fruits however were to ripen unknowingly, in spite of ourselves, throughout the action of our involvement.

Such action, at times harrowing, was ready to tear apart the web of our conceptual experience, in face of which Valerie might have opted for a series of talks alone with Philip. Nonetheless she knew now, as never before, what lay ahead on the path she had chosen since that initial night of the party – and her heart meant to stay with it.

CHAPTER 5

WE TREAD THE BOARDS

Friday came with an overcast sky, breaking into blue between April showers, then hazing pinkly over Ashdene's garden at the start of our session. I pulled away from the Sanctuary window, drew its curtains to allow only the altar lamp's gleam, and joined my companions seated within.

An air of expectance prevailed, for tonight we were to be briefed on the work and how best we could help. Even during the prayer Peter's head was nodding to its fall. Invisibly around us however, conditions felt more populous than last week – of earthbound people, that is – so it wasn't surprising to sense Philip squeeze through under noticeable duress. Recognition of him brought my will and any positive line to help pilot his struggle.

"Come on Philip… Nice and easy. You have all our support and welcome. Are you with us?"

At first he could scarcely part the channel's lips, and our concern grew when it took him some persistence to force an acknowledgement:

"Yes I'm… "

The throng of people must have seemed stifling to one without physical insulation. Uncomfortable from it myself, I had supposed that there would be a repeat battle of wills yet not against quite this many. As for Philip, his practical experience was limited to those four sessions so far in which pressure on our channel was still of manageable degree. All along though, the needy had been increasing like moths around a flame – drawn to psychism's light. His nibs on the other hand, having at last got their two-world project launched and given us the promise of special instruction, no doubt meant to make a showing as I kept up support.

"Well done. You were going to tell us about the work, how you want us to help, weren't you?"

"Yes... " he breathed under sufferance.

"We're eager to glean all we can, the four of us, and the channel seems relaxed."

"But crowded... There's a power struggle!"

At that, hope began to wane. Evidently one of the gangs had arrived who wanted earthbound people in their power, resenting The Seven's bid to entice as many as possible to freer localities. The known potency of a physical channel in doing so would rile such a gang even more. One could imagine how they might very well be occupying David, John and Brian's priority attention while Philip was left to cope with the dully pressing mass as best he could.

"Intruders you mean?"

"Yes."

Any prospect of talk looked bleak indeed. Then, across my review of whether to close the session or try some united fend-off strategy he shot a poser that took me aback.

"Do you all realise... what is... being asked... of you?"

My mouth hung open. It sounded as if he was expecting us to start work straightaway. No one else spoke, so I fumbled for clarification:

"What are you going to do?"

"David will give you... all the help... he can... because he is there. Do you understand?"

"Yes we understand," said my assumption that the others had cottoned on too. If Philip had planned anyway to lead us into a trial run after his talk, he now chose to bring that forward and drop us in at the deep end for our first lesson – back-up man in place. While he struggled through another acute minute we had hardly more time to think than he had to offer us the chance of quick counsel:

"Are there any… relevant questions… you wish to ask?"

My companions' hesitance again found me spokesman.

"Looks like they'll mostly arise in practice. We'll have to play it by ear and ask you later."

"If you are not… sure of… any procedure… please do not hesitate to call… for David… or Brian."

This was little consolation to Robert for the loss:

"Can't we do anything to increase your power?"

"It is not… in your hands… my friend."

Valerie feared the loss may be permanent:

"Will we ever be able to speak with you Philip?"

"Of course."

"We appreciate your having tried anyway," I said.

"I shall be with you… in the deepest sense tonight."

"We'll remember that Philip. Thanks for the effort you've made."

Yet the thought of his remaining a witness escaped most of us from that moment on, keyed up as we were over this unexpected turn. The scene, once he had slipped away into its benighted depths, is still vivid.

All four of us were drawn into a tight semi-circle before the settee where Peter's body loomed gaunt and still. Furthest off at one end Robert sat bolt upright, like a horse scenting battle. Next to him, and forcing herself into a composure she was far from feeling, Valerie leaned forward with the recorder clutched in her lap, eyes anxiously concentrated on the form in front of her. A bit to the rear at her left elbow, J.M's youthful, tense-lipped face gazed ahead too; while I sat foremost in waistcoat and shirtsleeves, sombrely arched over the channel like a cat crouching at its mousehole.

The wait was brief but intense. Valerie swallowed to relieve the constriction in her throat. We heard it and could identify.

"… Just call for David then, or Brian," she told herself by way of reminding everyone. Seconds later our nearest unhappy case pitched helter-skelter into the channel, releasing a sound which stole out so gently that the most timid could not be terrified.

It was a sound of weak, anguished sobbing. The body started to sway back and forth, hands wringing in vexation as the sobs grew loud. From their depth one could feel that whirl of emotional discharge with which, out of lonely and desperate straits, we finally rush into familiar or comforting arms. I offered mine without eagerness.

"Alright you're among friends now. We realise it's been hard for you and we're going to help."

But the lament continued, half-drowning every bid:

"What is it that's so painful for you?"

"My babies!" wailed the voice.

"Your babies?" I echoed to ensure the others heard. "Where are they?"

Instantly this triggered a further bout of sobbing which shook and choked the body as answers were sought:

"Do try to tell us more. Have you lost them?"

"Ye-e-es!" came thickly through the tears.

"Okay, okay. Can we know your name?"

"Shanti… "

"How did you lose them?" asked Robert.

"In the sun."

"How long ago was that?"

"Oh I've been looking for so long," she cried, scarcely articulate with grief. "Please, please get them! They didn't want me to have them and I … "

Her outpouring became inaudible. I cut in quickly:

"Hey, listen to us for a moment Shanti. Listen to what we have to say."

"Yes," she sniffled, making an effort. "Yes?"

"Now we have special helpers with us. These are people who can help you find them. But you must turn your attention to that help before they can close in and take you along."

"Oh please!" she implored. "I want my babies!"

"So tell us about them," suggested Robert. "Start at the beginning."

"You know! They took them from me and I really wanted them. I did!"

"Who took them from you and why?"

"The soldiers. I don't know why. They hit me."

"Are you alone? Give us all the information."

Here Valerie whispered her disagreement, that we should point instead to David or Brian. But already the poor woman was brimming over:

"It's hopeless," she sobbed. "They said they couldn't be left with me, and that I couldn't look after them. But it's not true! I wanted them so much... and they've taken them. They even trod over someone in the sand when they left. Now I go every day and there's nothing. No one'll tell me where they are. I can't bear it!"

One surmised the soldier's blows to have been fatal and that the body she had seen them trample in the sand was her own. Not realising her innate independence of it she would automatically assume the body to be someone else's, particularly if it lay face down. I missed this chance of explaining her state in an attempt to lure her sights forward.

"Well right now we have a friend who can help find your babies, and if you open yourself... "

" – Who, him?"

She could have meant anyone near. I took a gamble.

"Yes, if you ask the bright looking young man they will be found for you. He's one of many helpers ready to hand because you're not on earth any more, you see."

"... Not on earth?" Her tone held surprise.

"No, you've passed on into another world and are now using a lighter body that you had inside all your life. Once you can realise that fact, you'll find it just needs a thought to get help... where you are."

I was conscious in mid-speech of a brusque overthrow taking place. Another in the crowd, maybe ignorant of having jostled her aside, had encroached so quickly as to assume I was talking to him.

"Wot d'yer mean where I am? Do I know you?"

We made haste with a supply of names. His, given grudgingly, was Frank Bowldern. Our sudden appearance in his area seemed to puzzle him, and it sounded like David had been here on rescue forays already.

"You don't usually come wiv 'im, do yer?"

"No because we're on earth," I said.

"Wull so am I."

"What can we do for you Frank?" Valerie asked.

"Oh I just wanna go ter work."

"And what kind of work do you do?"

"I make 'oses."

She had never encountered anyone who made hoses. I hadn't either, and seeing her stuck for a response my fill-in was with the deftness of an elephant trying to execute a quick-step.

"That sounds interesting work."

"No it isn't, it's bloody boring, " he retorted, "but I'd still like ter go back."

"Why's that?"

"Wull for a start it's better than sittin' abaht 'ere. I don't loike this crowd very much."

The juncture to probe was obvious, even to myself.

"Frank, what's the last thing you remember happening at your workplace?"

"Oh a bloke got caught an' they wouldn't let me 'elp."

"Got caught? How do you mean?"

"In the press. I tried ter get through but they wouldn't take any notice of me. They wouldn't even look at me."

"Then what did you do?"

"Mooched abaht a bit. They won't let me go back, see. But I must, 'cos I got the keys in my pocket and they won't be able ter work it wivout me."

"Listen a minute Frank. We're on the earth… "

"– I know we are. Wot d'yer keep sayin' that for?"

"Because you're not here any longer. You're using someone else's body to speak to us."

"Don't be daft!"

Actually beginning to feel so by this time I paused, hoping for volunteers. But our pace had to be kept up or we risked his slipping away, which was likely unless my injudicious remark was explained pronto.

"No it's true Frank," I muddled on. "You have your body of course, but gradually you'll find it's a much more flexible one than you had on earth. You've left that behind you see. It's dead. That's why no one here can see you any more, and why we might look a bit blurred to you. It's not faulty eyesight. You're now in the afterlife, and free."

He was flummoxed, only half comprehending. If this touched off a glimmer of recognition to confirm sensory experience of late, reality was still the workplace:

"... But I've got the keys! They can't get it going wivout the keys!"

"They don't need those keys, and nor do you."

"But wot abaht that poor bloke in the machine? I've got ter 'elp 'im!"

I took a deep breath.

"It was *you*, Frank. You had the accident, and you left your old body behind in the machine, telling yourself it was someone else's because you couldn't face the horror of it. They couldn't see you trying to help. All they could see was your dead body with the original keys in its pocket, so they think you're dead too. You're not of course. No one ever is. But you must put all that away now, and go into a much greater world. It's all taken care of here, okay?"

There was an unabashed silence as the salvo took effect. When, shakenly, he spoke again it was to a figure on our left who had drawn close.

"Is 'e telling me the truth, Guv? Is that... what it is?"

David may have supplied the final answer to our hosemaker's release, showing him the way onward. All that we could see, like his former workmates had seen, was a body fallen from use.

"I think he's gone," said Valerie to me. "Do you think it's David taking them out each time?"

"Probably. I had the feel of him right here."

"So did I," vouched J.M., pointing to the spot, "and there's something like a click when they go isn't there? You know they're going, and you sort of think a little prayer. Then when the next one comes you know it's somebody else, but it's hard to explain how."

"That's what's happening then," she summed up. "David and Brian are able to take them out as soon as they come to understand. So what we say is vital obviously."

While another case was verging upon us I pleaded a fuller participation from everyone, because my tactics were potentially no better than theirs and we must pull together once contact was made. Nods of assent switched quickly back to the channel, for an incipient disquiet, advancing like rolls of thunder out of heat's stillness, told us that whoever had entered was in pain. Long, low groans heaved up with progressive vigour as the sufferer's state synchronised into physical expression, twisting it in search of relief.

"Alright we're here to help," I offered, "if you'll let us. What do you feel?"

The groans parted briefly in sudden cognition of our presence, but no word came. I tried again:

"Tell us about it. We'd like to hear."

"Are you in pain?" asked Robert.

"Ohh ye-e-s!" broke the stifled cry.

"Where does it hurt?"

"My chest."

"How did you get the pain? When did it start?"

" A long time ago."

"Have you been in hospital?" tried J.M.

"Yes."

"Was it an accident?" came back Robert.

"Ye-e-s damn you!… ohh… "

"Could you tell us more about it then?"

"Oh Christ not now! Ohh… let me die! Don't let 'er see me… please!"

"No don't worry," I assured, "it's just between us. We're going to make you well again."

"Not with that new doctor you won't. He's been trying to get me."

Such an unexpected qualm conjured up the image of some spurious dilettante from the crowd rather than David, who was again on our left. Uncertain, I felt it best to play safe and gain the patient's confidence.

"Well trust us a minute then. You want to get rid of that pain, and to do so you must… "

" – No let me die, I don't want to go on like this!"

"You needn't go on like it, yet that's precisely what has happened and you're now in a thought-world."

"Uhh… bloody wish I was. You're not a doctor?"

"No but we understand the condition you're in."

"You don't know what I'm in!"

"We do, I assure you. You're not on earth in that old hospital. They've let you go, and you're in an afterworld where there's no need to feel pain. You only think your chest is still painful because you don't realise that." Getting mere groans I changed tack: "Why don't you like your new doctor?"

"Oh 'e wants to stick me in one of those 'omes and I don't want to go. What's 'e saying to you?"

So perhaps the "doctor" was David after all. Not being attuned enough to pick up any hint he might be supplying however I had to bluff it out.

"He wants to rid you of that pain, and he can."

"Oh yeah? Where's 'e taking me then? What's 'e going to do to me?"

"He'll take you to a different hospital, said J.M., "where they know how to stop the pain."

"No I'm not going."

"But you see," tried Robert, "you have already lost your body, your physical body that is, so there can't be pain. It's all in your mind. Do you follow?"

"What?"

"You have no physical body," he repeated firmly, "so there can be no pain."

"What the 'ell are you talking about? You can see it can't you? Ohh I give up. Only don't let 'im take me! It isn't just the 'ome. I can't... I 'aven't... "

Indignance crumbled to tears. Valerie served one more tender spoonful:

"He won't hurt you, we promise. If you go with him he really will get rid of that pain for you."

But an early, surprise pull-out from the channel left her promise in mid-air. To connect this with any action on David's part never occurred to me, for his move toward our patient had gone largely unnoticed. So in the next few moments while we smouldered with chagrin among ourselves, we were attentive and a shade awkward to find that temperate mien of his taking over.

"Hallo," I sighed. "Are we making a mess of it?"

"You're not helping me terribly. May I just suggest that if you can't get them to understand intellectually, convince them that the hospital to which they are going is better equipped and more luxurious."

"That sounds good advice," conceded Robert.

"We have two of them," David went on quietly. "The old man was almost impossible to move. For some reason he fears us, and will return. Do you have any other problems or questions?"

I was about to ask our friend how we could identify him amongst others of whom the patient might be afraid or suspicious, though Robert spoke first.

"Er... David, are you, or one of you always with the person when they come through to us?"

"Yes, but only as close as you are yourselves."

"So we can point you out to anyone?"

"Yes, they should know who you mean".

"This is it," stressed Valerie, anxious to drive the idea home. "He's standing there all the time you see."

Robert nodded demurely then continued his checkup:

"And tell me, is it the suddenness of their accident which blinds them to where they are?"

"Partly," returned David. "But you must realise that not all these people are here because of accidents. Many see themselves still on earth from having already lived within a fantasy world there. As with the woman in the sand, her motherly grief is natural but she is also over-possessive. It isn't only her shell that is left."

"What about her babies?" I asked.

"We can find them if she'll come with us. Now, are you ready?"

"Yes," murmured all.

"Refer to me as if I was with you, because I am."

We took the hint gladly, though of course in watching his slow, characteristic surrender, questions sprung to mind that one had forgotten to ask. Valerie for example sparked off an exchange about which rescue had been the second of our "two" successes. J.M. believed it must be Shanti and that David's "if she'll come with us", only meant he didn't know how far his colleagues had got with her after she was handed on. At least we knew that he was being looked upon as a doctor by "the old man", and were primed for the latter's return.

During our confab there certainly had been a dim sense of someone churning around nearby, thought to be no more than an echo until David's mention of him, and then only distinct when laggard shifts back toward the vacated channel singled him out from much else at my side. As the oldster's chronic heaving and groaning sadly reasserted itself, a reminder of our new ploy was taken up by J.M.

"Can you see the doctor beside you?"

"Yeah, 'course I can," he wheezed.

"Well he wants to take you to a hospital where they are much better equipped to help your chest."

"Uhh... all 'e does is 'aul me about. You said 'e was gunna take the pain away."

"Yes he will in that other hospital where it'll be more luxurious too. He can't do it where you are now because they haven't got the equipment."

"Nohh, I can't... I told you. It's a bit awkward... I ... I've got... no money, see."

At last we had stumbled upon the block. David may have stood out in luminous contrast to our average NHS doctor on earth, appearing to the old man like a private specialist who required a fee. So talk of luxury would only compound an error which J.M. sought to correct.

"No that's quite alright, you haven't got to pay anything at all. He's doing it just to help you."

"I don't understand! What're you lot doin' then?"

"Well it's a matter of trust," said Robert with civil authority. "We know him, and realise he has means of helping you that cannot be had anywhere else. You must trust him for your own good."

"You sound like Doctor Gower. 'Ow long 'ave I got? Go on, tell us 'ow long I've got!"

"For ever. But you must trust our Doctor here."

"You mean it's not gunna get worse?"

"No it's all going to leave you," enjoined Valerie. "If you go with that Doctor you'll have no more pain. It'll all vanish."

We waived her slight exaggeration, for symptoms were slowing already with the mind's turn.

"You *must* believe us," Robert insisted.

"I do believe you, if you say so. An' I 'aven't got to pay nothin'?"

"Absolutely not. But it's most important that you go with him as soon as you can. You'll never, *ever* regret it."

"Can I go with 'im now then?"

"Yes you go with him now," answered Valerie warmly. He's waiting to take you."

"But... she'll only worry if I'm... You *will* tell 'er where I've gone won't you?"

"Yes we will," she assured him.

"An' you're sure I 'aven't got to pay nothin'?"

"Nothing at all."

"Is 'e gunna take me now then, or... "

"Yes he's ready," said Robert. "So put your faith in him entirely."

My call to David at that point was mere gesture, for a rush of activity had centred round the channel as if at least two people were eagerly hauling the old chap away. David's presence still felt the most obvious, the other having a tighter sense to it that flitted off with them – in the process no doubt of delivering him safe to their Centre's recuperative climes.

It all seemed very brisk and orderly. Nor did we have long to reflect before new life started filling the void. She slid in like quicksilver, a bewildered little girl with the tense, innocent impetuosity of a young fawn. Though guarded in her replies she was perhaps glad of our attention, and straightaway her main concern sprang clear from the darkness:

"Where's my mummy?"

General hesitation brought Robert forward.

"Have you looked for her?"

"Yeh I've kept looking."

"How old are you?"

"I'll be nine next year."

"What is your name? Will you tell us?"

"Gillian."

"And your mummy's name? What do you call her?"

"Mummy."

"Just Mummy. Where did you lose her?"

"By the car."

"Some time ago?"

"Just now."

"And where have you looked for her?"

"Oh Daddy said I mustn't go off. I must stay here and wait for Mummy to come back."

"Is your Daddy with you now?" asked J.M.

"No," came with a faint note of surprise.

"Is there anybody with you?" pressed Robert.

"No," again seeming slightly puzzled.

"Look around you just once more," he encouraged. "Look carefully now. Is anyone standing near?"

Brief moments let her review the scene.

"You mean that funny man?"

"Yes, what does he look like?"

"He looks like he's going to a party."

We laughed at this likely ruse of David's, and our negotiator continued with a smile.

"He's jolly is he?"

"Yeh an' he's all glittery," she added.

"I think he wants to talk to you Gillian."

"No, Daddy says I mustn't talk to people like him."

"Ah, but he's different."

"Daddy says they all say they're different."

Again we laughed, beginning to realise the varied kinds of obstinacy with which helpers have to contend. It being more excusable for her to talk to a group than strange men, Valerie's maternal semblance among us was possibly another advantage. That alone, if let forward, might have mothered the child toward David, but ad-lib we followed the direct option voiced by J.M.

"You must disobey your Daddy. He won't really mind in this instance."

"Yes he will. He'll be cross. Where's my mummy?"

"Well," resumed Robert, "I think that friend wants to take you to her, because he knows where she is. I expect he's waiting for you, and all he wants to do is take you there."

"Where is she?"

"I don't know, but he does you see. So if you want to find your mummy you must trust this man. Look at him again. We know him. He's very nice."

"But where is he going to take me?"

"You ask him and I'm sure he will tell you".

Gillian wanted more basic insurance.

"What's his name?"

"David. You call him that and he'll come to help."

"My daddy's name is David," she reflected.

"Really? Well there you are then. Talk to him."

"No I think I'd better wait for Mummy."

"You see," Robert persisted with a tender gravity, "your mummy doesn't know where you are, and you don't know where your mummy is. The only way you can come together is if you can trust David. So you must trust him, otherwise your mummy will not find you."

"But they took Mummy away!"

"Alright, so how is she going to find… "

"– She's coming back for me though," interposed Gillian quickly. "She only went with the other little girl to the hospital. Is that where she still is?"

"We don't know, but David does. In fact I think he's been with her. Ask him. He knows the answers."

As the prospect was timorously considered, J.M. tried to keep her on target:

"Can you still see him – the glittery man?"

"Yeh," she whimpered, "he's a bit like my daddy."

"Well go towards him," urged Robert. "Go closer and have a good look at him. He really is very nice."

We knew that she was edging out to a certain extent by the droop of the channel, though whether in line with these coaxes was hard to tell. Neither J.M. nor myself had felt David in his usual position near us, all along presuming that he was over by Robert to back him up. When she failed to return therefore, thoughts went after her that she would accept our guidance and not, for example, seek refuge in the parents' car.

Or what was left of it, for her responses added up to the family having had a motor accident. That "other little girl" was reckoned to be Gillian's fatally comatose body going off in the ambulance with her mother, while Gillian herself stayed bemusedly by the wreckage on the instructions of her father who must also have been dislodged from his body to have given them – maybe in a compulsive act before stupor overtook him. But one's focus dwelt more on the emotional impact, as expressed by Robert.

"That's beautiful," he recalled, trying to envision David's way of appealing to the child. "Dressed for a party!"

"Isn't it!" agreed Valerie. "A glittery man!" I bet she's gone with him. Wonder how many they're going to give us."

So did we all, with number five beginning to show. A mulish, forsaken air that moments before had percolated through to my senses now compressed itself into hard lines on the channel's face. Whoever was there remained stiff, knotted, as though labouring under a private strain yet conscious of our sudden appearance and unable to account for it. Indeed the strain was evident enough for Robert to declare:

"Gosh you look miserable!"

"Who are you?" came a gruff voice.

"We're friends," he answered.

"Huh! I never seen yer."

"But you've seen this other young man I expect," was said in hope of David's early return.

"Oh wiv you is 'e? Wot's 'e up to then?"

"He just wants to help you, as we do."

"I don't need no 'elp. I've always managed on me own an' always will manage on me own."

"So have you been doing anything interesting lately?"

"I bin trying ter git 'ome ain't I?"

"Where do you live? Perhaps we can direct you."

"Streatham."

"How have you been trying?" I enquired.

"Oh it's gettin' up them steps. Can't seem ter manage it no more."

"Up the steps? What to get to Streatham?"

"Wull I gotta git aht this bloomin' shelter first ain't I?" shot back with repressed annoyance.

"Er... did you say shelter?" zeroed in Robert.

"Yeah wot abaht it?"

"Wartime!" he gasped to himself, but was overheard.

"'Course it's wartime! Gor lumme where you bin?"

He had "bin" rather moved, collecting his thoughts.

"What's happened? Did you have a blitz?"

"Yuh, I 'eard the All Clear go but couldn't git up."

"Dear oh dear!" Robert was shaking his head with dismay as J.M. took over.

"And the man near you, has he been there long?"

"Na, 'e come just 'fore you lot. Who is 'e then?"

"He's a friend of yours."

"Garn!" was the incredulous reply.

"What did he say to you when he first arrived?"

"Darned if I know. Couldn't 'ear too well. Didn't pay much attention."

"You should have done. He can help you out."

"I'll find me own way aht thank yer."

"You don't seem to have been very successful so far," I said. "Why don't you ask his help?"

"Na, I'm alright. I can manage."

Robert could contain himself no longer: "But you can't manage really, can you, on your own? You want to get back to Streatham don't you?"

"Yuh."

"Shall we explain what in fact happened to you?"

The brows knitted together in silence.

"Do you want to know?" I reiterated. "We know."

"... Wot d'yer mean?" said a pathetic puzzlement.

"Well, when you were in the air-raid shelter... "

"– I *am* in the air-raid shelter!"

"Yes but there must have been an explosion which affected you, and the world thinks you're gone."

"Gawn where?"

"But really you're continuing in a subtler form."

"Wot?"

"Have you ever heard of Heaven?" gambled J.M.

"Course? Everyone's 'eard of 'eaven."

"Well that's where you are."

There was a slight pause.

"... It don't seem much like 'eaven ter me!"

"No but if you look more closely," he pressed, "you'll find it isn't the same air-raid shelter at all, and that the man standing here is an angel ready to help you."

It might have been interesting to see David's face at that moment. In any case these two attempts of ours to explain by means of over-diluted technical truth and common archetypes were proving ridiculously inept. The fellow, as we now found him to be, grew bewildered – not sure whether he was dead or alive and fearing, in the face of apparent evacuation, for the one security he had left.

"Wot abaht my wife and kids?"

"Oh don't worry about her, I said. "You'll meet up."

"Wot d'yer mean don't worry abaht 'er? I want ter git back don't I?"

"No she's been seen to by now I expect, further on."

"'Oo's bin seein' to 'er?" he demanded indignantly, which amid team chuckles had me do a quick make-over.

"I mean she may have already been taken on to where you're going, so you'll meet up with her there. But obviously you have to get out of the shelter first and this man can help you do that."

"Wot yer talking abaht 'eaven for then?"

One wished it had never been mentioned.

"Because, um… in a sense perhaps, Heaven is a place you're part way to. You're in-between as it were, and if you go with him he can guide you on."

"I just wanna go ter Streatham," he mumbled.

"Oh you'll find your Streatham… "

"– An' Streatham ain't no 'eaven."

"… but our chap knows where… Pardon?"

I had spoken over his last remark, caught by Robert:

"Streatham's not Heaven he says. Look would you tell us your name?"

"George Chandler."

"George… I think we must explain very frankly what happened to you, and you must try to come to grips with it. You see what Jules, our friend here, tried originally to say was that while you were in your air-raid shelter, a bomb exploded on that shelter and… what then happened to you was something you might call… died. Of course, you didn't die. All you did in fact was lose your physical body. But you see, you go on existing, and that is exactly what you are doing. You've only lost your physical body. That is in the rubble of the air-raid shelter. And when your real, shall we say spiritual body continued, this is the image it took with it. So you still think you're in that shelter. But you're not really. The war has long finished. The year is now 1972 you see, and all this time you have passed over as we call it. All this means is that you have lost your physical body, but as you know, you're fine and well. So you *must* now come to understand what has taken place, because if you don't, you will always, in your thoughts, in your mind, be in that air-raid shelter. You *must* come out of it, because only a little way beyond is beauty, and the young man standing here wants to guide you into it. All you must do is see and realise what has happened to you, and the help he can give. That's all. Do you understand? It's most important. What do you think of that?"

He had spoken very evenly, sensitively, but with a voice which rang true as steel. For a moment or two George was speechless, having listened with awe-struck attention if not blank astonishment. An almost solemn expectancy hung in the quiet room till he managed to collect himself, and when he did, his nerves struggled a little in his throat:

"S-Straight up?"

"Absolutely smack on the button!" confirmed Robert. "But it doesn't matter you see, because nothing worthwhile is ever lost. What's more we go on unfolding in a life of promise and fulfilment."

"So… So if I go with your mate, will I be alright?"

"Certainly. Trust him and you'll see for yourself. You can then forget about the air-raid shelter. You'll never see it again, ever. Just go with him and trust him. It's a wonderful world beyond, so leave that old shelter behind you now."

A sharp intake of breath, and George was gone. We sank back

appreciably relieved, though this time into a silence pregnant with feeling for the man and obvious indebtedness to Robert.

The pressure of people around us had lessened too, thought to be the result of those either spurred on by his advice or hived off by it. Some might indeed have followed David and George out of curiosity, while others seeking only amusement may have dispersed to more usual haunts. Yet remaining would be cases like George with whom tonight we were prone to deal, cocooned so fast in their bubbles of illusion that they were unlikely even to be aware of each other, clothing the helpers as part of that illusion – often an ignored or resented part. One could appreciate, for these self-exiled and forlorn, who clung to their subjective versions of life in death, how the comparative sharpness, hardness of earth reality through the channel made us seem more real, incisive, our world cutting into theirs like a knife but gently.

Soon, amidst a plethora of pants and gasps, the next came rolling in. He complained of an afternoon heat, thinking himself helplessly supine in his garden. We deduced this from a few terse replies which expected any passer-by to see his problem as elementary. For once our arrival on the scene was welcome however.

"My wife's gone in. I'm glad you came along," he said in a breathless, eager tone. "Just help me up will you?"

"What have you been doing?" I asked. "Did you fall?"

"No I was just lying here and then couldn't get up."

He had evidently passed in this position, perhaps from a heart attack. But I was unsure whether raising the channel bodily would do the trick, and decided in my impatience to try straightforward truth first.

"Right, the way you can get up is to realise that as you lay there you left the body without knowing it and changed dimension. If you look properly you will see that you have a newer form which is fit and free."

"Oh it's hot! And I don't need mental exercises. Just give me a hand up."

"But you can get up easily now, or the chap here on my left will show you how it's done. I expect you've seen him already. His name's David."

"That young whippersnapper you mean?"

"Yes, he can help you if you let him. But you can do it yourself."

"No I can't. Just help me up please."

My inefficacy drew Robert to the fore again.

"Are you otherwise alone in the garden?"

"Yes she's gone in. If you won't help, could you tell her I'm here?"

"Er... not exactly. Listen, raise your arms... raise them up. Can you do that? Now your head... that's it."

The effect was being estimated by slight physical response in the channel. Hope that he might discover his latent ability and thus his condition by suggested self-effort had us vocally supportive behind Robert.

"A bit more... that's it. There you are. It's not difficult you see."

"Give us a hand up then," he puffed.

"We are. Sit up now. Use your arms in support."

"I can't!"

"Of course you can. I know it's painful, but you can do it slowly. Try again. You're making progress."

"So why is your friend just nodding at me? Why doesn't he do something?"

"Because he's waiting to take you to the hospital where they have the facilities to put you right. It'll be much cooler there too. So try again slowly... a bit more... "

But the man took a sudden backward exit, I assumed on his own until realising that David also had moved and maybe pulled him clear.

"Are you still there?" called out Robert, glancing from the channel to me, then to Valerie.

"I think David's got him now," she said.

If he had, it seemed that the point of acquiescence was when he became expected to "do something". Such a crucial point, their key change to recognition of him, struck me as one that could easily go unnoticed by us. David might see the turn in them and either be able to act right away or have to watch our ignorance cloud it over again.

The thought floated irresolute as we made ourselves mentally ready for another case, each of us pondering how to streamline our approach and determined to be on our toes. Silence fell, then a stirring at which muscles tensed, but instead it was David popping in to offer encouragement. Our need of this brought Valerie forward almost before he had settled himself.

"How are we getting on?"

"Very well now," he said, taken to include success with the last case. Robert voiced a natural question:

"How do you cope with them in-between?"

"Brian's with me. He's handing them on."

"Is he the young whippersnapper?" grinned J.M.

"I think that was me. We have two more. Can you manage?"

"Yes we're happy to," I said of the general mood.

"You're doing much better."

"Thanks, that's reassuring David," was again said more for the others before Robert threw in:

"You must tell us one day how you pick them."

"We don't pick them," corrected David softly. "I just allow those able to use the channel to do so in turn. But there are many who cannot."

Only those, in other words, with qualities of a similar frequency range to that of the channel could blend into it enough to cause physical expression – a factor no doubt as palpable on his level as the law of gravity here. Those "many" left over to listen would one day become significant.

Promises meanwhile to continue doing our best saw his careful disengagement, and once out he must have turned to let the first of his "two more" hustle her way earthward in a welter of strangled breaths. She sounded momentarily unsure, then relieved at last to come upon human voices in what was for her an opaque, remote, watery fastness:

"– Ah!"

"Hallo," I acknowledged. "We're here to help you."

"Oh... 'ave you got a boat? I can't see."

"No we don't need a boat, and nor do you."

"You on the beach then? I'm nearly there."

"What happened?" asked J.M. "Did you go swimming?"

"Yeh we were in the boat, Jimmy and I. We've only just bought it y'see, an' we took it out. 'Ave you seen 'im?"

"No we haven't seen anyone," I confessed in truth. "But we can help you find him. Who are you?"

"Irene, an' I'm flippin' perished out 'ere. Got a blanket?"

"Yes there's a man here with a blanket for you."

Robert, guessing she had drowned, pryed further.

"And Jimmy, is he your boyfriend?"

"No my 'usband. I went for a swim and he rowed off and left me. I've got to find 'im!"

"Did you swim back?"

"Yeh I'm tryin' to," she said a bit tetchily.

"But you don't have to Irene," I urged, "because there's been a change. It's all different now, and a man's waiting right beside us to help you realise this. Can you see him standing here?... Irene?"

"No 'ang on a tick... let me get my... "

"Shall we tell you what happened?"

By now she had clambered ashore.

"I know what 'appened," said she. "Jimmy thought I'd swum back and I 'adn't."

"Look around you," Robert prompted. "See anyone?"

"Oh thank God, your friend's got a blanket. I'm frozen stiff. Bye-bye, and thanks for 'elping!"

We felt somewhat trampled over at first, but then saw how Irene's sense of contact with us had in fact homed her to the shore and linked her to David – he using her need of a blanket to entice her free.

It was during this afterchat, when attention had strayed among ourselves, that I grew suddenly aware of someone else's presence in the channel. There had been no sound or movement to alert us, though a lapse in our conversation at once startled that sense of a witness pending within, an air of heavy incumbence at my elbow which made me turn to see the head upraised, humourless and stern, as if surveying us broodily.

"Who are you, friend?" I asked.

"What do you want?" snapped an imperious voice. "And what are you doing with *him*?"

"With whom?"

"I think you know quite well who I mean. *Him!*" A nod went over to my right where perhaps David had come back to stand, since he was nowhere near me. "That young man. If you must barge into my house you'll kindly leave him outside."

"Er, we're friends," said Robert. "May we come in?"

"You seem to be here!"

"Oh, I do apologise, and I hope we're not entirely unwelcome because we'd like to meet you. Is this your house?"

"Of course it is!"

"Very nice," simulated Robert with a roundward scan. Where's your family?"

"They'll be home soon."

"I see. Perhaps I can introduce the members of our group. On my left this is Valerie, then J.M., Jules, and I'm Robert. We're very glad to meet you."

"Good evening, the name's Knight. Charles Knight."

"Oh good evening. You must forgive us, Mr Knight, because it will seem extraordinary to you that we're here, I realise."

"So how and why are you here? Who are you?"

"We're coming to that," steadied Robert. "But we must first assure you that the man you've put outside is a good fellow, and I'm sorry that you won't allow him in because he's actually here to help you, as we all are."

"I'm quite able to handle my own affairs thank you very much, and I certainly don't allow anybody of that type through my front door."

"What type is he then?" I asked.

"He's trying to sell me something."

"He isn't!" protested Robert.

"I shall feel a lot safer when my family gets home."

"How long have you been waiting for them?"

"Quite a while," was the sullen reply.

Robert chose his psychological moment.

"Mr Knight, um… we've got some rather… important… news for you in a way."

"Important? Don't say there's been an accident! Where are they?"

"No they're alright as far as we know. The news is about yourself. Would you like to hear it?"

"Oh. Do go on."

"Now it's vital that you listen to us. Jules? Maybe you could explain."

My heart sank, having fully expected Robert's savoir-faire to run on without recourse to me. But the dye was cast, and to quibble now might endanger our momentum. I took the plunge therefore, stiltedly ad hoc.

"Well… all of us, when we come to the end of our lives, we change. We lose hold of the physical body… "

"– You sound, sir, just like my daughter!"

"Nevertheless," I hurried along, "it is true that after the change we find ourselves functioning at a different rate, or dimension. Now some of us are so tied to habits of thinking that we often don't realise where we are, and… "

"– Are you trying to tell me that I'm so senile I don't know my own home?"

"No of course not, I'm… "

"You may have tea and then you may go."

Robert's intervention was never more timely.

"Mr Knight, I think we must point out that our news is not about your physical age, but that you and us are on different planes. That is why we suddenly appeared out of nowhere seated around you in your living room. You still find this most extraordinary do you not?"

"Well since you ask, I do rather. But what do you mean by different planes? I don't follow."

"I mean that we are speaking from one level of existence which is a physical, earthly one, and you are speaking from and are in, quite another level of existence which is nonphysical – however solid it may seem to you. The fact that we can converse at all with one another is entirely due to an earthly medium between us, invisible to you, but through which you are able to talk to us… "

"Good grief I've never heard such… "

"– Now before you dismiss this as preposterous we must ask you please to listen very carefully, because what we say can be ably demonstrated by that young man outside if, after I've explained, you will just give him the chance. He knows, as we do, that at some point you in fact passed out of your earthly body, or as we say – died, perhaps from an illness or naturally. But when that happened, only your physical body died, while your actual self, with its thoughts, feelings and grasp of your home environment remained the same, perceiving everything as before. So at this moment you are sitting on a lower edge of the afterlife which interpenetrates the old earthly world, and even though you're actually freed from earth and can no longer see it as it is now –this Friday evening of the 14th April 1972 – your mind's eye continues to project over it those last hours you experienced while still here. You overlooked the differences because your body's death happened smoothly like shedding an outer skin, maybe in sleep – and not realising you'd done so, your mind awoke still expecting to see things exactly as they are, which is what you see now. Are you with me?"

Knight had become dumbfoundedly silent, head turned toward Robert in unflinching, tense concentration. He might have suspected something of this nature all along yet been unable to equate or accept it within himself. After a second's hush his response was tentative.

"Do you mean to tell me… Is that why they haven't… ?"

"Your family? Yes that's exactly why they seem not to have come back. You see… "

"– No wait! But… but if I… died… where is the body you say I have left behind?"

"Oh that will be on earth, probably long found by them and taken away. You missed all that because when you left the physical world you were surrounded by an inner dreamscape of your own that entirely overlaid what was going on there. It prevents you even now from seeing the physical body of the medium you are using. What you see, in fact, is your own inner form which was there all the time creating your inner environment – and with it you are looking at my inner form, not my physical one. It's *so* convincing, it all seems *so* solid that you still think you're in your old physical body. Actually, we cannot see you. We can only see the medium through which everything you say comes to us. It has been kindly lent for this purpose, and that young man you've left outside has allowed you to use it. Do you understand? That man has enabled you to speak to us through this medium here in Kent. So you must realise that we're not really in your house at all, and neither are you in any physical sense. The young man can take you out of your dreamscape and show you your family still living back in that earthly home. They will not come into your dream. *You* must be taken to *them*. And the only way that can happen is by your acceptance of your *real* condition – which means that you must give up this idea of being in your house. It is a powerful photograph of your memory, your thoughts, the lingering process of an existence you have shed, and must leave behind. It is for you now to understand what has occurred. If you cannot do so, you will never see your family again, because at present they are separated from you by your dream. So you *must* go to this young man David. He will show you by demonstration exactly what we mean, and that what we say is true. Will you let him do that?"

There fell such an acute silence that it seemed as if no one present even breathed, waiting for Charles Knight to face his self-centred exile and bridge the gulf made with his family. At last he rallied with stealth:

"Are you… quite sure?"

"Yes we're absolutely sure," confirmed Robert. "This is what we're here to do you see, to help people who've passed over without realising it. We help them understand what has occurred so that they can move on into the most beautiful realms of their new existence. But what they have to do, and what *you* must do, is realise the change that has taken place. By so doing you shed altogether that world of make-believe and are then free to move forward into a real new dimension, one which will also allow you close contact with the life of your family whenever you wish it. So do please go and meet our friend. He will take you on."

"What is your name young man?"

"I'm Robert."

"And the young man next to you?"

"Oh he's here is he? This is David. He is waiting for you. He's a wonderful, blessed soul who long ago went through the same phase as you."

"I shall go with him for a short walk."

"Will you? Alright, just for a short walk."

"Did you come through The Oaks on your way here?"

"No," Robert chuckled. "You see, we never arrived. We're really on earth."

"I'll show David The Oaks."

"Yes he'd love to see them," said Valerie.

"But *trust* him," Robert stressed. "He's a good man."

"I'll see you when we get back."

And off he went with David, we assumed, bearing a proud mask of caution over the shock whose impact had evidently numbed any grasp of our real position – a hard one anyway while we still figured as part of his "dreamscape". But it did sound like he had taken the point, and maybe the step of a lifetime.

Since he was also the last of the evening we guessed that David would guide him straight on through "The Oaks" to their rehabilitation centre himself, leaving someone behind to replenish spent energy in the channel and make sure of it's owner's safe return. There were inklings of at least two aides, but in a finale of tacit, silent prayer we felt too ready for repose to pay much heed.

None of us however could ignore Peter's solid return, lumbering phlegmatic into a consciousness of eyelids that had become like leaden shutters, drowsily lifting them to recall an audience huddled round, and voicing dismay at the cramped, hot, used state of his body. Along with him we stretched our stiff limbs, stumbled out under the harsh landing light, and downstairs.

Little or nothing was said on the way. We were light headed from the intensity and variety of it all, from images that hung touchingly alive yet now felt far away, their power switched off. And it was over so soon too, shrunk within the surety of a familiar world again. I felt daunted by how hard to penetrate was the mindset around most of our cases, also a tad awed by Robert's ability to translate abstruse information into terms that Chandler and Knight could more readily understand. Without him, I thought, neither would have been freed.

Our descent was greeted by piquant aromas from Mary-Ann's input over the stove, enticing a newly vitalised Peter to scuttle out there and peek into cookpots as the rest of us spread about those sofas either side of the fire. Robert opened up a food hamper he had brought, wherefrom wine, French loaves, pâté, cheese, and tins of Mexican honey flowed onto the table like an outbreath from nearly two hours under tension.

As before, he was the opening bowler of queries, and after he had filled my glass the look that briefly held mine was rich with them. The first, at the forefront of his mind, sprung at me in lowered tones with a deferential eye on Peter out in the kitchen.

"He doesn't seem in the least concerned about what went on, does he?"

"I find they normally aren't, even the experienced ones," I said, glancing over my shoulder. "But raw novices like him are often the most confused about how they stand in relation to it, so they feel a need to distance themselves from the whole business immediately afterwards. And that need can persist, because however feasible or authentic the output may be there are doubts already in the mind from deep-seated cultural prejudice – especially when they have no background in the field. Being able to place it in a given framework of knowledge can be a short term relief, except that the old assumptions are held onto, and will conflict. By avoiding the output they avoid the conflict. They know it'll bring up the awkward feeling they harbour of their oddness, apartness, embarrassment at phenomena which appear quite unconnected with the everyday self they've been used to. A main fear is of arguments imputing the subconscious of course, which brings up their core doubt."

"Like when you've been drunk the night before," J.M. offered, "and you're nervous of what you might have said or done, hardly daring to ask."

"In a way."

"But he finds us supportive surely?" plied Robert.

"Oh that's just seen as gullibility around him, or as a certainty he feels unable to share. He knows that, to us, it's at arm's length, easy to be detached from, talk about, dissect – whereas he's the subject, part of it and yet mysteriously not. I wonder if we'd feel the same in his position."

"Yes I've been wondering that," Valerie pooled. She was brandishing the live microphone again, new cassette swiftly installed. "And I suppose for him to know it's all on tape too is a bit of a... thing, although he can't expect us not to record it. I mean if I found out that someone like Philip had been talking through me I'd be absolutely bowled over."

"But that's not his position," put J.M. "You're into all this and he's not."

"You'd feel in-between perhaps," I suggested, "unable to speak with them physically, and your belief reducing the problem to how much is you, how much them."

"Yes I suppose so," she conceded.

"Say you didn't believe in them though," J.M. spun at her. "I bet you'd find it pretty scary. Wouldn't she Jules?"

"It's a fair bet, because then the experience is of mental phenomena which disbelief says shouldn't exist at all. Peter certainly found that scary, so for peace of mind he's had to adopt a tenuous belief in what is given him as the source."

"Not so much a belief," mooted Robert, "as a way of coping. In which case, if their communication is heard to contain insight or knowledge greater than his own, this makes it more scarily phenomenal to him and the prospect is avoided?"

"Yes," I replied. "Sometimes a medium for senior discarnate teaching can feel guilty over not living a spiritual life beyond reproach. The Seven are rescue workers not teachers, but the effect of what they say can be similar on a novice like him and hatch another reason to push it away."

"I can understand that guilt," Valerie said. "It might be how I'd feel. Simply remembering we're hand in glove with seasoned discarnates makes one a tinge in awe."

"It does pin your ears back," spared J.M., "though you can expect too much because of it. They seem to me as basically human as anyone else."

"Which reminds me," Robert began, but was halted by Mary–Ann and Peter bringing in the meals. A glance from Peter swung on the cassette machine as if it were Pandora's box, then shied off into humorous vein. He liked to be appreciated of course for the secular chap he was, continuing with pleasant lightheartedness to uphold the commonplace of occasion and thus his honour in normality. Appreciated well enough, it overlaid whether or not he could recall anything of his stint out of the body. Not until after we had eaten was the question thought politic to broach. At once his usual animation was suspended and he became distant, hazed in memory as from a dream.

"I remember that weird tunnel thing again," he said, "and then a lot of shouting. I thought it was you lot at first, then realised it wasn't. Couldn't be. They weren't your voices and it was a street scene. People standing about in hats. I didn't like it. But someone was close beside me. Didn't see the face. Then we went away. I can't remember anything else, except waking up to that hot, stuffy feeling and you all so close. Did you have a chat then?"

"We had a rescue actually," said Robert.

"A rescue? I thought… " Puzzlement darkened his face at this shift from the agenda he had been told of. "Who was it, one of those people?"

"It was a trial run Philip let us into," explained Valerie. "We tried helping various cases. I don't think they were the ones you saw. Do you want to hear the tape?"

"Of your rescue?" His flinch was obvious.

"Or maybe you'd just like to hear Philip?"

"So they did speak?"

"Oh yes, although he couldn't carry on. It was mostly David whenever possible."

Our sensitive's expression had grown deadpan, maybe trying to comprehend the new angle. But he made no answer, and before Valerie could think of some further incitement Robert broke in.

"That's the matter I wanted to ask about – Philip not being able to make it tonight while David could."

"Oh because David's nearer us," she responded, "and I think he only came when the struggle had died down."

"Okay. All the same we were promised an important talk, perhaps crucial. I'd have been particularly interested to hear how Philip himself would recommend approaching these cases, how he'd do it in our place. He was going to give us specific advice wasn't he?"

"Yes he told me that tonight he'd explain what we were about to become involved in, and how best we may help. Those were his words. Seems a pity he couldn't I agree, but he did ask if we had any questions."

"I know, I felt caught up in the unexpected hitch and didn't think he could say much. On the other hand, shouldn't he have foreseen such a contingency and been prepared for it? What do you say Jules?"

"I doubt that even if he expected the power struggle with intruders he'd be able to foresee how much it would inhibit his use of the channel. In effect it may well have distracted his aides from their job of easing the pressure on him."

"Who are these people you call intruders?"

"Well they can be either the kind of hoodlum who on earth disrupts a village meeting, or they can be the bullies, like gangsters, who want to hold earthbound prey under their thumb and are annoyed with rescue workers coming in on their patch."

"I see. So we've got Philip not knowing how it felt to sit in a channel surrounded by both earthbound and intruders until he was actually doing it?"

"He probably had an idea of what he was up against," I replied, "but he wouldn't be able to judge its actual effect on him or the channel's subconscious beforehand. Remember too that with precious little experience even of normal trance control he's having to allow, for the purpose of rescue, adverse conditions which any veteran control would avoid like the plague. Quite an incubus for him, and David."

"Yes of course, one forgets how deceptively easy it all looks from where we sit, and the odd circumstances they're in. Anyway I wanted to discuss David and the rescuees because at times I didn't get the picture."

His scrutinous intent had us snuggling involvedly into position, except Mary-Ann who now went to make coffee and Peter who had already cut away to finish a wedding bouquet in his shop. Again, the deadline of Saturday marriage trade overcame those strong social instincts to oblige of him the peace in creativity he most needed. But our need was that of a newly-fledged rescue team trying to learn from its first lesson, and there was the tacit sense that we had to learn it well.

"You see, the one thing spelt out this evening," frowned Robert, "was that we'd hardly convince anyone on earth, walking up to them in the street, say, and telling them they'd passed over. So what's the difference when they are discarnate?"

"The thought-effect," flung J.M.

Our inquisitor swivelled, frown deepening:

"Whose do you mean?"

"Ours – which a discarnate is particularly sensitive to, as they don't have the physical insulation we have. Our thought toward them has more power than if they were on earth. Jules mentioned this last week, and I've come across it in communications I've read."

"It was in The Country Beyond," supplied Valerie. "Scott had to remind the medium Jane Sherwood, when she worried about him invisibly affecting her, that in the beginning it was *her* thought that could be so easily impressed on *his* brain. I think we should bear it in mind you know."

"I am," said Robert, his own recall focusing on Mary-Ann who had whisked in with a cloth. "Didn't you get a response from one of our chaps along these lines M.A., when we last sat?"

"Yes, from John. I asked him whether prayer is more effective from our side or theirs. He said more from our side, definitely."

"Did he say why?"

"He didn't know," I intervened, seeing her at a loss. "He said we should ask Philip. If we did, his answer I suspect might involve both their lack of physical insulation and our fullness of it. In other words, our every thought coming out of physical density toward them is stronger and more accurate because of that density, like shots from a big gun embedded in concrete, and without the same basis they're very susceptible."

"But our cases have Peter's body for insulation."

"No, in using the physical remember, they're not as embedded as we are – just impinging to varied extents. They borrow his gun barrel so to speak, rather than sink into his emplacement. That comparative looseness, plus our sudden appearance with earthly voices I'd say gives us the advantage you made the best of tonight."

"Fair enough," said Robert. "Although at first the only difference I could see between talking to Charles Knight for instance, and someone here, was that deep down he must have known his true position but refused to consciously accept it. After all, whatever reports say, death must be a very basic change to go through and it must register on some level."

"I think they'd all felt a change," offered Valerie, but couldn't recognise it as death because they still felt alive. And as Jules explained, we're in an ideal position to... well, tell them".

"Convince them actually. Yes I understood that."

"Besides, it can't be such a very basic change to them when they stay wrapped up in the world they've left, and which they think continues around them."

"Although that's a replica don't forget."

"Yes but it's the one they've lived with throughout their life on earth. We all live inside our replica of the world don't we?"

"Some of us more than others perhaps."

"Oh right," joined Mary-Ann, "but Mummy's saying that our private world is more real to us and more basic than any change, even death."

"We'll all be earthbound then will we?" smiled Robert.

"No, because as you said, it's in different degrees that we're wrapped up in it... and ways."

"Or directions," I prompted, getting her nod.

"Yes that's what I mean. If you're earthbound you're bound by earthly things and situations, caught up in the opposite direction to where life is going. But if your inner world is wider than these things, if your values are to do with quality not quantity, let's say essence not form, then you're open to deeper, wider experience and you're not bound by your personal replica of earth."

"Every case we had tonight," said J.M., "was bound up in theirs to such an extent that they couldn't even see each other."

"Surely because they weren't seeing people when they were here," Valerie came in again. "I mean we tend to project on each other don't we? Seeing our projection rather than the true person in front of us? Obviously not half as much as those people were doing tonight of course. Their whole surroundings were projected, making David into a salesman and a doctor and what-have-you."

"Or he was just mistaken for both," slid in Robert.

"Well in any case," she held, "I've read that helpers like David *do* get painted in an extraordinary variety of forms by the people they're trying to rescue, everything from an AA road man to a great saint apparently, out of desires and expectations. And they can also change form at will can't they Jules?"

"Yes, in the same way that discarnate relatives make themselves recognisable to newly-arrived kin."

"But if the newly-arrived don't have any expectation or desire in the first place," put Mary-Ann, "maybe they don't see anything at all, or only see… sort of common ground. I'll always remember that bit in Lyall Watson's book about an early explorer, Magellan or someone, who moored his ship in a remote Pacific island bay, and the natives there had no concept of a ship – never mind any desire or expectation – so at first they couldn't see a thing in the bay! Incredible!"

Her mother was off on another tack however.

"I've even asked myself," said she, "whether that vision Mary Rogers saw – you know, the one she had me paint – whether it was actually Jesus as she thought. I do like to believe it was Him, and use the print we have for a change of focus now and again. But it could have been anyone, a guide say, whom she only pictured in long hair and white robe, or he just appeared in that form to encourage her."

Robert's slight impatience seemed that of sincerity.

"Oh I'm sure there are dozens of characters roaming about the astrals in long hair and white robe, Fugs. The issue I feel we should take a closer look at is our means of rescue and the guide's position in it, don't you agree?"

"Yes although they aren't our guides."

"Okay – helpers, friends, whatever. But there was the business tonight over that old wheezing chap having to be coaxed into hospital and David advising the lure of luxury, whereas in fact he was quite wrong as things turned out. This was the very block holding the fellow back, because all along he'd assumed he'd have to pay. How then could David be so mistaken? And secondly, we can't always rely on his information can we?"

"Why should one expect to?" I replied. "We don't make such a high demand of everyone here, even those of highest merit, so it's unrealistic to demand it of a rescue worker who happens to be discarnate. He was just mistaken that's all."

"But the difference is," tussled Robert, "that unlike us he knew and could see the case he was dealing with, and surely should have known its main problem."

"Not unless he's a mind-reader," said I. "It sounds as if you're attributing him with powers he hasn't got. Put it this way: if you're talking to a helper on the other side of a wall in grounds you can't see, you may be able to rely roughly on his info about those grounds and a word-sketch of the people there, but his judgement of their motives will be a personal one, and incomplete."

"True, yet last week when John spoke to us he said: We know what they want – implying telepathic insight."

"Well David knew what the old boy wanted," cut in J.M., "which was release from pain. It probably never occurred to him the block was over money. He hasn't had to pay a bill since 1933! I think John must have meant telepathy on their home plane anyway, not with the rescue cases. With them they'd have to use their own judgement, and be expecting us to do the same. In fact they're forced to rely on our judgement because we're closer to the rescuees' materialistic hang-ups, while knowing we're also fallible. As I see it we're cooperating teams, or one team on two sides, depending on each other's position to do one half of the whole job, and any suggestions which fly between us are fair game. If David and Brian had failed every time to take rescuees out and on, or if we'd failed to win a single case, then there'd be cause to worry. But even in that main job there'll be mistakes on both sides because we are all human beings aren't we?"

J.M. was not given to length of utterance. Undefeated by the fact whilst conscious of our wonder, he added a final touch with colour in his cheeks.

"The minor sort of mistakes you're talking about are bound to happen along the way, like when that same old boy saw David whispering a hint to Jules and asked what he was saying. Do you remember? Jules hadn't a clue, wasn't aware of it, so he felt a bit awkward. But there was no problem or question of unreliability, only David trying the once and finding it didn't work. I could try and fail in communication with a girlfriend, not being wised up to her true state. It doesn't mean she then starts seriously doubting me."

"No of course not," Robert granted, before rounding on me with new curiosity. "Why did he think you might hear him at all Jules? Wouldn't he know that you're not er, clairaudient, which I assume you're not?"

I shook my head. "No, he must have been talking to my inner self in the hope of it filtering through as an idea to my ego. I'm obviously not in tune, or I wasn't at the time. Give him half marks for trying!"

Robert applied himself with satisfaction to the last dregs of his wine and stared at Valerie's turning over of the tape.

"Does one take it then," he rebounded, giving her a start, "that being from a different plane, discarnate helpers are in general almost as cut off from the cases as we are, and this is principally why we're needed as their go-between?"

"Oh absolutely it in a nutshell," she said, dazing him with her approval. "We're between Heaven and… well, Charing Cross."

"Ah yes," he brought to mind, "*pitched* between was the line in Thompson's poem. Anyway I'm trying to get more of a perspective on our exact role."

"One would hope we'd grasped that," she muttered.

"I know, I know. It's just a matter of clarifying *why* the helpers are so help-less, as it were, with the earthbound and where we must fill in for them. Now last week John told us that many cases are too frightened to go up with them. Perhaps helpers look ghostlike, but obviously this didn't apply in our cases tonight who saw David in rather innocuous guises as a part of their dream. I also accept that we have the greater impact as Jules described. This could be why George Chandler heard us and not David. Only then you might ask, when it was such a simple message, why David couldn't have found some way to explain as *we* did – albeit within the dream."

"Lack of attention surely?" suggested J.M. "If you're in a dream, do you hear anything outside your assumptions? David must have known it was impossible from experience."

"Yes but isn't it a bit of a hairline margin? For instance do all the earthbound depend on earthly help? If so they've got a fair old wait haven't they?"

Whilst the tragic humour of this last remark didn't escape us, J.M. offered a solution.

"Another thing we were told last week was that many from earth help with these cases during their sleep-life. Actually I think you said that once in class Jules."

"Yes I did, and Dr Crookall compiled a whole book of examples called During Sleep. Their memory of the work is suppressed by materialistic beliefs on waking, but I gather they do a grand job because the astral body's usual association with the physical gives it a denser, familiar look when out – which makes them seen, heard and understood better by the earthbound."

"If that's true it certainly lessens the burden," Robert admitted. "You're implying then, that otherwise any explanation by David wouldn't have been heard let alone taken in?"

"Especially not by a stubborn type. What you have to remember is that the mindset, whatever it is, gets more acute when its physical body is shed. It's now in a mindset body and a mindset world. So if it's not of a mind to hear any sound, it literally won't hear that sound. Sense experience is now mind-governed by and large. The eyes won't see, either, what the mind doesn't allow them to see. If you have a stubborn type *mind* you have stubborn type *senses*, and the condition becomes chronic."

"Ah," he said, "it was the extent of mind shutting off the senses I hadn't fully realised. Therefore when they enter a physical body, our channel, that condition is lessened by denser matter."

"Yes, they're within the channel's physical senses and are more likely to hear or see what before they'd shut out, even though they're still dreaming."

"And it's the stubborn types mostly that we have to wake up and make see-hear-recognise the helpers?"

"Because their dreamworld remains real, and still clothes the helper, but they can hear and see us much louder and clearer than anyone since they left earth – which hopefully starts waking them up."

"More than sleep-life helpers do?"

"I should jolly well hope so! Wheeling us lot in means that contact is loosely between physical bodies like us talking now, except that for them it's starker against their dream and can make a keener impact."

"Okay. I'm only left with my question of how much dependence is placed on earth help."

"It's not a total dependence, just a great deal easier if they let earth people help the earthbound. I don't know what proportion these are, but none of them is ever ignored we're told. No one is waiting for help. On the contrary, each one is monitored, waited *for*. The point of our channel, which is brought in as a high-powered piece of equipment, isn't aimed at that mainstream of earthbound, although The Seven will make use of it while they can for whoever's in need and can blend in. It's a rare facility which by far increases the chance of success where the helpers have failed."

"Like an amplified microphone between levels?"

"That's right. It's also luminous with Peter's high psychic energy and more noticeable to earthbound whose dark thoughts have literally created a dark world round themselves. As you say, the channel amplifies both us and the helpers. So all of this *does* make our position different from walking up to someone in the street and telling them they've died. That's the weak position a helper is normally in, you see. I assume it's why the earthbound often disdain or ignore them."

"And why David said he was only as close as we are to them?"

"It could be. Without the channel he's a nonentity to the stubborn types, helpless because projected over, or frightening because he can suddenly vanish and then appear again somewhere else. Now he's on an amplified footing alongside us, except that to start with he's known on near-earth levels as that twit who comes up to you in the street talking nonsense. So our exact role is to mediate, be his mouthpiece, waking these characters partly or fully out of dreamland and coaxing them in the right direction. We *do* have the upper hand. What I find difficult is how to play it."

That difficulty was acknowledged as a general one for us all, despite the evening's measure of success, and we fell into heated debate. How indeed was our role best played other than in the spontaneous way already tried? Should we attempt to force a Robert-style explanation of their state first instead of last, or would it be more practical to concentrate simply on coaxing them toward the helper? Should we take any one line when the cases were so various that it might be more realistic to play each by ear? Did we need to know their circumstances, or was curiosity wasting valuable time? Valerie and Robert were opposed here. Could we do with any special effects to convince people of their changed state, and what effect might do so? How about storing a set of psychological ploys up our sleeve? Might Philip have supplied one or two in that preparatory talk we never had? Why, after he found himself prevented from giving it, had he let us carry on? Did this denote confidence in us, or in spontaneity itself?

These among other questions filled the next hour or so without definite answers. All that our tired minds could agree upon was to continue the trial and error process until some clear format emerged, which put an awkward tag on a memorable evening. But at last my job was disentangled from any notion of ability at rescue. "Consultant engineer not Captain", trimmed Robert when expounding his view of team parity, and with Peter now flurrying in to join us I was glad to be let off both hooks.

The effect of him was like that of a butterfly blown into a board meeting. Straightaway our axis changed. We let ourselves be alighted upon at random, which gave me room to try some amateur observation. Not rumbled before, and according to Valerie habitual wherever they went, was his passion to maintain a grip on external things – as if by teasing, overstating, highlighting the shallowest interplay he could stay airborne or in control, avoiding a depth in himself which perhaps he feared was depression. Humour and exuberant charm were the two wings he used for defying gravity. So, when laughs faded down from weariness one could almost see him wondering what to get a rise out of next.

An impression began to form in my mind that he mistrusted the mediumship above all because in it he had to let go the superficial level to which he clung, and thence let go his need for setting the pace. Beneath this level ego control was lost from lack of emphasis, subject to a faculty he feared to understand lest it threaten his idea of selfhood. Yet at a deeper level his actual self was in control, had in fact accepted exit of the body via trance, and had then returned him easily and calmly.

His current extrovertive play among us did, for me at least, conjure up the image of a core stability from which the anxious ego was pulling away on a stretch of elastic as it were. Most of the trance sensitives I had met with, though some underwent those initial qualms of novicehood, seemed to fluctuate on shorter elastic and nearer their core. They were characters whose behaviour showed nothing unusual that I could see. Peter's easy ability to move within, on the other hand, appeared to be frightening him in the opposite direction so that he pulled outwards and clung to the other, almost desperate extreme of surface relationships and doings.

This stressful reaction to unfaced ability could have been the pattern for years. So what of his future with us? I figured that if, trusting The Seven, he ever let his ego consciously relax into its natural flow within, the practice could gradually resolve his fears and find him living from a profounder, securer level of himself than anyone in the room tonight. At once a new interpretation lit up Philip's words: "If only he would accept us, his life would change."

There and then my speculative train of thought was neither mature enough nor appropriate to air. Robert and J.M. had got to their feet, Valerie was arranging that I sleep on a camp bed in Peter's room in case he suffered post-rescue traumas, while he was in no mood for a matter hedged about with arguments and precepts it tired him to think of. He preferred the know-how, the briskness of spirit given to piling trays with our glasses and plates in last round chatter. Even a firm date being fixed between us for next Friday merely saw his shrug of relative insouciance.

Relative that is, to our dawdles and hoverings as an incongruous little team's strange debut together hung onto the common cause of laggardness here at midnight. For there was something about this cosy room, perhaps generated over many years by our current of thought, that exercised a pull of easeful belonging underfoot.

Valerie's impress no one would deny. Preoccupying her just then were those cases we had failed to rescue, so it was her withdrawal to pray for them awhile that finally and respectfully dispersed us. When I joined her in the Sanctuary, Robert was giving J.M. a lift home and Mary-Ann had yawned out of sight. Only Peter remained below. In no hurry to go to bed he sat down beside the fire and opened his newspaper, from which a pack of tiresome esoterics had kept him.

CHAPTER SIX

STAGE FRIGHT

With each new dawn the inside of Ashdene now looked to me like a theatrical set, its props ready for the next novel performance. If there overnight I would be the first to rise, slipping quietly down to wash remnant dishes and tidy a little on my way out. Behind closed curtains the household lay slumberous and dark, immune to workaday village stirring, but once our cast were in play some irregular or exceptional development may very well have occurred by the time I got back.

They were sweet mornings on the whole, tinted by that promise, contentedly at home whilst keen to the thought of dodging away before a gamut of goodbyes and through Happy Valley – favourite shortcut to my roost. In an Easterly direction my trail wove across Tea Garden Lane into tree-lined footpaths until, on a plateau where huge rocks sprang from their woodland bed, the earliness of hour gave excuse to pause.

Far beneath slopes of bracken, pretty lakeland on the valley floor had long submerged among rhododendrons and mixed forest, tending one's view, from that promontory of rock, across the treetops to a distant horizon. I would sit here in simple reverie, or else weighing up the validity of our events by trying to approach them from a different angle. Then the last stretch along Cabbage Stalk Lane to my flat in Broadwater Down was taken knowing that Valerie may summon me anytime to a fresh turn of events around Peter – on occasion the result of her own approach.

She was especially liable to make one while such primrose days were vanishing his winter of unease. As will have been gathered, he had outgrown the injury to his leg and become superactive to fulfil the demands of his prosperous flower shop. Goodwill was not hard to come by locally, for once the strains of convalescence had gone his friendly enthusiasm got the same in return. Withal, it revealed that charm of boyishness which to women customers was often attractive in a man who had actually left his boyhood behind him.

The fervent, diverse round of business and social life, flowing on top of milder trance aftermaths, had lessened his tension about the mediumship almost down to nil. If Valerie had told anyone of it beyond our immediate circle then at least his reputation was still intact. When he had also, one must recall, felt the reassuring hands of Philip enough to recognise him as an invisible guardian, and found that even a gaggle of earthbound folk – whom he was astounded to hear on tape – left him little the worse for wear, it soon scarcely mattered to him in what circumstances he "nodded off" after a hard day's work, provided they were comfortable. To me it mattered a great deal, but I was not present on that following Tuesday evening.

Valerie had asked him to sit for a private session in the Sanctuary. She craved another talk with Philip, remembering how a week ago he had promised to come if she was "in need of comfort at any time". The strict truth was that his promise had been of a *nonphysical* attendance for comfort. Use of the channel he seemed to regard as secondary. She skimped these finer points however, and her need was not one of comfort.

Years of secret wondering at her altar table, of prayer and solitary endeavour, of reading the lives and paths of adepts, ingesting esoteric seminars, applying herself to meditation, had welled up depths of assurance but never the first-hand access to answers which she now saw on tap. The cogent downsurge of discarnates over her life, including that of pitiful earthbound, had put extra value on spiritual growth and its importance, as if the heavens had opened with responsive sunlight which cast normal activity into the shade. What inspired her nowadays was the hope of a graphic picture direct from one who may be resident on levels of growth barely even glimpsed by writers on earth. Moreover he was of her own spiritual group, a qualification thought likely to make his report foreshadow her future experience.

That certain factors were necessary to safe communication itself rated about last on her checklist. High aim, she felt, transcended advice from psychic booklets which warned against the danger of sitting off-guard by oneself with a novice trance sensitive. Any problem she attributed largely to forces outside her control, except the need for vocal support. The presence of quality friends was a known help, albeit for unknown reason so dispensable if lacking at unknown risk. Her experience of communication happened always to have been in the company of at least one au fait person or in the security of an earnest group, the exception being recently with Philip. Their successful chat, because it had escaped serious intrusion, she took to be further licence.

But overlooked was the effect of a rescue session since that time, and of its expressly open door having lured a still greater plethora of earthbound. Although some degree of ongoing risk was accepted with Peter's mediumship, her habitual regard for the Sanctuary as a haven of self-protective peace made little allowance for its changing use. She also tended to equate her chances here with those obtainable at the College of Psychic Studies from a competent professional, which of course Peter was not. Neither did his discarnate colleagues have the maturity of practised cooperation with him that the controls of such veteran mediums enjoyed. Philip had only managed to hold his ground in somewhat embryo, rough circumstances, asking us to bear with him while adequate cooperation was gained at all.

Nevertheless I explain rather than criticise, and when Valerie's mindset was known to overshoot these parameters any blame for her evening's result may as well lie with me in failing to stress our new position. And her try was by no means disastrous, just a sneaky gamble onstage that showed the lone gig was pushing her luck too far.

At an agreed hour after business Peter trod upstairs to find her completing a tape of sacred music. His mood was relaxed, lackadaisical, with mildly grinning bathos on his way to the familiar settee – that throne which for him held more of an association with sleep than bed. In a short while, and before either of them anticipated, the closing measure of her chorale in those soporific surrounds turned her to see him a still, silent spectre of his former self, head heavily inclined over the merest sufflation of breath.

Having sent Philip the required "beam", her concern not to miss one word from him surged her immediately forwards with the tape recorder, chair dragging aft. But instead she found David there, maybe on guard duty, moving in to hold the fort as best he could. While conditions afforded him hardly a thread of sound in greeting, she recognised his manner almost straightaway and covered her disappointment with that slight falsifying for the sake of politeness:

"Oh I'm glad it's you David. How very nice. But you're having difficulty without more power are you?"

"Yes. I can't… " he strained faintly.

"You can't talk? Never mind David."

"I… want… to."

"I know. You just hang on a minute. Maybe more power will come, or one of the others could manage it instead. The problem is not enough power is it, or… ?"

"I don't know… It feels stifling. Getting better."

"Well hang on and we'll hope for the best. Peter was very relaxed this evening so there shouldn't be a great block. Anyway it's more intimate with the two of us. You were a painter on earth weren't you?" she homed in, seeing the chance now to assuage curiosity about our man behind the rescues.

"Yes… "

"Right, I'll go on talking for bit because apparently it helps. I'd love to know what sort of painting you did, and how you felt about it, and how you've felt about it since leaving earth, and if there's any of your work we could go and see… "

"I painted ships," said David, noticeably stronger.

"Oh did you! And were you successful as a painter? I mean in the worldly sense. Not that it matters of course."

"No because my father thought it was an effeminate thing to do. He made me join the Regiment."

"And give up painting?"

"Yes."

"Oh what a shame. And do you paint now David?"

"No I've become too involved here really. But I used to sit on the quay by the bridge at Bristol and paint in watercolours. Do you know Bristol?"

"No I've never been there. It's a place I've always wanted to visit though. So there aren't any of your paintings in art galleries or anywhere at the moment?"

"Mother used to hide them."

"Did she feel the same as your father about it then?"

"No, she hid them from Father."

"Oh that's very sad isn't it! I don't suppose you wanted to go into the Army did you?"

"No I didn't. At the time I thought it was sad, but it isn't really. It's rather insignificant Valerie."

"This is what I feel now about painting of course."

"I like your work."

"Do you think I should go on with it though? Because I feel nowadays that it's so unimportant compared to all these major issues teeming around us – you know, the vital need for growth, and prayer, and attunement."

"People often say this when they finally come out of our hospital. But Philip always reminds them that life has to be lived. I think he's right."

"Yes but painting does seem a bit superficial, and although I know it gives people happiness I wonder if the kind of happiness they get from it is ... well... "

"Does it give *you* happiness Valerie?"

"It used to. But now I'm beginning to feel that I ought to be doing something more worthwhile. Besides, it's frightfully commercialised today you know. I find everyone's painting for money, and what will sell, and all that seems so ridiculous."

"I know."

"Do you agree?"

"Yes, but if it makes you happy it's not wrong."

"No. Still, I'm going through a phase of not doing any painting. And where I was doing it, Peter's got his florist shop as you probably realise – which is going very well. So we'll just see how things work out. Um... Is there anything you'd particularly like to say now we're on our own and fairly relaxed?"

"I shall have to get Philip because somebody's trying to get in here over me."

"Oh dear! There's no way of avoiding that I suppose. Well Philip," she quavered, addressing the air, "I hope you're going to come because I don't feel I can handle distressed ones by myself except through prayer. I'll always pray for those who are drawn here, and in the rescue sessions we'll do all we can for them with people like Jules and Robert around."

"They're good people, " said David, struggling.

"They are, yes I know."

The people that are trying to use this channel are good people too," he defended.

"They just need help don't they?"

"Oh I'm not sure what to do, whether to go or stay."

His uncertainty worried her. "But... er, could we call Philip before you go, so that... " Halting, she thought to do it again herself: "Philip, would you please come and help? David is having a problem."

There were a few anxious minutes between them until the inimitable presence of that man, either in direct response or because already alert to the situation, at last began descending into the channel and let David slip out safely alongside. He might only have brought enough power to refuel spent energies on site, priming it before he ushered back its owner, but Valerie had other ideas.

At first thankful for the deliverance , her usual awe in his company was outstripped by the desire to hold onto this originally expected contact. As her target steadily took command she mustered her questions.

"Oh good evening Philip. I'm so relieved you came. You're in control now aren't you?"

"Yes," came a terse reply.

"I don't know whether conditions are good enough while you're here to say anything more about the group soul on your side, but I'll just ask and you can only say yes or no. Are you in fact losing identification with your earthly personalities?"

"In our particular level of consciousness… Philip has ceased … to be."

"To be a person in the earthly sense you mean?"

"Correct."

She noted his singular reserve. "I suppose communication is rather difficult for you at the moment?"

"It is, yes."

"Anyway that's perfectly clear. I don't know whether you've heard me talking today to different people but I think I do understand."

"I believe you do. However, I cannot be present at … every conversation. You must now close. The Channel has come with me. Please do not prevail upon us lightly. Next time… if you will… bring those… whose hearts are… lifted with you."

"Yes I'm sorry Philip. I will be more careful."

"One more thing. David wishes me … to convey his… intimation… that you can paint certain pictures which… will be of outstanding beauty… because they are landscapes of foreign origin. They will have sunset skies… of red… reminiscent of the skies you witnessed… in that other continent. If you make yourself receptive… to the flow which comes… then a deeper dimension may be added to your life."

"Well as I said to him earlier, I haven't actually wanted to paint for quite a while. Will I receive some sort of clear inspiration on this?"

"You will receive help from David. Goodnight child."

"Thank you very much Philip. Goodnight."

Shamefaced though she felt over his censure, her mind dwelt more on the care of a fellow artist casually and kindly offering stimulus with the reminder of a holiday spent many years ago in Africa. There, the late skies had certainly been flooded by shafts of scarlet and ochre – a marvel she had thought too superlative for canvas.

Skies were not her forte anyway, and her landscapes were those of West Kent and Sussex not foreign. That word, she mused on the other hand, could mean *astral* landscapes – which gave the offer some interest value as an experiment between them. His wider discarnate vision might have noticed in her a latent ability, one never tapped because outside the earthly stricture she placed around painting. Far from being any prediction of success therefore, she supposed that its outcome would be up to her.

When Peter came back into the body his recollection was merely of the last transient moments away, a drone of muffled voices from the limelight ahead of him and low down in front of other people. He had been staring at the nape of a man's blonde neck – someone he knew well in the "dream" but no longer did, if she saw what he meant.

"Oh that must have been David."

"I thought it was Philip you were going to talk to."

"Well I did briefly, after a chat about painting."

"Painting?"

"Yes, then it all got into a tangle I'm afraid. I'll explain later."

He was miffed over what struck him as a pointless use of their hour, having possibly assumed they would be discussing spiritual matters, which reaction made her suspend the nub of the tale in case that near miss with an earthbound darkened impressions further. She had good reason to be wary, for his improving opinion of The Seven was still young, untried. In the event, he switched subject to the mealtime chores.

It was through the ease of wining and dining that his half humorous, half-tender indulgence toward Valerie brought her to confess the problem she had caused, which endeared her to him all the more. Barriers thus melted away in a spirit which fast became frivolous, and her slight exaggeration of how David, under imminent threat of intrusion, "got the collywobbles too", amused as well as interested him rather.

Perhaps this gave him his first clear evidence that they might be human after all. From here on at least, the consistent naturalness of The Seven's attitude – serially heard from extracts of tape – did build up to quieten Peter's misgivings about them, nerving him to treat their invisible fellowship without awkwardness.

★ ★ ★ ★ ★

The next afternoon, a Wednesday, proved convenient for Valerie's follow-up trial. Her writing partner Betty was due at four again, Mary-Ann was at home, and the steady downpour of rain on this early closing day had confined Peter indoors. Had I not been away at a trade exhibition in Nottingham I might well have demurred over these extra-curricular sessions of hers, thinking them too much of a drain on our channel in the same week that he was expected to take earthbound cases aboard. My view however tended to err on the side of a Taurean caution, while her Leonine flair would leap at the golden chance. So even my absence that day was seen as opportune.

And for good measure, an extra guest sat coolly in one of her armchairs. Rob Morgan was in his twenties, of tall, lean, sinewy build with a face which one might almost describe as ascetic. Its spare, boney contours, beneath raven hair and a steeply tranquil brow, caved into modest eyes that I remember being turned on me with piercing enquiry. Small, fine lines puckered humorously at their corners, and there was balance in the average, thin-lipped mouth. Sparing in speech he preferred to listen, and from his expression these days we hazarded the guess that he was inwardly debating some moot point. If so, then one could count on it having more to do with a growing interest in Mahayana Buddhism than with his worldly profession as a building surveyor.

Valerie liked him. She trusted his discretion to keep our work under wraps, needed all the "hearts lifted with" her that she could get, and in an attempt to enrol manpower felt she had done quite well. Their ostensible motive was meditation, though no one had rallied there as an innocent pawn – not even Rob. The early stages of his path-seeking led him into any avenue thought germane. When he was briefed by phone of our goings-on, he understood that if Peter were to join their traditional drift upstairs the scenario could radically change.

Truth to tell, we were seldom sure what Peter would do at a given juncture. At the present one, for reasons which Valerie alone suspected, his levity was edging its way into her group's chinwag about meditation techniques. Heard to involve "conscious withdrawal from one's outer world", such practice was being grasped anew – not as the passive slide which before had made him unconscious, but as an active tool to his purpose.

He was tired of hearing his voice in misty snatches of dialogue supposedly from another realm where Valerie said he withdrew in trance and met up with "colleagues". He wanted first hand experience of that realm and of their validity in it. Everyone was drawing upon his capacity except him. Not only, unlike him, had they read about the place. They were also able, apparently, to speak with the denizens in person, develop a relationship of sorts. His mere listening to tapes was cold comfort. Warmer and more enticing was the possibility that self-awareness through the blackout could bring him to his own visible, direct encounter.

It didn't occur to him that meditation's withdrawal from the outer world applied on every level. Conscious withdrawal in some form of course was how we hoped he would accept The Seven, gaining easier than ourselves a soul-link which we believed Philip meant by the edict, "his life would change". And since Valerie had nursed this idea long before me, she was archly careful not to nip our hope in the bud by alerting him that the button pressed, as it were, for meditation takes one up soul's liftshaft to experience levels of awareness without looking round their departments.

Besides, he was listening to beginners who had barely got past level one – whose bookish concept stretched far higher than practical ability. To tie in his aim with theirs must have been all the more confusing for him because the debate covered different schools East-West. When it came to Sanctuary practice however we each suited ourselves, and would retire into a unity of aim transcending individual approach. That said, the heart of Ashdene was Valerie's, which took uplift from mystical devotion to "God" or definedly "The Presence Within". Her home-made tapes often formed a sort of bedrock to sessions, whether or not one chose to follow their contemplative lead. Culled from Brunton, Happold, Rhodes-Wallace, White Eagle and others they would have sounded faintly Christian to Peter, yet to take full advantage of them required maturity of esoteric usage plus a profound yearning for the Divine. One would have to identify totally with the speaker through a process of letting-go, self enquiry and affirmation before coming out on top.

What in effect he had gleaned for use by "up there" time beggars the imagination therefore. He told Valerie of his minimum resolve, made as they all trooped aloft, to stay conscious with them throughout the session. She gave her encouragement but privately doubted success at first try, minding that his capacity for unconscious trance equalled ours for sleep after extreme exhaustion. Most of us under those circumstances might need practice in staying awake if given our usual settee let alone the downy, word-laden music about to enfold him.

Confident that he would leave the channel free anyway she thought not to diffuse his aim by telling him of hers, which was a comparative doddle. Philip had asked her to, "next time bring those whose hearts are lifted with you", and she was taking his advice, though why he hadn't stipulated this on the previous interview alone with him puzzled her a bit. Was it because he had felt her questions important, or from first-time tolerance? No matter. According to a borrowed booklet meanwhile, "where two or more are gathered together sincerely in the name of prayer, spiritual knowledge, or attainment, their safe aegis is assured," and today she had fitted the bill.

Upon Ashdene's front door was pinned her hand-written note: "MEDIATION IN PROGRES – PLEASE KEEP QUIRT", whose spelling the rest of them were amused to think might at least strike the erudite caller dumb. They nestled themselves now into her old Sanctuary chairs, resigning from ordinary physical concerns and orienting inward along their own paths to another dimension of quiet. As one draws down a sunshade or narrows focus to concentrate, we drew the curtains so that meditation's private nature was reinforced and extraneous elements minimised. From hi-fi at the altar table, where grain incense had been lit, spiralling strains of Barber's Adagio were ignored by some, warmly imbibed by others in calm prelude to the voice of prayer.

Indeed everything followed its normal course until, near the end of the music, Betty opened her eyes to a subtle and premature development. On the settee to her right Peter's head hung heavily passive, he having long given up the struggle. But then she saw it beginning to be levered in slight jerks to a midpoint at which, nearly horizontal, his deadpan face was in silhouette. There seemed to be steadier respiration taking charge, lids still closed while it gently turned a few degrees each way. His mouth moved a little also, though whatever sound may have come was unheard beneath the music. She thought to alert Valerie in case these movements were of trance control, but her clues died away and the body slid back into its former leaden state.

Their free-floating period ensued after the tape's run. Not even Valerie knew what had briefly occurred, presuming with eyes shut that yesterday's episode would have Philip wait for optimum conditions before venturing earthward again. An onset she did notice presently, in a scan for results, was the look and feel of David close upon them. His feel she always found tough to describe except by one's catch of a friend's familiar footsteps, and it would need a painting to portray the look of him in minutely distinctive posture. Maybe he heralded his C.O. Like a flash her impulse was to record every word, hitching her chair forth, portable clasped in lap, which signals rallied group interest around her.

Having established contact it took further moments to get into dialogue. For besides being the most taciturn of the band he was ever the longest at gaining control or leaving, and possibly felt apprehensive after his last shift.

"Until you get better David," she obliged, "shall I go on talking rather than ask questions?"

Thence his weak "yes" got nothing but questions.

"Did you hear our meditation tape?"

"No I was trying… to help Brian… use the channel. He was here… just now. When he comes again… you can support him."

"Oh we're going to meet Brian at last, the fifth one of The Seven! You're both on duty together then?"

"Yes."

"And can you tell us where Peter's gone, or did he just disappear?"

"We… think he's at… the hospital."

"Oh, so he whipped off without bye or leave?"

"Not quite. He says… bye… and leaves."

David's soupçon of humour tickled the audience. In slow dribs and drabs while his control improved, they understood that Philip had "doubled the guard" on Peter, a guard which had tried to help him stay conscious. But he fell into his blackout again, consciousness broken till his inner self took over and left them with the empty channel. Its need of an occupant to fend away the earthbound led Brian's eagerness to have a try at control, hoping not to disturb meditators. Sole witness Betty was keener to get on than boast.

"As you seem stronger now David, is there something you want to tell us?"

"I'd like to say something about the rescue work."

"Gosh," said Valerie, "I forgot all about that when we spoke yesterday. It was fairly satisfactory was it, from your point of view?"

"Yes, but the people who were allowed to come through are a minority. So don't expect the same success another time."

"Oh. You will always be there won't you David, for us to refer them to you?"

"Yes. If not I, then somebody."

The subject drew Betty back, mindful of Robert being abroad on a ten day business trip.

"Er… it was said that I'm not suitable to join the rescue. Is this to be permanent or can I come in when a team member is away, like this Friday?"

"I see no reason why not, but you must ask Philip."

"Well it was he who said I wasn't suitable. Is that for my sake or because I wouldn't be of any use?"

Given that source, David banked on one reason.

"For your sake certainly. Are you happy today?"

"Yes. That's helpful is it?"

"It helps us all."

She did yearn to take part. A pained Valerie knew it well, had glossed over the truth to avoid hurt, and was hoping that the heavy hint just dropped would sink in. Then she wondered if Betty's clairvoyant faculty would have been useful in rescue, which brought to mind doubts of herself being inspired in art.

"David, about the message you sent me yesterday via Philip. He said that you were offering inspiration with my painting. The point is, I don't think I'm able to be contacted psychically. I never receive anything like Betty does for instance. How would you do this?"

"If you allow me to walk with you when you go out with your canvas, I can guide you inwardly. Please do not talk in this way, because there are many things you don't understand about your consciousness. I can help you even though you are not aware."

Her block dissolved. It was a mere matter of one's internal consent. "Really? Okay David, I'll stand by. Right, another question was about the concert you were rushing off to enjoy last week. Could you tell us what that's like?"

"If you wish. We go to The Hall, where we sit in an auditorium which is in the shape of a horseshoe. Before us, leading up and on, are silver steps with an archway at the top in shades of blue. From within the blue our music comes, making every shade fluctuate, sometimes becoming as deep as infinity. We listen, but it isn't necessary to see."

"Is this music coming from a higher sphere?"

"I don't know. It seems to come from within the arches."

"Can you tell us the name or type of music it is?"

"No because it doesn't have a name, and is quite unlike yours. I couldn't describe it to you. It's more a state of mind. Even the greatest come to sit with us and wonder. The auditorium is one of the most beautiful places on our sphere. As part of the treatment we give in the hospital, those who would benefit are often taken along and placed at the foot of the steps."

"Music is a form of healing then?" gathered Betty.

"Very much so. The notes are blessed you see. Their rays penetrate and uplift. The idea will filter through to earth one day."

"And what's happened," asked Valerie, "to people like Beethoven, Brahms, Mozart, and all those great composers? Do they continue to compose?"

"If that is what they want to do. Most find still greater work."

"I can believe that," said she. "Tell me, do any of us work with you at night?"

"If you allow us to work with you. Often you don't wish it. But I can help you in this way if you want me to."

"Well I would, rather. Is it a question of putting one's mind into a certain attitude before sleep?"

"It's a question, really, of getting your desires in the right perspective. When you expect, during your normal day, to receive a visit from a friend, do you not inwardly and outwardly prepare yourself? You are aware of those outward adjustments, but if you observe, there are inner ones too. There is the desire for instance, to alter your mental perspective into that which you believe is most pleasing to your friend, or which you consider will create a certain impression. In a way, you do the same when you prepare for meditation, except that there you alter your perspective from outward-going to inward-going desires, or aspiration for God. We have seen this in you tonight. It increases your attunement to the plane for which you are most fitted and from which you may live on earth more fully. Each one of you lives from that plane inside you, even while you tread the streets. But your society tells you to look outward always, not inward. So you forget from where you are looking at one another, and the inner grows dark. To come here is as natural as breathing. What would happen if society told you to breathe outward only? You think sleep is unconsciousness, when it is really your self breathing inward while the body rests. It is a time when you may turn to your roots, by getting your desires calmly in the perspective, not of creating an outer impression, but of relaxing to your inner impression and becoming more completely yourself."

"How interesting, thank you," she said, appreciative that his extended answer was a specially outstretched hand. "I have insomnia as you know, and this right perspective is something I must aim for. It's awfully difficult though David!"

"You find it so only because you're human and because earth's density tries our strength in both directions. But remember, at any stage you cannot contain more than you can cope with."

"There's a thought. Anyway, before one goes to sleep at night one should concentrate hard on this?"

"Better if you do almost the opposite."

"Empty one's mind you mean?"

"Just relax and turn the perspective inward. There's no point in keeping the brain awake with a mind to leave it, is there?"

"No that's true."

Mary-Ann however sought outward-bound counsel.

"David, do you think I have the capacity to bring this knowledge into my earthly life and help people?"

"Yes. Very soon, when you have completed your present stage, your psyche will feel much more at ease, and we can guide you to earth it better. Then later on, when you come home to us, you will have gained enough strength to continue your natural work."

"Thanks."

"Now you can all talk to Brian."

David edged away at his usual slow pace, though the head didn't have far to tilt down again. In my recall he never brought it up as high as the others, leaving the neck muscles fairly loose. By and large one got the hunch that he and Philip were reluctant users, just bowing to the yoke of their mission's necessity.

In contrast, Brian's entry had a cool deliberateness, quick to take over from his colleague. The tangy impact of him permeated the rhythm he set – direct, tight-knit, expressive, and already adroit in his use of the channel. Within such close range however of the clicks and whirrs from Valerie's machine as she changed cassette, he had a rather sardonic air which she mistook for pleasure.

"You're liking it in there are you?"

"It'll do, but I'm not used to all this taping fuss."

Audience stiffness broke into chuckles.

"We're recording what you're saying you see."

"I'm not saying anything much."

You're doing well though," she credited. "Is this really your first time?"

"My second time."

"He came through," said Betty, "during meditation."

"Oh yes. Still you're very clear, even holding the head up. What would you like to say to us Brian, now you're in the seat of honour?"

"I always hear you people ask that question," he said drily. "Do you want me to talk forever?"

"Yes please!" she laughed. "Well I know you were here last Friday assisting with the rescues, and David has said we'll get more difficult ones this week, so be prepared. Is the rescue work a subject we should discuss?"

"Go ahead. It's just that I'm overwhelmed with… thought, and a bit befuddled how to find the right tack with you."

"Is there lots to say?" asked Mary-Ann.

"There's everything to say."

"Can you see us Brian?" she hung on interestedly.

"Yes, I see you as you were, as you are, and as you will be."

"Are they very different?"

"Yes."

"Would you know," angled Betty again, "whether it's alright for me to sit with the rescue team this week, as Robert won't be here?"

"I think you should ask Philip."

She had evidently not registered the hint dropped by his deputy earlier, and was now sad that chances of cornering the elusive man himself before Friday were slim. Her temperament must have been thought too prone to attack or injury under rescue conditions. It drew Valerie's wing of care into a question designed for two.

"When we started the work, Philip said that we must be prepared for a rough passage. Did he mean that one would be slightly overshadowed by some people we'd be rescuing?"

"Yes he could have meant that."

"So one might get depressions and things coming on?"

"I don't think there's any doubt about it."

"Oh. No wonder I've been feeling depressed today."

"Have you?" Brian voiced concern. "Because it isn't overshadowing in the sense that we overshadow the channel. It's in the contact sense."

"Could you explain that?"

"I'll try, but of course it has to be explained in your … " He paused. "You have shops don't you? Well if you enter a shop and you're served by a charming young assistant, when you leave, do you feel happy or sad?"

"Happy," answered Valerie.

"If you enter a shop where you're served by… "

"A dreary person?"

"Yes. Does that person not contact your feelings and make you rather sad?"

"The thing is," she queried, "how are they able to contact one during the day? I suppose they sort of hover about."

"Perhaps. But you don't have to see the same person every minute of your day to feel sad for the next few hours do you?"

"No, their thought form could stay in one's aura."

"You see, this is the trouble with talking to you all. It's hard to explain because you're always trying to equate what we say with your background on earth. Do you seriously think that a lost one has the same degree of effect on you as a shop assistant does?"

"Heavens. No wonder one's going to feel low then!"

"So if Philip did in fact warn you about this, it's really for your own protection isn't it? I gather you have knowledge to apply."

"Yes, and now we've got you in front of us we mustn't miss the opportunity to learn more. There are so many things!" she stressed frustratedly.

"Why don't you ask them?"

"Okay. I'd love to know if you lead a reasonably normal life with sleep and day, like us."

"Oh dear!" His light-hearted dismay raised giggles. "No because… Oh he's right isn't he!"

"Who's right, Philip? He told you about our… "

"Well if my body was the physical kind which needs sleep, exercise, regularity of cycle, would I be here?"

"No of course. Sorry Brian, I should know better from books I've read."

"And yet from those perhaps you'll appreciate how whole worlds of people still live in that pattern, sometimes because they don't realise they have left earth. So you have no need to feel too sorry."

"I'd like to ask you Brian," returned Mary-Ann, "about facing and dealing with the kind of problem one meets in physical life. For instance I want to help people in the best way I can, but I'm not sure how to do that without making them suspicious. I have the desire but not the know-how."

"The know-how is knowing yourself first," he offered. "Don't forget that the inner you – what Philip calls the part of you which is

The village, with Ashdene by distant white car

Valerie in 1972

*Her impressionistic oil painting
of Peter, 1972*

Robert Riddell becomes 'Swami Chaitanya Sagar'

J.M. as 'Swami Devadas' in Poona

The author in the 70s

Mary-Ann

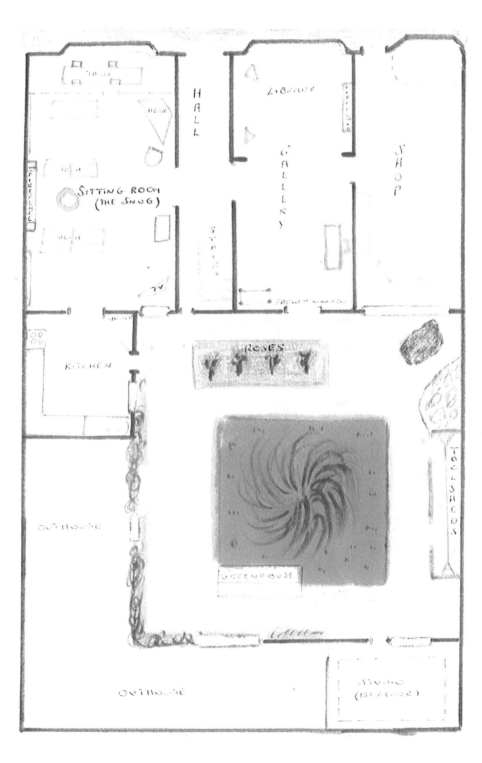

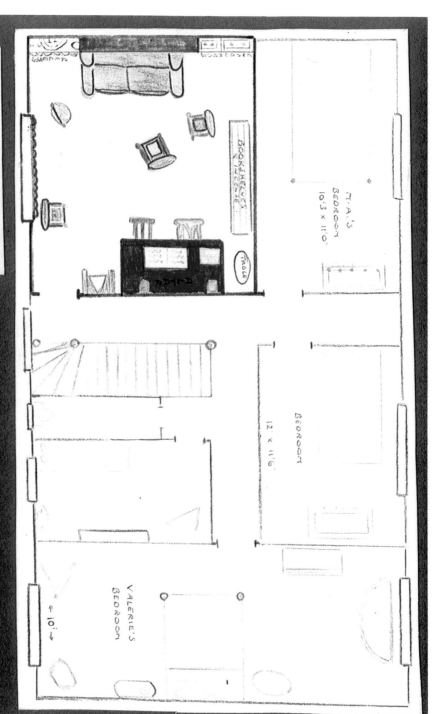

always with us – if it is coloured blue and you try changing it to red, your help cannot function."

"By colour there," said Valerie, "you mean her actual soul nature don't you?"

"Yes, her true individuality."

"And the soul is all the time controlling our earthly self isn't it?"

"Not like a puppet, but in the sense that it is your source and sustenance daily, and the only part of you which understands your potential, your whole reason for existing."

"Now in terms of the Eastern path," she probed, "where in yoga schools and ashrams they spend almost all their time in meditation, trying to reach God-realisation, how do you regard this from your plane? Do you feel it's the ideal way of occupying oneself, or that it's better to balance life out in the market place?"

"Do you mean us collectively or me personally?"

"Oh collectively, for anyone who is on the path as it were. Here one finds this continual, one-pointed emphasis on attaining enlightenment, and that not until then can one lead a valuable life."

"You're saying they believe that such attainment is necessary to lead a valuable life with us?"

"No here... leading your life absolutely from the soul instead of leading one which is often independent of it." She dried up and laughingly ridiculed herself. "I don't know whether you've understood that rather muddled... "

"No!" he confessed, raising general amusement. "I think you should refer to Philip."

In fact this was a question she had ready for Philip.

"It seems to me," opined Betty, "that one's time is better spent serving humanity."

"I'm sure," said he. "And when I was going to answer the young lady, it was to say that people are naturally suspicious of unorganised help, although I don't feel it should prevent you from offering any. You see, giving our view is difficult because... it's a matter of root assumption on your plane. Let me use an example. The people you're keen on helping, or otherwise have in mind, are coming to us eventually. That's inevitable. And my point is that in the comparatively short time they are with you, those questions, issues, problems which have become huge to them – maybe to some of you – we can't even see."

The notion threw a momentary dumbness over the four while Mary-Ann figured her own slant.

"So if I'm not properly attuned within myself to help people on earth, not only will their true need be missed in all that superficial stuff but my true colour or way of helping can't be applied?"

"Don't let that prevent you from the trial and error process until you've found it though," he tipped.

In Valerie's sights, help to prevent the earthbound by means of education on earth was a true need.

"But right down to simple, practical knowledge of the afterlife," she posed, "John said that if we could just try to explain briefly to people here, or give them a book showing first experiences in your world, this saves them an awful lot of trouble and makes the position much easier for you when they arrive."

"Did John say that? It's true."

"To drop the smallest seed is important isn't it?"

"A seed for when they come here, yes. When we go on the rescues, those with some knowledge, however small it is, can usually understand where they are, and be brought up with us to a level where they can face their deeper problems realistically."

He had summarised the axis of rescue, we felt later, whereby people trapped in their superficial problems are guided into the hands of expertise adept at tackling the true need underneath.

"Is there more than one of you in attendance with our team?" enquired the wistful Betty.

"David and I are there. John isn't always able to do it. He stays near the hospital, transferring the cases we pass on to him."

"He did say he got too impatient," Valerie marked. "Back to you though Brian, you said that our issues seem insignificant to you. Have you almost forgotten your earth life then?"

"Not at all."

"Only you asked earlier if we had shops."

"Yes because I don't know where you live."

"Oh we're in a highly populated corner of West Kent with a lot of shops. Where did you live on earth?"

"Bishop's Stortford. My father was a doctor in the town. My sister passed over shortly after me, and so I was able to help her."

"Does she work with you now?" asked Betty.

"No, she rejoined her group. I see her occasionally, when she isn't busy constructing."

Valerie's creative instincts were aroused.

"Constructing what?"

"Well, people who have… vision isn't the right word… imagination will do – and build beautiful environments here, they and my sister have constructed what we call The Pools, which are… I'm looking for the nearest word in the channel's mind… Oh dear – concrete!" he decried, drawing laughter. "It'll have to do. Anyway, they are suspended – please don't ask me how! – with clear blue water flowing over the sides, and cascading down into rivulets which stream through the surrounding area."

"Sounds wonderful," she acknowledged. "This rather brings us to the point that imagination must be very important in your world, because everything is created by the mind isn't it?"

"It is in yours too, more deeply than you realise. So don't make that word to mean fantasy. In fact what shakes most people when they come up further with us, is the brighter realness and aliveness, perfectly solid-feeling although more instantly mouldable. That's why their ignorant use of imagination carried from earth trapped them between our realities, as you've found. Like everyone they have to adjust in stages, learning to use it correctly, and those at my sister's level have undergone special training. Otherwise we'd soon have buildings all over the place wouldn't we?"

Mary-Ann was taken up meanwhile by his mention of a sister. It had jogged her memory of an uncannily vivid dream where she and her mother lived as fond sisters in France during the Middle Ages. Their present rapport made such a past credible, and worth a trial feeler.

"Brian, if we reincarnate with the same people but in different roles, could Mummy and I have been sisters in another life?"

"Yes perhaps, although my sister and myself hadn't been together before. She was simply anxious to go back and I was there. If it is wished, it's arranged."

"Did Mummy and I arrange to join up in this life?"

"I've no idea. Shall I find out for you?"

"No, please don't bother about it."

Betty's reading had left a firm precept.

"Don't you have to reincarnate with someone because of unfinished business, for example to work out some wrong you did them?"

"Not necessarily," he replied, "but that would be a reason for doing so. The trouble is, you all have many questions but they are… shall we say, limited? Your concern seems to be with the same sort of question. You see, we are still individuals here – as we always will be, even when on the path of human evolution we realise our Oneness – and the steps we choose for ourselves on that path are always uniquely individual. So if a soul on one step toward the Oneness feels they should incarnate to find a solution with another person, they will. If this is not necessary, they won't. Do you see? In the same way, people who choose to reincarnate together might not have problems to work out but enjoyment to seek, or potential to unfold. For everyone the path is unique, in that everyone *is* their own path. If you want me to, I'll talk to some friends and try to learn a bit about you, but I can't promise anything."

"Yes please Brian," urged Valerie. "The disadvantage we feel is that most of our growing knowledge is from books, not like this from someone near to us."

"You're thinking I'll give you a personal diagnosis."

"Oh no!" she begged off quickly.

"I believe you are. I can't find out specifically why each of you are on earth, because the problems that deemed it necessary for you to come back – if indeed any did – are not the kind you have over money, ill-health, partnership, shall I or shan't I change my career, my religion, whether to become a yogi or stay in the market place. They are complex character problems often so tied up with your individual past that if they could be told, you may still not understand. Daunting isn't it?"

They were hushed, then Betty threw a stipulation.

"If we turn our back on the problems we face here, we have to return and try again presumably?"

"Do you mean the problems in your world?"

"Yes."

"But these are earthly effects, not the reason why you would have to return."

"Surely though Brian," picked up Valerie, "they're part of the soul's development aren't they? In other words, an aspect of our soul, the inner part of us here, takes birth needing to perfect itself within a certain discipline."

Noting the confusion he tried a simpler approach.

"How many emotions do you have?"

"Umm… Seven or eight I think."

"So you see, as you can only conceive of seven or eight, it might be hard for you to accept that there are at least twenty-five. And that is just a measure to show you how your real problem, which may prevent you from fulfilling the purpose of your incarnation, could be involved with any of those emotions apparently unknown to you."

"Yet how do we deal with a problem," Mary-Ann put to him, "if we can't understand it?"

"The inner part of you can, and *does*," he emphasised. "Old patterns of behaviour are carried through into new effect of course, and from inside you are born with right impetus which your earth ego is free to accept or reject. Your job is to deal with the earth effects you face by applying the right impetus provided. The applying steadily works out your real problem in steps at your own pace, without being overwhelmed by the whole complex of it. Nevertheless, if a problem really is unaccepted by your earth ego, then it is worked out by that inner part of you during sleep life."

"Golly," said she in quietened tone, and her mother shared the sentiment:

"That's a reminder of how terribly important our sleep-life must be, not to mention our waking life. I wonder if we aren't wasting both. Quite a tip, Brian."

"Yes," agreed Betty, "I found the last bit helpful."

"It was intended for you."

Conversation hove to a standstill.

"Do you wish me to go?" he asked of Valerie.

"… Er, heavens no Brian," she said. "Sorry, it's just the enormity of whether… "

Her speech faded into pensiveness, allowing Rob Morgan's low profile to take up the slack.

"Can you remember any of your former lives, apart from the most recent one?"

"Yes, but I don't choose to."

"You don't want to remember them perhaps."

"Only because they are no longer of use to me, but I can well remember my most recent time on earth."

This awoke Valerie's inquisitive spirit.

"Was it a happy life?"

"Very happy, as far as it went."

"Were you married?"

"No."

"You were fairly young then, when you passed?"

"Yes I was twenty-three. I was going out of the front gate and some slates fell off the roof."

"None of our rescuees the other night seemed to realise they had passed, did they?"

"No. Those people's independence was so fierce that it made them unaware, which kept them from help too. The majority who do realise they have passed you'll never encounter. That is not to say you won't be dealing with a residue of them. In my own case, I spent a short time contemplating the scene of sadness from above. My only desire was to comfort my parents."

"And were you able to do that?"

"Yes. Later on I went into the living room and found it was just possible to move my father's favourite book significantly under a vase of flowers. It was Pilgrim's Progress. Then I lay on my bed and slept. When I awoke I was still on my bed, but by this time it was my bed's double, and Philip and John had come. I had no hesitation in going with them. Then, after resting among some beautiful mountains here, I went on to train under Philip. Now had I not been aware, I might have remained in my parents' house, eventually perhaps to be approached by a team like yours."

"How well did Peter manage when he passed?"

"I don't know. He was here when I arrived."

"And already training with Philip?"

"They were certainly together a great deal. But do you sit around drinking coffee and going over your earliest memories? We don't hear of them. Why should you think we do?"

"I just wondered whether you knew anything of his actual experience there before he came back in 1941," she fished. "For instance he and I weren't sure what to make of it when Philip asked us to tell him that "the woman in his life" was exactly as he knew her in your world."

"The truth has gone in, whatever his earthly mind says to you, and Philip has consoled her. I don't think we should talk about it."

"No, well that's… understandable."

"Changing the subject Brian," thrust Mary-Ann across an awkward hiatus, "you all refer to beings called The Golden Ones as leading lights much senior to yourselves. Are they evolved by having lived many more lives on earth and reached a high level of consciousness, or are they altogether distinct entities from the human?"

"The beings in our group whom we call Golden Ones are evolved from many lives on earth, but there are Golden Ones who never take earth form. They belong to an order of evolution distinct from the human although parallel, with the same life essence as ours of course. The order has many grades of being which rise from those you call nature spirits, on the ethereal level of your world, to those whom in certain earth cultures have been set up as gods, or angels, or lords of flame. This is because of their great, fiery, flowing auras which primitive people believed to be wings. A few of the very evolved from our race sometimes choose to transfer into one of their grades which, as I've said, run parallel. I don't know whether any of our group have done so. But we call ours Golden Ones because they look similar and are often seen with those described."

"They sound like the Devas," said Valerie, "mentioned only briefly in the books I've read. It's significant isn't it how, the higher the planes of evolvement, the more united the various orders are in their work?"

"By the very nature of things," he affirmed, "they realise their Oneness the more. Now the Channel has arrived, so we'll have to say goodnight."

"Okay Brian, thanks for that marvellous chat with you both. I expect you want to get off home. You'll be with us again for the rescue session on Friday?"

"We'll be there," said he loadedly. "Goodnight."

His going was nimbler than David's, she noticed. He struck her as academically minded, on the sharp side but informative, flexible and potent once the right connection had been made. What could that connection be which they had kept missing with questions he found "limited" or negligible? He savoured of assets untapped, filling a broad range between John's nitty-gritty and David's rarefied genre under Philip.

She chafed at herself for not asking why Philip had seldom responded to her "beams". It had been suggested by both of them tonight that she refer certain queries to him. Did he know these in advance and consider them unnecessary to our spiritual assignment? That could be the connection missed with Brian. Channelling rescue was for them a pivotal operation and a slippery slope of work. They had harnessed themselves to raw novices at the job, were aware of their dependence on us with the security risk it brought. She had gradually noted, during talks with Philip, David, John, and now Brian, that their keenest responses had been over issues in some way work-related: practical information about it, assurance of a fatherly eye from their seniors, our satisfied wellbeing, our trust in their integrity and in a familiar working partnership. She realised too that a chat like tonight's had helped to cement our partnership with them, and would familiarise our trust when David and Brian stood by us in the work. Probably they all knew it would do so, this being more useful to us than her curiosity about high-level experience or lower incidentals.

Her puzzle dissolved into another picture. Philip's earliest wish to be sent a "beam" was no idle gesture, but in order to stabilise the channel at that time and better explain their mission. His promise to be beside her in comfort's need was succour against the rough passage he predicted through baneful earthbound cases about to surround her. He meant the soothing of her ruffled spirit from within, the cleansing of negative effects which Brian had now confirmed were inevitable. That confirmation had startled her enough to set about streamlining her image of these men.

They were not here to chew the fat, indulge our whims or pull our chestnuts out of the fire. In Philip's own words they had "a serious job to do", through a Channel who is "inclined to take it rather lightly". Had she been guilty of the same? Not quite. Hers was the guilt of projecting her own desires on the set-up. So instead she decided to restrain herself and follow their cue, calling on them solely when the pressure of events faced us with a sine qua non. The sensed rightness of this decision, albeit based on conjecture, let it rest there. For after Peter had woken abashed from his failure at staying conscious, and her group had dispersed thoughtfully with little said, a question of some significance refilled her mind – a relevant question whose "enormity" she felt must tremble in the balance.

Peter's aim in that session of breaking through his deep trance blackout was not of course the same as ours for him. He wanted to keep the transition conscious so he could remember seeing The Seven, a temporary affair. We hoped he would use it with their guidance to align with his astral or inner self as planned, a permanent transition wherein "his life would change", as Philip had said, and very likely our ball game too. By and large the idea looked unrealistic to me, at least in his case. However, on the morning before her session Valerie had received by mail a booklet featuring talks by Sufi teacher Pir Vilayat Inayat Khan. In one, he described transition through a blackout to live permanently at the truer level of self. Khan's reputable stature worldwide, and his seeming to have experienced such a transition himself, inclined her to read his account again over supper:

"One has to go through a blackout and maintain the continuity of one's consciousness at the same time. There is a blackout unless one is a highly experienced contemplative and one has enough courage to face the blackout with full consciousness. But in the case of most people there comes just that moment when there is a transfer of consciousness from one level to another, and at that moment another consciousness takes over from the ordinary physical consciousness. It takes a certain amount of courage to leave that physical consciousness behind, because one thinks one is dying.

"There has to be a sense of continuity in change – of being another person and yet the continuation of the person that one was. There is a continuity which is very important, but you accept that you are not the same person. You leave your personality such as it was, behind, as you know that that person cannot experience what you are about to experience, cannot reach where you are about to reach, or go where you are about to go. Talking metaphorically the secret of it is to displace the focal centre of consciousness and place it in a more total part of the being. This requires a certain amount of selflessness, and the secret is love.

"One shifts that focus out of the narrow limits of earthly experience, and that is the stepping-stone to higher levels or degrees of reality. The psychologists would say there is a transformation in the notion of the self. It is as though you have awakened from your past. That now seems of little importance compared to the richness which you are experiencing. Your experience now is that which was always there behind you, but you had not been aware of it before."

A tall order for our chum. Taller in its demands than she had imagined. Yet her hope lived on because that moment of transfer to another consciousness was available to him each time he went into trance. Also, during their session, when they learned of the "right impetus" being given us before birth, she had faded off into pensiveness because Khan's secret of love was then dawning on her as a crucial mainspring of the prebirth agreement Peter had made. It had suddenly occurred to her that his own right impetus must be love, spiritual love.

Why else would an inside part of him surrender up his physical body to such a harrowing, racking purpose as the release of tormented lost ones? Surely it is the destitute and helpless who call forth the highest and best in human nature? And surely by applying that impetus, that "certain amount of selflessness", could he not shift his focus out of those "narrow limits" to realise the richness of his truer being? Of course the gap between his earth mind and Khan's did seem enormous. But to her that only increased the enormity of whether he would accept or reject his life impetus.

★ ★ ★ ★ ★

"It's all black... black!"

With galvanic abruptness the cry tugged us emotively into our second stab at rescue work, a somewhat nervous trio warned of more difficult cases and without Robert. His urbanity would not be there to smooth-talk us over the gaffes, while Valerie feared that "more difficult" spelt violence and along with J.M. found it convenient that I was nearest the channel. My own nervousness stemmed from being in that position as doorman rather than out of the slightest competence at rescue. For me, "more difficult cases" meant more likelihood of my vantage making an irreparable gaffe.

It did enable me to monitor the comings and goings, or hear faint mutterings which were essential to relay back, but it set me up as spokesman beyond my bounds of conscience. This was latent with our first poor bod, whose groaning exasperation muffled the rest of his cries. Persistence however revealed that his name was Derek, and thus encouraged I tried to focus him in our direction.

"You're not alone Derek. We're here beside you, and have come specially to help. Do you see anybody else in all that blackness?"

"No. If I'd stayed," tore the heart-sick voice, "I know I could have saved him."

"Saved who?"

"My boy… "

"What happened?"

"He was on the train with me. Oh it's all black now!"

"Your boy was in the accident with you?"

"He was killed wasn't he! But I got out… got out and *left* him! Oh I should have stayed… I should have *stayed*!"

"Listen Derek. You haven't lost him. He'll be there somewhere. All that's preventing you from seeing him is that blackness, which is all your dark thoughts of grief and remorse. To get out of it you must look for our man David who's standing right here, waiting to unite you both again."

"Oh it's getting hotter! I don't want to live."

He broke down into guilt-ridden, sobbing diffuseness which drowned his words even from my earshot. When the catharsis was spent, one symptom rang clear as usable:

"I feel so sick all the time. Oh I should've stayed!"

"Can you hear me Derek?" My chivvy at least held him. "Look I know it's hard, but if you can let go of all that horror just for a minute and think of getting some medical treatment you'll begin to feel better. We've brought a highly qualified man with us who can treat… "

" – No it's too late! I see it all. If only I'd… "

"It's not too late friend. It's your big chance to get out of this blackness and see your son, make it up with him."

"But he's *dead*! Don't you understand? I'll never see him again."

"Yes you will Derek, because you are too. You both died in the accident. Do you follow? And he'll want to see you just as much. Are you listening?"

"Oh I wanted everything for him," the dream groaned on. "He was my whole life you see. Oh I can't face it. I'll never forgive myself!"

Another tack was tried, though again wide of the mark:

"Okay, talk about him. What was he like?"

"Like me. Everyone said he looked like me. But he looked awful afterwards. I saw him. Oh god he was only six!"

"Don't think of that anymore. That's just the damaged physical replica he's walked free from. What you must do is try to lift yourself out of those memories by thinking how you can get to him, because he'll be on the other side of it, and our friend David can lead you to him. Your son isn't far away, really. So go with David."

The fellow became still, as if transfixed.

"He's David?... It hurts my eyes... I can't... "

"What's hurting?"

"That light. Oh he's getting bigger – look!"

It sounded like David's astral facility to impress.

"Right well you go with him. He'll help you find your son and you can be together again doing all the things you always enjoyed."

"Why doesn't he say anything?"

"He doesn't have to. He's just waiting to take you out into the light of your new world. You can relax yourself into his care now Derek."

A few extra displays were obviously being created to fan the flame, watched with gasps of amazement:

"Hey did you see that?... Hah!... Oh Christ I don't believe it! Is he an angel or something?"

"Sort of. Anyway, go with him and you'll be fine."

When Derek left without further hesitation we assumed success, due mostly to our friend's tantalising floorshow. We saw no reason to believe that he had realised his own physical death. Yet perhaps his being able to cathart emotion through the channel gave necessary relief, and help had to be identified with a brightness which might otherwise have frightened him away.

"The best we could hope for Jules," said Valerie.

If that was an example of "more difficult cases", our next entrant was to prove testier. As soon as she flopped in we could feel the apathetic vapidness with which she had surrounded herself. After sparing her name, Janet Barton, she appeared to glower sulkily at each of us. I welcomed her, remarking on this, and asked what she made of us – only to receive a bored cynicism:

"What's your game then?"

"We've come to talk to you."

"Yeh alright," she mumbled in world-weary tone.

A bit stuck, I rooted for subject matter.

"Is there anything you'd like to tell us?"

"Nope."

At the impasse my half-baked resort was to cajole.

"I must say you know your mind, and sound quite smart."

"Don't make me laugh!" Her scorn rang off into silence.

"What have you been doing Janet?" I chanced afresh.

"Not much. There's nothing to do."

"What do you see around you?"

"Load o' people."

I brightened that one of them could be David.

"Have you talked to any of them?"

"No, why should I?" she retorted dully.

"Because they might have something useful to tell you."

"No they 'aven't. They never want to do anything for me."

"We want to do something for you."

"Yeh? I've 'eard that one before. What do you want to do then?"

"We're going to help you into an exciting new world with plenty to do. Aren't you bored here?"

"I manage."

A ruse occurred to me that might shake her up a bit.

"Do you realise that you're using someone else's body?"

"Umm, suppose so."

"You do?" It was not the seismic reaction expected, so I threw in a booster. "A man's body?"

"Is it? There's not much difference."

My vacuum was filled by Valerie.

"What did you do on earth Janet? What was your job?"

"I worked in a pub."

"And what happened in the pub?"

"Wot d'yer think 'appened in the pub?" she sneered with a cattiness that made Valerie falter.

"We don't know," I said. "What caused the change?"

"Change?"

"From working in the pub to here."

"Oh I 'ad to go into 'ospital."

"And you realize you're on a different dimension?"

"I'm dead ain't I?"

"Well those you left behind probably think so, but… "

"I don't give a shit wot they think."

"No but you can now will yourself out of your… "

"Oh I'm getting fed up with this!"

"You don't want to talk to us anymore?"

"Not much," she grumped, beginning to retreat, so I hurried a last tempter off the top of my head.

"There's a handsome young chap here who's anxious to meet you, and take you on a fun trip with great sights."

But it was too late. She had slunk back to a haunt which at least was believable to her.

In the shadow of failure my ad hoc tactics looked pretty feeble. I could only think to allow longer pauses for the others to have a go. Maybe Valerie's feminine instinct and craft might have won Janet over if extra seconds had been given, though as said before, the longer the pause the greater the risk of losing our quarry's attention altogether.

Next was Linda, who in spite of a livelier frame of mind than her contemporary still hugged the same sphere of mental withdrawal. Yet hers was for a different reason, which she told us straightaway when, having learnt her name I explained our wish to help and tried to draw her out.

"How do you feel Linda?"

"Scared!"

"What are you scared of?"

"Everything," she confessed meekly. "I have to keep… It's all bars, an' I… " Her fadeout left one guessing, apart from the logical relation of bars to fear.

"Don't you see people around?"

"Yeah on the other side of 'em. They keep takin' 'em down and when I turn round they're all up again."

"Are we on the other side of them? I don't see any bars between us."

"You must do. You've got your hand through 'em."

This was probably because of my bent forward position, intended to screen Valerie from Janet's depressive effect. Now conscious of its absence I sat back more.

"Do you mind talking to us Linda?"

"No, it's better than those others who come 'ere and talk to me. They think I'm mad."

"But you're just scared aren't you?"

"Yeah I am. What's over those 'ills?"

"Over those hills Linda, is a land of light and love which dispels fear, and we know a man who is waiting to take you there – a man in white."

That last phrase of mine was meant to offer simple romantic appeal, but turned out to be a gaffe.

"I don't like men in white. Before I come 'ere there was always men in white."

As my toes curled up, Valerie did the redress:

"But our man is very different. He's an angel."

"Oh no I don't want anything like that."

"So what do you want most of all?"

We were unprepared for the inventory which followed.

"I'd… I'd quite like some curtains in 'ere, and I'd like a telly, and a nice comfy couch, and um… "

Valerie shrunk a little in her chair, face turning to me for a stall of the flow, so I ploughed in.

"Ah, well if you won't go with our friend you'll have to wish hard that he'll bring these things to you, and give you a taste of what's over those hills."

At her scepticism I explained how to concentrate desire into effect on her level, banking on the hope that David would support me and materialise the goods anyway. It was a risky hope, since he would doubtless have preferred us to lure her out instead. But minutes later she gave a gasp of surprise:

" – 'Ere! There *is* a telly! Where d'that come from?"

"It's a small measure to show you what we mean," I said shiftily, hiding my relief.

She said nothing of curtains or couch, evidently so delighted with the TV as not to mind. Valerie then dared her a step further.

"Now think those bars away."

"Oh no, they're always there."

"Well like you've just done, only the opposite. You wish, and they won't be there."

Linda knew she hadn't done the first trick however.

"Does the telly work?"

"Yes I'm sure it does," I resumed, "but you see, that was merely a sample of… "

"And did you bring any apples? People always used to bring me apples in the 'ospital."

"But you're long out of hospital Linda. You're a free agent, free to go over those hills where you can enjoy far greater luxury than you have here."

"Oh I don't mind so much now I've got me telly. And they won't think I'm mad, seein' it 'ere, will they? Hang on, what about the bars? Still, they'll keep people from comin' in and watchin' it."

"Or you can leave those people and the bars altogether if you want, taking the telly with you."

"Oh no it's quite big. I couldn't"

"That's easily solved," said J.M. "Our man will carry your television for you over the hills to freedom."

"No I wouldn't like that. I don't want anyone. No I think I'll stay here."

"Alright," I sighed. "If you ever change your mind though, our friend will be available."

"What's his name then?"

"David. Just think of him strongly and wait."

Meanwhile it seemed her neighbours were in tumult.

"… 'Ere! What're they all shoutin' at?"

"What does it sound like to you?" asked Valerie.

"Um… dunno. What *is it* they're shoutin' at?"

"I expect they're watching a game or something. Do they sound cheerful?"

"No… " she murmured distrustfully, as if supposing a fight. "No I'll just sit 'ere. But I won't be able to hear the telly if they keep that up, will I?"

Perhaps she had come to regard life as dangerous and herself as powerless, her cloistered den a bastion of safety behind bars. Threat of one kind or another would therefore be her general experience from those of like mind who believed in it as a solution. Whatever the case, at that moment we were unable to improvise any other means of allure. So we gave in, consoling ourselves that we had left her an escape route via David to the therapy needed. It became necessary to edge her gently out of the channel by force of will, because she sat tight – watching the telly we assumed.

Then a man burst in, huff-puffing with frustration. Hindsight would make it easy to deduce that he had been a miner of some sort, asphyxiated after a shaft collapse. Ignorant of his changed state he had tried to burrow into the rubble, and hearing my voice presumed the pit rescue party had arrived.

But we started off as clueless as usual, my choice of an opener coinciding with his darkened world:

"Hallo, can you see us?"

"No I can't. It's me Ted."

His impatient puffs and snorts flickered a bit to hear, in the 'mineshaft' ahead, Valerie's feminine, genteel voice ring out:

"Is there anything you'd like to tell us, er… Ted?"

He somehow managed to overlook the anomaly.

"… Gawd! I dunno 'ow you can keep chatterin' on when I can't… Oh no!"

Another section may have collapsed, unbeknown to me:

"Because we want to understand your problem and help."

"I'm just tryin' to get out!" he spluttered vexedly. "Why don't you… Ohh!"

"Get out of where?"

"Out of this tunnel! Where d'yer think man?"

"Okay Ted we'll have you clear in a jiffy. See our friend's light at the end? It's showing you the way out."

I imagined that David's lucent effect could stand in for an underground rescuer's headlamp. But despite it the hapless pitman faded away, muttering to himself. Almost before we could blink, a spry young lad of unknown origin dropped into his place:

"What do you mean?" he chirped with indignance. "I don't want to get out."

Announcing his name as John, this boy obviously thought my entreaty had been addressed to him:

"I mustn't go anywhere 'cos it's my birthday soon."

"And how old will you be John?" I enquired.

"Eleven," said he proudly.

"Gosh that's quite old isn't it! You're a big chap."

Unused to children and self-conscious at having perhaps sounded patronising, I felt worse at his next announcement.

"I'm gonna have legs for my birthday."

"But, um… you've got legs already haven't you?"

I cringed inside as he began to whimper.

"Don't say that! It's what everyone says."

A fleeting pause saw my mind race. Whenever physical limbs or organs are absent or damaged their counterparts stay intact of course, and are normally found so once the outer body is shed – unless mental habit dies hard. Was "everyone" seeing his inner legs except him? Yet children are reported to adapt quickly to the new world, and I was puzzled by John's tardiness. It impelled from me a rather rash half-querying device:

"Can't you see your legs? They were always there."

"No don't tease me!" he begged. "I haven't had any for as long as I can remember."

"How far back is that John?" Valerie asked.

"Oh I remember playing with my brother. They got burnt. But I'm gonna have some for my birthday – *real* ones, 'cos I don't like these."

My guess was that an idée fixe of artificial legs may be the hold-up, David having nudged him toward us with the birthday as trigger-point and a twinkle of promise.

"Hang on," said I feignedly, "isn't today your birthday?"

He tensed alert, yearning to believe me.

"Is it?"

"Yes it is!" explained Valerie, catching on. "That's why we've come, you see. It's all been arranged for you."

"Golly!" And something more than eagerness thrilled in his voice. "Can… Can I have my legs today then?"

"Yes," she answered strongly. "In fact you're going to get them any minute now. You close your eyes, and when you open them you'll have your new legs. Say One… Two… "

He did so with us: "Three… "

"Now. Open your eyes and… there they *ARE*!

"*OHH!*" he cried in wonderment, enthralled. "Oh I… !"

"Isn't that marvelous? Now you can walk all by yourself!"

He was touched to the quick, almost trembling at the fullness of body which was his again. For us, it was at last a pleasure to share the glory.

"How about that!" I grinned. "Aren't they great? You can go anywhere you like."

"You can run!" fired Valerie. "You can run right away now. Happy Birthday John!"

"But… you haven't sung it," he insisted.

So, more or less together, we sung him Happy Birthday. Not the finest of performances one has to admit, though enough to satisfy a truly happy boy. When his gratitude surrendered him into David's care our faces shone with having delivered the goods.

As to why David couldn't have done this particular feat himself, I thought along the lines of a psychologist M.D.'s rating that the ordinary influences of one mind on another is always greatest with strangers. Arguably it bore out on our older cases like a damp handshake, but in John's case a windfall appearance by strangers enacting the birthday task, plus our earthly advantage of impact, was calculated to guarantee breakthrough upon an already expectant and susceptible young mind – provided we got the idea, which we did by a whisker. Valerie bet that the opportunity was also given us as a morale-raiser.

Unable to argue there, because suitably uplifted, we were sitting inches taller for the next challenge. It came however in the form of Barbara, whose mind had hooked onto an anxiety which made us peripheral.

"How do you feel, Barbara?" I opened gamely.

"Nervous. I have to go in today."

"Where do you have to go?"

"Court number four."

"Who's on trial?"

"No one. They're going to listen to Frank."

He, I ascertained, was her husband.

"A civil court then is it? What's he been doing?"

"He's gone off to her house."

"Ah I see – divorce. How did… "

"I can't tell you any more, I have to go in now. I've waited a long time for this and I want to get it over with."

"Do you know who we are Barbara?"

But she rushed away – so quickly that for seconds my stare hung fixed, mouth still open, mind in a fog as to how I could have kept her. That remained about the sum of us through the lull before certain, rather unpromising signs from another entry took form.

Heavy, shuddering breaths came with the gradual ingress. A mood of conflict had me warn the others and brace myself. It showed soon enough, snarling in a twist of the body and a lash of clawed fingers which all too narrowly missed my ear until J.M. and I were able to grab them firm. Valerie had abandoned her seat. Off its front edge swung her loose microphone, picking up my demand – once we had our captive held down – that reason assert itself over the snarls.

"Right. Now what's this about? Who are you?"

The captive writhed away awkwardly as if expecting a blow.

"I'm not telling you! It's on my arm."

"What is? I don't follow."

"You *know* it's on my arm!" was shrieked in disbelief.

"No you're mistaken. We're friendly newcomers. My name is Jules. Won't you tell us yours?"

The resistance ceased, giving way to suspicion:

"If you're one of us, where's your star? Why aren't you wearing it?"

We let go our grip on each wrist and gingerly resumed our seats. From a corner behind us Valerie likewise sidled into hers, retrieving the microphone.

"Can't you see my star?" I bluffed, with a try at mental suggestion.

The man, as I felt it to be, made no answer. Instead, concluding that we posed no immediate threat, he settled back to his grind:

"Three… four… five… six… " he whispered to himself.

"Why are you counting?" I broke in.

He stopped concernedly:

"You don't have to ask things like that do you?"

"We do," said J.M., "because we're new here."

"You'll find out," he warned, and went on counting.

"But who's going to tell us?"

This time he was brought up short:

192

"How did you get here? Don't you know who they are?"

"No. We don't know anybody here except… "

"Have you just come in today?"

"Yes we're the latest," I affirmed, trying to disarm him. "It's only us and David. He's the one in that light."

" – David! What's his last name?"

"Er… King I believe."

"Is he Jewish?… But we're all the same," was muttered on reflection, "all treated the same."

"If you mean like cattle," I said, "we wouldn't treat you like that."

"No but you're one of us, so you'll be treated like that."

"We won't friend. We're outsiders you see."

"How did you get in here then? You've come to trap me haven't you? Sent to spy on us. That's it, isn't it?"

"No nothing of the sort I promise you. We simply wandered in. There wasn't a soul around except yourself."

The scent of disbelief saw J.M. put swift rationale:

"And they wouldn't have us just wander in without stars if they wanted us to spy on you, would they?"

"Uhh… I don't know."

"It's true," urged Valerie. "We've come with David to take you out."

"What?" The decisive note seemed to arrest him. "How can you? Is it finished?"

"Yes," she told him squarely. "It's all finished."

He drew in breath, afraid to believe. Was it true? How else were these outsiders, among them a soft-spoken female, to be accounted for? As the dawnlike concept opened, still he could only think in terms of his murky hell-camp environs.

"And I don't have to count any more teeth?"

"No, because it's truly over," she pledged with feeling. "It's all over. The Allies have won. That's why we could wander in. And you can go out the same way. You can go out right now, with David."

"Oh… And no more men coming down?"

"No, no more of those," she assured him. "Everything has been stopped. Your guards have fled or been taken away."

"What about this, on my arm?"

She tried the birthday-John device again:

"That'll go too. You close your eyes, and when you open them again it'll be gone. You do that. Close your eyes."

"But what are you going to do when I close my eyes?"

"Nothing. You can trust us. It's alright. Just do it, and when you open them the mark will have vanished."

"No... No I don't want to. I can't... trust."

That unhappy snag let me reclaim our ground:

"Anyway the camp's deserted. You can stroll off as you please."

"You're free now," underlined J.M.

At the very notion however, he shrunk with fear.

"Ohh... I don't know where I'm going to go!"

"Just start forward in faith," was my prod, "and you'll be shown the way."

"... But where shall I go to?" he wailed, rudderless.

"Where it looks lighter and open. Where our friend is. Do you see him?"

A hush. "No. Which one is he?"

It took some moments for the pitiable fellow to discern David through what sounded like ghost-forms in the "fog" nearest to him. Then his eye was caught by one figure who was slightly luminescent against the paler haze beyond, an upright young man turned towards him, standing quietly with arms outstretched.

"What's he doing? Why doesn't he speak?"

"Ask him," I suggested. "He's inviting your attention, wanting your response. Go and meet him."

"Over that mud? Everyone knows it's worst there."

"Don't worry," said Valerie. "Concentrate on David and you'll be able to walk across. Is he beckoning or calling you now?"

"I can't see his face. It's too far. Why is the light round him only?"

"Because only he can show you the way."

"And what's outside of that circle? It's got so dark."

We supposed David to have thrown a strong spotlight on the area to be crossed, darkening all else.

"The dark is a side-effect," I hustled. "Look straight into the light for your freedom."

But for one convinced he was still on earth, the quite unearthly guide we offered had become a phenomenon.

"He's coming now, look!… over all those hands. What are they doing in there?"

That was anybody's guess, and given the neighbourhood we preferred not to. Expectations were instead bent on David having moved closer with the favourable tide of interest shown him – closest to Valerie by the sound of it.

"What's he saying to you Miss?"

"To me?" she sat up. "Is he saying something to *me*?"

"Oh I don't understand!" he cried in sudden disarray. "You people don't make sense. I'm dreaming aren't I? You're not really here!"

"We're trying," said she, "to help you out of your dream, out of this place. I couldn't hear David, but I know he wants to lead you away into heaven, if you'll go with him. He's been sent by the angels, who watch over and love you. You've got to believe it, because you're going to a place where angels visit."

"No leave me alone. Just leave me alone!"

At his retreat I hurriedly laid it on the line.

"Go with David and he'll show you where you belong, your true home. He's waiting for you to take that vital step out of your misery, which only you can do. He won't pull you across your mud. He can't. The choice has to be yours, a spiritual step if you like, which must be made entirely of your own accord."

We had both felt that to make an issue of his death here would ruffle the profound simplicity of stepping from a hell-camp to heavenly freedom. He wavered between, though presently distracted by a step of David's.

"What's he doing now?"

"Tell us how it seems to you," said Valerie.

"He… He wants me to walk on those flowers."

"Ah yes," she clued in, "he's putting flowers down to show you there's no need to wade through the mud. He's laying you a path. You go on those lovely flowers. Are they daffodils?"

"No, yellow and white ones. I mustn't walk on them."

"You must! There's plenty more where they came from. Don't you see that where there was mud and those awful hands it's now all flowers, and that only a divine power could have done that?"

But the fellow was held agape as David drew nearer:

"Hohh!… Is he real? Why's he done this for me?"

"So you'll recognise where he's from, and how he's come to give you deliverance. He wants to take you under his wing and lead you into a new, full life because he's a friend who cares for you, a friend who's been waiting for you to accept him."

"What about all the others?"

"They'll be watched over, those who are left," her calmative voice told, "but you're one of the first to respond. And then, when you've been nourished and healed and restored, you can be his bridge to them because you'll understand. You're like someone specially chosen, more awake in your heart than the others, so that afterwards you can come and help him reach them too."

"… Yes… Yes, I… " trickled to us from his comprehension, widening under effects from David no doubt.

"You see?" she pursued. "That's another reason why he has come. He needs your help. So will you go with him?"

"Yes."

"Make those beautiful flowers your path out into life."

"… Why is he crying? I don't understand."

"I expect in his joy over your release at last."

"Ohh, it's… so… !"

Choked with inexpressible emotion he shook off his years of imprisonment and was gone. Much later we were told that he did indeed return to help reach the other inmates, then absorb himself in the use of colour for healing.

Still, we were too aflush with the hue and tone of that success to carry it far when already, hard on his heels, rather wearisome griping in front of us signalled a fresh arrival. On enquiry through it I got the name Ronald and that he was tired, which drew the natural question from Valerie:

"And what have you been doing Ronald, to get so tired?"

"Uhh… There are two of me."

"Two of you?" she queried. "What do you mean?"

"I can't get together," was the newly baffling reply.

"Can you tell us a bit more?"

"Every time I want to talk, *he* sits in."

Valerie's blank expression met mine. J.M.'s brows were knitted, mouth open. The term schizoid flashed into my mind, though not how to proceed.

"What was it like before the second Ronald?" I groped.

"There were three of us."

I didn't think to ask where the third had gone.

"But we only find one of you. Why is that?"

"Because he won't join me. He doesn't want to come. I want to come but he doesn't."

"Well," I said, deriving no sense, "we reckon you're sufficient in yourself. Leave those others behind."

"Hmmph!"

And on that note he left. In the flat silence I chewed on my lip, thinking we could have thrown some obscure label over his psychosis and steered him to our specialist at the ready. Euphoria from the previous win however had dulled initiative.

As Valerie's lively cassette-change resharpened us to the fray an uptight, avid character slid in, brushing my gambits aside:

" – SShh!"

"Pardon?"

"Be quiet – they're coming soon!"

For twenty seconds we honoured the ban. Then J.M joked that "they" might be lost in fog, and with a grin I prodded:

"Who's coming?"

"You wait and see. Are you new here?"

"Yes we've rolled up to lend you a hand."

"Ah, you'll never get out now!" was the cynical jeer.

"Actually friend, it's you who we plan to get out."

"Don't be daft. Haven't you seen all them girls?"

"Girls? No. What are they going to do?"

"Same as they do every day. You must be really wet behind the ears."

"Okay so give us the lowdown. What happens every day?"

"Oh they all come and you're never allowed to get near 'em."

It emerged that our fancier, conceivably male, was dreaming a troupe of showgirls who paraded before him and did a regular dance routine. "The Police", he said, always stopped him from approaching them.

"'Cos I've got to be punished."

"Why?" I asked. "Have you committed a crime?"

"I don't remember. But I've got to be punished."

"You're the only one who believes that. You're punishing yourself. We're in touch with someone who knows all about your situation."

"Who's that?"

"David. He wants to tell you it's a mistake. You don't have to be punished at all."

"I don't know any David."

"Not his name maybe, but he's been watching you very closely and can see a way for you to leave here."

"It's time!" exclaimed the man.

"For you to leave?"

"No, for them to come. I told you."

His attention switched away altogether, and dead on time he was off – mesmerised by the parade.

"Strange!" Valerie whispered, though J.M. and I were thinking it less so. How to pull someone out of his outpictured male guilt-fetish, and pretty quick too, was the strangeness for us. The following three were equally problematic, and much briefer. They passed through in fleet succession, the first vapourish after having climbed a mountain. Asked where, he or she limply said:

"At the end."

"Talk to us about it," encouraged Valerie. "Did you reach the top, or did you miss your footing?"

"No I just climbed it," sighed the voice, floating off.

The second passer-by shivered, although our room was warm, in an effusion of heavy, rather ominous breaths, their depth and power mounting while I bid blind:

"Hallo? Speak to us. You feel cold?"

"YE-E-EES!"

That full-throated penetrating scream rent the air. It could well have been heard several doors away. An offer of warmth and comfort brought no response. Nor, when asked, had our visitor any remembrance of name or willingness to unburden, instead seeming to regard our entreaties with blunt, apathetic indifference before sloping back into the gloom. A third of the same ilk came and went, this time not even deigning to speak.

But our final caller was quite different. Friendly, responsive, and wistful till it hurt, "Dickie" believed himself to be a certain pop-singer of acclaim – one whom no doubt he admired. Or maybe he was in fact that singer? At first anyway, relishing the thrill of sudden focus on him, he settled eagerly into the channel to find me closer than an average fan should be.

"I'm very... near you!"

"Yes you are," I granted, ignorant as yet of the case. "We'd like to learn something about you because we think we can help. Will you let us, and introduce yourself?"

"I've been forgotten. Don't you recognise me?"

At a tricky moment Valerie came to my rescue:

"Are you somebody we'd remember if you gave your name?"

"Yes," said the small voice, "but nobody knows me now."

Naturally that acted on her like an aperitif:

"Oh do tell us! Then I'm sure we'll know you."

He paused. "Shall I sing something instead?"

"Yes, sing us a little song. We'd love to hear it."

So he obliged by crooning two verses of On a Slow Boat to China, then awaited the happy event.

"Do you remember?"

"Of course we do!" she beamed, scrabbling fervidly for the singer's name. "We remember that very well."

"It was my first record."

"Was it *really*! First record! Gosh… " the flannel went on. "We still hear it sometimes… " and while racking her brain was thankful of J.M.'s fill-in:

"I bet it made you world famous didn't it?"

"Yes," said he cherishedly. "But not anymore. Nobody recognises me."

"Well you see," came my own flannel, "it's your distinct presentation which stays in our mind, not your label."

"And we do know your song," appended J.M. hastily.

Unsatisfied, our crooner sought to prompt us.

"Dickie… ?" he began, causing audience unrest. "You can't remember!"

Yet the lead was fastened on by Valerie:

"Not Dickie… umm… It's Dickie Valentine isn't it?"

"Yes!" he cried, at his source of honour.

"So that's a boost for you Dickie, and you must know that your talent gave pleasure to millions. Are you not singing any more?"

"No," was the humbled reply. "I'm not doing anything now. I want to go back. I want to be famous again."

"But you've remained famous," I said. "Your name and your songs are still known."

"Not here!"

The plumb disappointment in his answer typified that of others whose earthly fame had not followed them. But assuming he was indeed the singer, Valerie pointed out the plus side.

"Oh you can do much greater things where you are, and be far more famous than you ever were on earth, because in that rich world it's so much easier to do wonderful things for people. You did such things for people here didn't you? Not just with your singing I mean."

"I want to do them again," rang his pineful note. "I want to be back there, in it all, like I used to be."

Faced with this nonstarter, she counted upon David.

"Can you see a young man standing anywhere near you?"

"Mmm… No, why?"

"Well he came with us to ask if you'll join him in a special project for the needy. He feels you'd be a terrific help."

Dickie was circumspect. "What could I do?"

"He wants you to sing," I abetted. "Top of the Bill."

"Absolutely," she said, "and uplift whole crowds of sad, bewildered souls he brings to his Centre for healing, as well as inspire other young talents. You've got a tremendous job ahead of you there."

"But I want to come back. Nobody knows me here."

"The thing is though Dickie," she pressed, "it's very difficult to come back in that way. You can't just come through a door and have everything as it was. You'd have to choose new parents, new circumstances, and you'd be a rather different version of yourself in a world that will have changed enormously since you left. You must go on into your present life first, grow to realise the truer being within you. Only then can you know your real needs and direction to plan another earth life properly. Meanwhile if you join our friend at his Centre in the greater world beyond, you can increasingly have the sort of life you want."

"He'll warm up the people for you," said I, "telling them of your fame on earth. So they'll be expecting you to sing for them."

"Yes," she took over again, "there are so many people who'd love to hear your singing. This is the whole reason why he's come to fetch you. The sound helps to heal them."

"Then why hasn't he come before? And why didn't you know my name?"

Valerie's artful tongue smoothed a trouble spot:

"Because it wasn't necessary. He just needed us to explain in advance from the earthly point of view, that our world here is changing fast and already isn't the same as you knew it. And this is the first opportunity we've had. So he was waiting for us, and now he's going to put you back on stage. Won't that be marvellous?"

The prospect unnerved him slightly after such a gap:

"… I don't know if I can sing again. Maybe… " and he was hesitant. "Do you remember: C is for the candy trimmed around the Christmas tree, H is for the happiness of all the family?"

"Yes we do. You mustn't worry though Dickie. People there say a talent flows easier once you're really free from earth. It'll be just as much fun as your golden days if you join our young man."

"Will I be famous again?"

"Yes, famous for your good works too," she hinted. "You'll be happier altogether than you were here, involved in lots of super ideas to help people and touring round all sorts of fascinating places."

Yet his anxiety's sole ear was for a stage return.

"I hope I can remember the orchestrations… "

"Oh they'll come back to you in due course. Besides, with the endless scope available, and far greater artistic freedom, you'll be able to create whole new adaptations. It really is exhilarating further on, you know. We all long to go, as a matter of fact."

That last remark got her a dubious glance from J.M., while to me she had merely overspun how one looks forward to summer holidays after boarding school – and here was Dickie stuck midway without knowing it.

He drew a long sigh in might-as-well vein.

"Where is this friend of yours then?"

"Good," she said. "You'll find David nearby somewhere if you look carefully, in a brightness perhaps. Can you see him?"

"No… I can't ," was reported after a scan. "Unless… You're not talking about that one in the middle are you? The fair headed one they're listening to?"

Does he seem as though he's in a light?"

"Yes. But he's more famous than I am!"

"Oh it's not how it seems Dickie. He's quite unknown."

"Then why are all those people around him?"

"Because he's brought them to hear you. They'd like you to entertain them. It'll be your new world premiere."

"They're not even looking at me."

"Ah but they will. They can't see you until you stride confidently into that light, casting away your fears. They know you're having a chat with us first, as I said, and will be ready when you are. So meantime he's acting like a… a sort of promoter for you, spreading your great name till you can pluck up the courage to go out there and sing with all your heart."

Such promotion of her own set his mind at play.

"… So once I'm in the spotlight, what shall I give them to start with?"

"Well let's think. Why don't you give them… umm… now wasn't there a very successful one about a top hat – or am I thinking of someone else?" she faltered, eyes on me.

But my eyes went to J. M., who put in a request.

"You could give them that number you sung for us."

Our star idled. "Or Walking My Baby Back Home?"

"Perfect," declared Valerie. "That's the one."

"Will they look at me then?"

"You'll have to assert yourself first," said she. "So rise up and be brave. Hold your head high."

Pendulous seconds passed.

"Yes he's moving! He's looking at me!"

"Now you're ready to join him you see, and one of these days you'll be telling us how wonderful it's all been."

"And… And you can see how wonderful I shall be?"

"Yes we'll see that. But you are anyway."

"I know. As long as they're going to like me."

"Oh of course they will. Do you want to sing us one last song before you leave?"

A lungful was released with gusto:

"Gee but it's great after being out late, walking my baby back home!"

"Jolly good. Don't worry about our old world any longer Dickie. You'll never need to think of it again."

Thus hooked, he was pulled out by David's call.

"... Yes I'm ready!"

The pathos of this character, as far as we could see, typified a sad ego lost in the belief that his self worth was not at all based upon his own authority but must be earned under the weak tyrant of public opinion. To cast such priceless worth into the power and caprice of the crowd, common in human tendency, echoed up to us from some lower level of our minds. "I want to be recognised by my herd," feels an animal. "I want to be famous," says our child mind, and the fact niggled in us while scrunched round that settee relishing our success. We also became aware, with no sign of another entrant, that our session's last curtain had rung down.

Whether or not he had been Dickie Valentine mattered little in itself. Yet how could he sing to them if he were not? In J.M.'s view "without applause" judging by the "naff auditions". These I argued were no criterion since every input was limited to the channel's ability. If our rescuee was simply deluded, then the people he saw could have been a mirage projected by him around David from our mental suggestion. In either context, deluded or Valentine, we imagined he would need to live out his heart's desire until sated enough to heed the truth of himself. Valerie had taken him at face value. She felt that anyway he was in need of all the positive thought he could get right now, and that knowing the truth David must have arrangements in hand – which had kept him from saying goodnight.

Peter's return, fuzzy and bog-eyed, was to a brain used by twelve strange minds, of whom we had rescued four. They had been cut loose from entanglement here and pushed toward real healing skill. Each, no doubt, would be enabled to discover their worth and capacity beyond earth props. Our usefulness to The Seven tonight, at a disadvantage without Robert, was uncertain. But reviewing our failure in those more difficult cases we did question where actually he would have succeeded.

★ ★ ★ ★ ★

That weekend the chill of early Spring still lay in a breeze which ruffled Langton's tall evergreens, and for Valerie, watching them sway from her bow window, the winter had not outgrown its mysteries either. She shifted forward to her street view, where along the huddle of shopfronts a dozen or so village folk, small, overcoated, mostly with bag, trailed their even pace. Odds and ends of conversation, bursts of motor traffic, were insistent and numerous on her ear, though not as loud as those sentiments of John's one wintry eve which replayed on her mind.

Would such people seen here in this Kentish village be among the "so many who have nothing, no preparation at all" when they passed over? Any one of them might find themselves there tomorrow. Would they know that on encountering dull or unpleasant conditions they must realise these to be subjective and call out for guidance to higher realms of healing? Our caseload so far had not been of rare background but of a fairly ordinary cross-section. Why had they been ignorant of the lucid and substantial testimony claiming to describe afterlife conditions? Surely, as John said, "if they had read one book" and not accepted it as true, on arriving they would recognise that the claim, in his words, "wasn't so wrong after all"? What would a disbeliever have to lose by pocketing the knowledge just in case?

Maybe they had never read any testimony because put off by a ubiquitous kind which reviewers disdained as the incoherent, subconscious ramblings of uneducated mediums. Or else they simply hadn't read much. That was a likelihood with several of our rescue cases she thought, one which further lessened their chances of ever having come across the core of quality material which reviewers praised.

Yet in fairness it seemed to her, from many an educated acquaintance and rescuee Charles Knight for example, that this core material had never reached the public en masse, staying as a rule within specialist bookshops like Watkins off the Charing Cross Road. A publisher friend had once stoutly informed her that each book required £5,000 of his investment, which now made her sympathise with the risk of manuscripts liable to have limited circulation. Why were these books in poor demand? Why was the knowledge so unwelcome as to leave people unaware that it existed? Even New Age enthusiasts referred to ancient Egyptian or Tibetan dogma on the subject rather than to New Age material here in Britain.

Reminded of how, eight years before, my schoolboy innocence had set out to tell the world of such vital knowledge, she caught herself smiling and was onto a clue. For the smile she caught was not at innocence alone, but at innocence of a world which her maturity knew better. From there she began to discern, under joe public's creedal or intellectual resistances, his hoary preconceptions and prejudgements, another layer which held them fast.

Head on side she watched old village women traipse by, waddling with the burden of their years. They lent focus as her picture grew of a mass belief in which the individual felt less worthy, less authoritative than established world doctrine, a pawn subordinate to giants who implied that official truth is their domain. By solid vote, echoed the pawn, since mainstream science, religion and philosophy knew nothing of an afterlife then one need look no further. Evidently there could be little with which to prepare oneself except faith and hope. Personal objections to an alternative method of enquiry could have free rein, for if anything was to be definitely known it would sooner or later be discovered by authority's revered one.

Masses would not open themselves to the challenging of that long-established belief, because for them it was a condition of reality rather than a belief. Not unlike rescuees who came to mind, they would shy from new experience, fail to explore beyond the mould, their fear being stronger than their sense of adventure. Comparatively few would stretch over the fear, look beyond the belief for some working hypothesis to guide them in case revered supposition was wrong.

The availability of channelled information revealing how, as John said, "a lot of problems could be avoided if they knew beforehand what to expect", might never occur to them. Not having reached them from the authorised sources it must be non-existent. If, according to this belief, there was no valid data to be interested in, not even clues toward life's purpose, she wasn't surprised that when they did think of such matters they were content usually to ask what they presumed to be unanswerable questions about either. Or one heard the sadness of that conditioning which has only been left enough reason to offer the hackneyed quote: "There are more things in heaven and earth, Horatio, than you and I have ever dreamed of."

She knew this must be far from a complete picture, but fancied nevertheless that if the high priests of scientism declared their full acceptance of discarnate knowledge tomorrow the mass mind would pick it up like a box of groceries. As things stood, their current widespread belief could be keeping demand low, and an output almost wholly confined to specialist bookshops leaving thoughtful folk untold. Were these the ones Philip meant when he spoke of the "few between" in whom he was much interested? She had never quite understood that reference, and always forgotten to pump him afresh.

Whether he was referring to the earthbound, or the thoughtful "few between" in our world, raked up a poser. When speaking too of Peter's pledge his terms had been of a "liaison with us here, telling people about the many and varied spheres that surround them". Perhaps they originally aimed to inspire him, or still did, as their earth spokesman – rescue being a needful prelude?

Was there more to The Seven's plan than we suspected?

After our call to rescue she thought he had meant earthbound people, in neglect that he had already defined it as, "knowledge of a kind to an intermediary level of your plane which many people miss entirely". And then: "We think even you Valerie, have missed this… with your friend", meaning Betty. His drift hinted at an ambition rather above the use of recorded rescue examples to do the telling, especially since he had not asked her to record them. What level had she and Betty missed? And what lay in store from these men?

Her thoughts scrambled into confusion. Beyond the window it had become a showery afternoon, so she turned to her snug settee by lamplight. Under its glow a salient remark of John's made her next course of action obvious. "I'd rather talk to some people there with you," he said, "before they come over. I haven't got much knowledge, but I'd like to try." She was going to give him that chance, and picked up the phone to make arrangements for it.

Remembering that Rob Morgan's parents were heard to have shown interest in his line of enquiry these days, she rung his Mayfield, Sussex home at once. He chimed in with her idea of allowing John's talk, and after brief consultation promised to bring his parents the next evening, their freest Sunday. Short notice though it was, they were her main target and she had no intention of letting the opportunity slip. Before ringing off she had the prudence to cadge a lift for friend Winifred on their way through Tunbridge Wells.

Winifred Wild was an elderly spinster thought to fit the occasion, not just because handy time-wise but as having the compatible, respectable vintage of an ex-schoolmistress in sympathy with Ashdene's genre though lacking the gen. She had taught pottery at an independent girls' school and retired to share a house with two of her age-group who from the floor below ran a local branch of the Churches' Fellowship for Psychic and Spiritual Studies. Their London headquarters had sponsored the publication of Frances Banks' Testimony of Light, which account Winifred had read without close review or much awareness of the others. Whilst also a friend of Paul Beard, College of Psychic Studies President, she was no psychic student either – preferring metaphysical enquiry. Her regular home meditation group included Rob Morgan. She had shared the odd healing or prayer circle with Valerie elsewhere, and had sat in Ashdene Sanctuary. So the mixed grounds upon which she was now roped in by phone to sit there tomorrow were that she might blend with the Morgans, lend ballast to an uncertain venture, and perhaps be edified too.

The trickiest bit, that of actually staging the show outside rescue hours, Valerie left till last. As it had been requested by John, no breach was seen in her volte-face away from channel misuse – and to lure Peter she counted on his keenness to meet new people. Simply asking him if the parents of our budding Buddhist might have a session was found quite enough bait for his inquisitive nature: What did they think of their son's "weird" predilection? Were they Buddhists too? "Have they told the neighbours?" he added with an impish grin.

She had no idea; but he was welcome to quiz them tomorrow when he got back from Sunday's jaunt with his children, after which the Morgans would appreciate a sitting. His "okay", half drowned by the shop doorbell, sped her off to phone Betty at Southborough. One of their writing sessions was hastily convened where they put through the message via Orlando that John's chance had come. Then, with everyone synchronised, she took her ease scooping extra data about The Seven to use in an introduction she would give the Morgans.

Twenty-four hours later they were alighting from their car outside Ashdene, Winifred in tow. Since Betty was unable to attend, Mary-Ann remained her mother's sole support as a bevy of sanguine faces appeared round the coffee table. Instead of plunging straight into her role of compere she clung to the preliminary chit-chat, nerves on edge. So often had she resented the waste of time spent in skimming the surface and denying the depths, yet now she herself was denying these, putting them off. She had many a good cause to be anxious.

Tonight, for the first time, total outsiders would peer into our privately cherished world of The Seven and rescue work. Her invite moreover was asking them to believe a phenomenal contact largely unaccepted by the culture – not unlike claiming that in her cottage bedroom they must prepare to meet a spaceman from Venus without actually seeing the fellow. Sudden wariness, here in their presence, of just how hard a bargain she expected to drive, then of the forgotten bargain with Peter against exposing our work to strangers – albeit to a harmless enough couple – rather sapped confidence as though her very integrity were at stake.

That Mr and Mrs Morgan might be readier to go halfway with the concept of an unseen discarnate did little to assuage her fears. For was John equal to the task, able to give a fluent talk, bear the brunt of possible scepticism? Alongside the others he had only answered questions before, and sympathetic ones at that. To her knowledge he was a junior rescue worker, no more a speaker or teacher than they – of whom perhaps he was the least mature. With neither the stature of Philip, the temperance of David, or the intellect of Brian, could he put their case convincingly? Come to think of it, why *should* the Morgans, on spec like this, accept his separate identity anyway, when they had no basis, no soil of study, evidence and experience in which those roots of belief grow in the dark all unknowing?

But as she got herself started at least to provide them with an explanation of The Seven's background, her major headache was Peter. He had not yet arrived back. It was long past the time he had agreed to join them. The awful possibility of a motor accident she tucked away into a corner of her mind. He was a good strong driver, careful and adroit. No, the trait in him to which she had grown accustomed was that he would not phone with the cause of delay – simply be late.

Meanwhile she put together for them her gleanings of how in 1933 Peter had been an Army doctor whom with three colleagues had frequented a bookshop in Charing Cross Road; how one fateful night their Morris car had crashed, pitching all four into the next world where they passed through near-earth planes fraught with thousands needy of release and healing. She could now mix in those scoops from Orlando.

On earth the four had been much moved by a book, Thirty Years Among the Dead, detailing the removal of earthbound cases from the patients of Dr. Wickland via his medium. But later, our four's first-hand experience with the earthbound had shown that the real problem was not of privately obsessed patients here. It was of collective purblindness *there*, carried over with false ideas from earth and rebounding here as a broad negative influence on psychological behaviour. Dr Wickland acknowledged such a rebound effect in principle. These former readers of his, once they were discarnate, confronted the fuller actuality.

They realised that any countermeasure of theirs could only make a hole in the problem, but passion to do their utmost willed them as one to try. Their subsequent compact and plan, formed under the aegis of a senior group soul council, had involved from among them a nurse who took rebirth early. Peter however elected to come back as their primary means.

Valerie ended her narrative, feeling it was all the Morgans need know, mostly letting Mary-Ann answer their questions because this review went on unabated within her. She thought how easily a higher level of him had made promises and how easily they were broken by the lower. It had happened before, so prebirth he chose to make up spiritual leeway – solemnly pledging to the group council a wholesome life and body as channel for reaching those cases which normal discarnate help could not, pure enough to let his group speak through it without fear of intrusion, sufficiently attuned to remember the tryst. He laid the foundations of his life in accordance, which for a start had meant linking up with two "earth guides" and via them his group leader Philip. By the time he was in place and due to link, additional colleagues of his had been mobilised into a fit working unit of seven. They waited.

That time came and went, forsaken. His earth ego had become distracted, "as usual", said leader Philip when belatedly Peter did turn up – more by accident than design. "He is behaving true to form. Now the game must stop. We have waited too long," was the comment presently recalled by Valerie, having in turn waited too long, her hope alert for sound of him. The time at which tonight's session was due to start had come and gone. She saw Mr Morgan check his watch. Peter would be home shortly, she offered them, stomach tight, and spun out the performance a little by telling them of John's eagerness to speak.

Then with her play for time wearing thin a car door thumped in the courtyard. Wood-panelling jarred open and shut, there came a dash of feet, and in burst Peter's gladsome yet penitent face which always disarmed her. The relief of it won instant forgiving, his apology unheard beneath introductions.

Very soon the whole party had filed aloft, he taking it in his same hurried stride. Valerie reverted to the rest of her pre-session worries: whether John would be impressive enough, whether instead it should be Philip or one of the others – tonight of all nights – though nobody had asked except John. He alone had put himself humbly, boyishly forward to address any from outside who would come. How much would this audience innocently expect of him?

In her sanctuary's close quarters she threaded post-haste among them, feverish with last minute preparations: the tape recorder, the curtains, the room temperature, the ensuring of everyone's comfort, the glass of water to be placed beside Peter, who sat in neutral readiness for oblivion as if wondering why all the fuss. His most pious concern, he chaffed later, was that some discarnate colleague would quickly relieve him from the "embarrassment of sitting in front of these customers like a potted plant". Procedure up there was hocus-pocus to him – but not to John, who was about to blame lack of magnetic clearing passes for his difficulty in the channel.

Way back, I had twice used these to soothe Peter's nerves. Even *he* knew I had left them off by the first rescue session however, not wanting his trance to become dependent on them, and in my absence Valerie had no mind to do them. Their last time of use had been on John's last but one visit. He might have seen me doing them and supposed they had brought channel clarity at that session. Anyway, in my view he was mistaken over the blame.

It is a session's psycho-climate, the combined mental state of medium and sitters, which largely determines success or failure – not mere clearing passes through the medium's aura. Our Sanctuary's psycho-climate was by then much changed from the one he had known. Rescue work had since attracted many earthbound to press in upon every session. The moment Peter sat down they will have flocked around him. In addition to their own anxiety states, Valerie was anxious herself and mentally nearest him. Nervousness effusing from the others, plus doubt or suspicion, will have compounded the negative admixture making John feel decidedly sticky, heavy, pressured and vulnerable. His inexperience would mistake what he knew to be Valerie's omission of those passes for the cause of it. She knowing no better was bound with guilt to presume him right.

What she had actually forgotten was a prime need beforehand to "seek the peace within", so a swelling fear that her speaker might not come tended to keep her on edge. Should she have told Peter the exact purpose of the session, or would John just turn up as arranged via the writing? Responsibility for his doing so, for two guests who looked somewhat out of depth, and her own unaccustomedness to strangers in our Sanctuary, dogged the minutes until Peter's release. She envied him that, as she did everyone else for just being onlookers.

Her resort was prayer. Then, while face down, she saw her daughter's hand move upon hers, thinking it merely sympathetic. Yet its press bore witness to familiar traits showing up in the channel. Even after his longish absence John stood out quite evocatively, chin jutting foremost, shoulders poised in that youthful willingness to serve. Only his customary hint of good humour seemed to have failed him tonight. Instead she discerned an awkwardness, and wondered why.

"Good evening John! Are you having trouble?"

"Yes."

"Oh dear. What's wrong?"

"You haven't cleared have you?"

"Gosh no, I forgot. Shall I do it now?"

"No it's too late."

"Is it? He's otherwise alright this week."

John evidently decided to outface the odds.

"Well how are you Valerie? It's nice to see you again."

"And you too John. Shall I introduce who's here? I expect you know."

"Yes Orlando told me. I'm very glad to see them."

"Oh good. Now these are friends who've come because you said you'd like to talk to some people from outside our normal circle."

"Yes I would very much."

"So we gathered this small band together of Mr and Mrs Morgan, their son Rob, and Winifred. Mary-Ann you already know. We thought perhaps that after you've given your talk they could ask questions."

"Yes I'm sure they'll want to," said John, and to the trio: "It must be very difficult for you to believe what's actually happening."

A constrained silence had Valerie step in.

"I think you did find it quite difficult didn't you?"

"We did rather," admitted Mr Morgan shyly, and got John's warrant:

"I can assure you that it's true."

Again Valerie tried to bridge the gap.

"They've had a briefing on the whole position, but I thought maybe you'd like to start with a summary of your actual work before going on."

"Alright," said he, "I can tell you something of what we do here. I work with five others, all men as it happens, and we run our rescue hospital. You must excuse me if I sound a bit stilted, but there's a slight problem this evening."

His mention turned her to the Morgans:

"Yes I didn't clear the aura, which would have made it easier for him – that's why."

"You see," he continued, bravely starting out on his modest talk, "a lot of people when they pass over to us have no knowledge at all of an afterlife, and some of these people find themselves trapped in a state that they've been unconsciously creating throughout their time on earth. Our job is to rescue them from that self created state and bring them to our hospital. Sometimes they need a lot of healing and general help, other times very little. The object of the whole exercise is to help them readjust to our world first, so that they can eventually reunite with their soul. Now if you know anything about the soul you'll realise that when people leave here for a new life on earth they leave a greater portion of themselves behind. This is the soul, the portion they'll sooner or later unite with again when they come back here. It's the real individuality, and decides the next course of action.

"Anyway," he said, getting into his stride, "that's rather a complicated procedure and something maybe we could talk about later on. What I do want to try and tell you, those of you for whom this is the first chance to speak with us, is that we are very much alive and well and living, and that you will be too. Our lives go on in a similar way to earth except for the fact that it's much more basically a thought-world. I don't mean its imaginary, in your sense, because it's as solid and real to us as your earth is to you. Actually in a funny sort of way it seems more real to me than earth did. But I mean that strong thought can create or change an object under your very eyes. It's a bit weird at first, although you get used to it, and whole areas are created in this way. For instance we can create, with our thought, things that we need to use, or which make our work easier for us. The buildings, and the landscape they're in, are created by special people in our society whose job it is to do such work, and in fact our own hospital has been created by that group. So none of our buildings are built in the way that you build on earth. It's an important difference, and might sound very improbable to you, but it's the way it happens. Even if the group whose job it is to build wish to use the methods they've used previously on your earth, then these methods are readily available to them through their own creation.

"The special reason I'm explaining this, is that people who pass over here with no knowledge at all don't realise how their strong thoughts, in one way or another, have been creating their world here throughout earth life. You see, in a way, it's as if you're really here all the time but standing with your back to us and looking out through your physical bodies. You don't realise that your thoughts, which are really here, are going out in our direction as well as the physical one.

So when that body dies or is killed, a lot of people stay in their thought-replica which they've been solidly creating for years. It seems so very real because they have created it themselves.

"Quite often they haven't had strong enough thoughts to create their own replica, so they fall back into a mass creation of other people's. Anyway it can get very frightening when things start changing under their eyes, and a strong fear-thought only changes something again into whatever they most fear – at the same time making it even more real. They create myths and devils and whatnot. But then there are whole communities, whole worlds of people who mass together without this happening because they haven't had any stronger idea than to stay in a very humdrum existence which makes no demands on them and feels safe. So they continue with the same surroundings and way of life that they had on earth, and most of them don't seem to know or care what's happened.

"I've only mentioned three types out of the many we come across, but all of them are actually nearer your earth than they are to us. This is why we need an earth group, like the one that meets us regularly, to get through to them. Being closer to them, this earth group look and sound more acceptable than we do when we go down there. Going down doesn't mean descending into some imagined fiery hell, but just going to their level which is lower than the one I live on. There are many levels or worlds here, right to the top level of our sphere where the Divine ones are. My friend Philip says that many incarnations are needed to achieve their state of Oneness, and that all souls work towards this by stretching parts of themselves out as personalities into earth experience. Anyway our work is primarily concerned with helping the personalities who get lost or stuck to make a proper sort of link with their soul again so that they can find some direction in life. So we must go down and try to reassure them, and help them to believe that they've actually come over to us. As you'll hear later it's a very difficult task, made more difficult by the fact that not only do they have no idea of an afterlife, but their attitudes are often wracked by conscience or an emotion that has…

had the strongest... bearing on them ... while they were... living... on ... earth."

John was running out of his personal energy, rather as we might run out of oxygen underwater. Indeed at such moments one was reminded that our environment must seem similarly sluggish. The mustered supply brought with him might normally have sufficed, though as we have seen he was in adverse conditions from the start. Now it sounded like the pressure of earthbound bidders sapped his energy by the minute.

Having to face the fact was a sad blow for him no doubt, since he had awaited the opportunity so long and knew that nothing could be done to retrieve it. As soon as his sentence faded into its untimely end, Valerie did her compere bit.

"Thank you very much John. That's explained a lot I'm sure. Somebody's trying to get in are they?"

"Yes... " was all he could manage.

"Okay, we'll wait in case you're able to add any more. You've got lots still to say, I know." She switched to the Morgans: "This is because there are others in the room who are pressing in upon him, the very people he's been talking about in fact, who are drawn to the channel almost without realising it you see. They don't mean any harm. They only want to talk because they don't know what's happened to them and feel very bewildered, as he said. So he's having to resist them in the hope that they'll eventually go away. There always are people in here nowadays because this is where we do the rescues, and it's creating a slight problem tonight."

Mr Morgan attempted a casual-sounding enquiry:

"Do they sometimes overpower John, or... ?"

"Not John himself yet," she said, "because he's managed to control it so far. Most of the four who speak to us have had trouble, although they usually weather the situation. It means we have to wait a while till things clear, that's all. But if you'd like to ask a question it does help John to remain in contact. Our voices give them a sort of temporary boost."

"Yes I've been wondering what happens when you reincarnate," the man responded. "How do you choose when to come back?"

"Er... John can probably explain that. It's quite a complicated thing." She saw the afterlife theme going adrift, as John may have done while straining feebly from his beleaguerment:

"If I... could put it in a simplified form for you, it is a choice for growth. To progress in our world, reincarnation is necessary... and after uniting with your soul to find your direction... you receive advice on the earth time, place... and circumstances... which will give you the most... oppor... tunities for... gro... "

At his lapsing again, Valerie took the channel's hands in hers. "I don't know if that helps, John, does it?"

No reply. She enlisted audience appreciation.

"They're still pushing on him you see. It's hard to imagine what he must be going through. I'm told it's like being suffocated. I'm terribly sorry John, but maybe if we go on talking... ?"

"Yes."

"Right. So if we discuss whatever you all want to know for a few minutes the situation might get better."

Mr Morgan's low voice returned.

"John was working on earth with these people was he?"

"No I don't think so," she replied. "He only joined them when he passed over."

"Has he met people he knew on earth?"

"Oh I expect he's met several. But because masks are off, so to speak, you tend to see people as they really are, and find your true affinities very often among those you never knew here. Or they may be friends you've known from lives before – not necessarily this last one. You do remain in what's called the group soul though, because that's your true native family. Sometimes part of that group is on earth and part on the inner planes, but your life comes from it always and you move on with it." She reverted to the difficulty: "How are things now John, any better?"

"No."

"Is there anything we can do?"

"It's too late I'm afraid. Ohh… you must make… sure it's… clear Valerie!"

"Yes it's absolutely my fault. I was thinking the numbers and the quietness would be enough, forgetting of course that I should have cleared the aura. If you really feel it's too much for you, we can arrange it again."

"I'm going to… ask David," he spluttered, "to take over… till our friend… gets back. Alright?"

She agreed guiltily, and John began to edge himself out with a caution that would safeguard the channel for immediate transfer. It drooped a little nonetheless.

"Oh that means he's out," she said. "Conditions must be bad actually, because John's the strongest of them in an earthly sense, being nearer us than the others. You'll find that David doesn't raise the head so much. I don't think he likes coming in at all really, but he knows how vital it is for the rescues and for us to understand various things. This is him now."

His lighter impress was felt by her taking control. He could well have been nearby, though outnumbered in any attempt to steer the worst away from John. What he did have was more oxygen, as it were, to survive in our channel till its owner was retrieved. Drawn upon impromptu however the supply would be limited, his use of it economical.

"Are you fully in yet David?"

"Yes Valerie."

"Oh I'm sorry about the conditions tonight. I forgot to clear the aura. Are they very bad?"

"Yes, but… " He saved his breath.

"John was just giving us a talk, and then he found it too difficult."

"I know. Can I help you?"

"Well yes. Mr Morgan was asking about reincarnation and how it's arranged. Perhaps you could continue?"

"I will try," he said patiently. "Each one of us has a guide which is our higher self. If we think of this guide as a multi-faceted gem, then the principle is easier to comprehend. We arrange to reincarnate into a particular earth experience which can polish one facet of the gem."

His soft modulation, weakened further by discomfort in the channel she guessed, had been barely audible and worth a sound- check:

"He tends to be rather faint I'm afraid. You have to listen carefully. Did you understand?"

"Not quite," Mr Morgan had to say. "Each of us… ?"

"Well many sides of the soul have to be perfected, so each incarnation is trying to perfect another side."

"But… each of us has a guide?"

David supplemented:

"The guide is a higher part of you which stays with us. When your effort and experience have taught you to receive guidance only from that higher self then you will find the Oneness and be able to live eternally here."

"Is that a bit clearer?" she asked Mr Morgan.

"No I still didn't quite get it."

"Well never mind, I'll explain afterwards. David, could I just ask you what effect sleeping pills have on one's sleep-life?"

"It depends upon the person Valerie."

"Yes, but on Peter for instance. What about him?"

"It's very bad, because he is forced to leave the body unnaturally."

"Although he says that you force him to leave it in trance anyway."

"I am surprised to hear this. He knows very well that we would never do so, and cannot. When we come, he gives way to us willingly. Otherwise we could not do what we do, and I would not be speaking to you now."

"I see. So perhaps he's using this as an excuse for taking them. But I'm not sure what we can do about his sleep, because it's not good."

"We know. It is a direct result of his head injury, which will heal."

"Would it help things along then, if I gave him healing before he goes to bed?"

"It might. Brian will support you whenever you wish. Is this conversation helping the people here?"

"Oh sorry." She turned to them. "Now if there's anything you want to ask David, please do."

At that, Winifred spoke out from behind.

"I was wondering if a group united in prayer could help in the work that you do."

"Yes very much," said David. "Prayer can help a great deal altogether, not only those you call departed but us as well in our efforts to reach them. Please do remember all such people in your prayers, and you can help them to depart."

Her home circle in view, she was aware of the rub.

"Yet it is difficult to maintain a quality in prayer, because our egos are so different, hard to unite in a group. Having in a sense to lose the ego in united aim is not easy, and this must affect the quality of the prayer put out. Could you say anything about this quality required?"

"The various degrees of quality depend on for whom, and for what one is praying, as the degree of sincerity will vary. This is why meditation is important beforehand to detach from the little ego so that your group find their natural unity within. Then a deeper quality of prayer should result."

From a voice that by now had wilted considerably, Mr Morgan "didn't catch what was important", but Valerie again promised to explain afterwards and let his son put a question:

"Could you give us some idea of the distinction between prayer and meditation?"

"Yes… " granted a weary David. "Prayer is having a direct result on those to whom it is directed, while meditation is having a result on yourself. Meditation helps you find your true self, and prayer helps others to find theirs."

In sight of the poor fellow almost dropping, Valerie yielded to close the session. "David, I think this is too much for you having had to take over so unexpectedly isn't it?"

"Yes. John… has brought the Channel."

"Well thank you very much for your efforts in his place meanwhile.

Perhaps we can arrange another night when the conditions are better. So we'll say goodbye for the time being, and thanks again David."

"God bless you," he whispered.

When he had gone her care shifted earthward.

"Peter should come back in soon. Try not to be staring at him. Just relax. Are you with us Pete?"

Our man made a safe landfall, but was puzzled to find a different Valerie than he had left. Her anxious mood had sunk into a downcast one, which she could hide only from her guests. Its cause was as unknown to him as why they seemed in sympathy with her.

Beside her guilt over "not doing the aura" and thus spoiling John's talk, there was an extra cause of which he was also unaware. She had since seen that her promise to him yesterday as bait for his cooperation, namely an indulging of his curiosity about the Morgan's life, would have to be allowed now because of his late arrival at the start. It was going to scotch her aim of practical on-subject explanation and discussion. Experience of Peter knew no way of her sharing the floor even if he took part. His garrulous personality, given an inch, couldn't help but overflow into a mile or two of red herrings.

So once everyone was resettled downstairs she let him have free range, mindful that he had fulfilled his side of the bargain in good faith. Watching them fast become his monopoly made her realise how little feedback they had given John's talk, as though attention had been clouded by the phenomenon of dialogue with a discarnate. But she consoled herself that they could always hear him again on tape, that at least she had given them a chance to avoid the main hazard in passing over, and that she had enabled him to impart a fair dose of his theme – in which he was more proficient than she expected. On the other hand thinking back through our latest sessions, she did reflect that once an irregular kink developed their ongoing course generally remained somewhat erratic.

CHAPTER SEVEN

A PRESAGE OF INDIA

The evening rush-hour train from London's Victoria rattled its way southward through commuterland, a dusky procession of carriage windows. At one of them sat Robert Riddell.

He was peeking round his newspaper, eaten up with curiosity over a young woman seated opposite. Her obvious merits had not escaped him. Neatly curved, of medium stature, about twenty-five he guessed, she had a high forehead and sleek chocolate brown hair centre parted to fall breast length either side of her face. This was ovoid, trim and elfinly individual under creamlike skin. Her long eyelashes were genuine, lowered toward a hardcover book she was reading: The Inward Revolution, by Bhagwan Shree Rajneesh.

He had seen her on the train before, but with her gaze fixed outside and not into a serious book – let alone one whose title hugely intrigued him. Nor had he imagined in her the peculiar devoutness of concentration which, since they left London, had enwrapped her near rigid figure. He was also keyed to the fact that she would get off at Morden. It was the next stop. There was no time to lose. He put down his newspaper, leaned across, and politely expressed his interest in the book.

Without her otherwise moving, up came those eyelashes. Clear, curvate eyes regarded him" in that feline manner", he told, "which looks as if they know something you don't." She handed him the book, saying little. In a moment he was among its pages, found to contain not writing as such but the recorded interviews of a newly-arisen savant in Bombay. The interviewer was direct:

"Bhagwan, what do you teach and what is your doctrine?" rose first from that conventional stratum of philosophies and religious doctrines. The answer sounded appetising to a seeker who had grown beyond these.

"I am not teaching a doctrine. Teaching a doctrine is rather meaningless. I am not a philosopher. My mind is anti-philosophic. Philosophy has led nowhere and cannot lead anywhere. The mind which thinks, the mind which questions, cannot know. There are so many doctrines, and there are infinite possibilities for many more. It is not a discovery but an invention. The human mind is capable of creating so many systems and doctrines. But to know the Truth through theories is impossible. A mind stuffed with knowledge is bound to remain ignorant.

"Revelation comes the moment knowledge ceases. The known must cease for the unknown to be. And the true, the real, is unknown. There are two possibilities: either we think about it or we go into it existentially. Thinking is something roundabout, never the real thing. One can go on thinking for ages. The more a person thinks, the farther he goes from that which is here and now. And to think about it is to lose contact with it. So what do I teach? I teach an anti-doctrinaire, anti-philosophical, anti-speculative experience: how to *be*, JUST TO BE! How to *be* in the moment that is here and now – open, vulnerable, one with it .That is what I call meditation."

Fascinated, Robert was far from being in the here and now. This fluid advance on his own view, where borrowed knowledge – the sort vital to rescuees for instance – was a poor shadow of ultimate self-knowledge, lost sight of time and his fellow traveller, who touched him on the arm. They were coming into Morden. He returned her book, quick to enclose his card in it, and was surprised at her assent to visit him over the weekend.

With a dash she was gone, except that from his window seat he glimpsed her along the platform. She appeared to him a sylphid creature, hair blowing slightly in the wind and a look now of belonging to the weather; a creature elemental and remote, inaccessible save through the book. At least he could taste her name, Christina Woolf, plus the spice that she had met Rajneesh a year earlier, her full personal link of discipleship still unmade – though she left our friend unaware of how personal was her link already.

★ ★ ★ ★ ★

The next thing we knew, two saffron robed disciples from their North London Rajneesh Centre had descended upon Ashdene.Evidently they were sprung by Robert, who wanted to share his find with us. Their arrival was no big deal however, or thought glaringly incongruous. A private home it was, and remained, yet as our meeting ground it had also become an impromptu look-in for devotees of the spiritual growth movement burgeoning at that period. Approaches to self-realisation were rife.

Any activist might appear from the rich diversity of guidance which arose about us worldwide. We had learned to avoid its somewhat fanatical and tacky fringes, sadly aware of their being the only aspect known to people at large. Our open door was discriminative while of course welcoming the news of scientific pioneers, the flourishing upsurge of channels, centres and organisations that claimed to herald a golden age of planetary awakening. Their cross-harmonisation of fresh insight looked enormous. Besides, each of us had always brought our divers coloured pebbles from the metaphysical beach and laid them in a pool which was Valerie's.

A well-seasoned listener therefore, she was inured to the guru syndrome. None of its cults had so far impressed her – or the rest of us, including Robert. Since he was neighbour friend of her son Nigel at Jevington, hearsay soon reached her about the train-carriage episode with a budding disciple. She guessed that some form of ashram delegation would "be down to court us in two shakes of their wagging tails", had said as much to me over the phone, and here they were making themselves comfortable on her settee.

But she found them a picturesque young couple. Just off the plane from India, their bronzed, handsome faces, blonde hair and bright saffron robes with mala necklace sporting Bhagwan's photo had exotic impact. They called him "Acharya", saying it meant teacher, and deemed him to have the calibre of a World Teacher equal to Buddha, Mahavir, Jesus and Mohammed.

Such vainglorious claims were expected of course. On the other hand these disciples were unlike any she had known. To her mature mind they began showing an integrity and discernment which befitted their stand as qualified psychologist and psychotherapist. Their conviction about Rajneesh was based partly on work, where he had "the most practical answers yet". They didn't seem the gullible type. Neither was he, by their account, an ordinary guru.

His non-suppressive line – don't be ascetic, don't deny yourself, give free rein to emotions, sexuality, and the physical release of inhibitions, do everything with full conscious awareness – had raised eyebrows in India as well as in the more libertarian West, whose avant-garde therapy techniques he blended with Eastern Tantrism. His radical understanding of the human psyche, they said, had drawn the attention of successful practitioners throughout the world. Certainly he had enthralled the present couple, along with several older colleagues. Much travelled on the guru trail, their search was over. They had been staggered by the charisma, the power, the authority and presence of the man. He seemed to offer everything they sought. It all made Valerie wonder, softening her resistance.

Mary-Ann rolled in from college, followed by our would-be Buddhist Rob Morgan who had given her a lift home. At length he grew curious to hear their meditation method as compared to his own. The disciples told him that although in the past a succession of spiritual masters had devised precise techniques for inner growth, these are no longer effective because humanity has changed. So their Master had devised a hybrid revolutionary technique specifically to help the modern mind. His Dynamic Meditation consisted of four ten-minute stages, for which one should wear as little or as loose clothing as possible – standing upright and blindfolded!

The first stage was of fast "chaotic" breathing with use of the whole body, a vigorous pump-out of nasal breath to break tension spots and emotional blocks from their repressive hold. The second stage allowed release of that emotional energy, often sudden and violent, for one was encouraged to express freely anything felt, and throw off pent-up tensions through crying, screaming, laughing, or whatever came. At the third stage a Sufi mantra, "Hoo!"was shouted forcefully down into the body, hammering on the sex centre to stimulate the kundalini and charge the higher centres also. The majority of our blocks, they affirmed, are sexual ones, crippling us emotionally and spiritually. The fourth and final stage was, "of dropping exhausted, emptied, non-doing, into a psychological void free enough for the natural experience of meditation to flow from within as divine grace."

Rob could try the technique in London if he wished, then go on to a meditation camp at Mt.Abu, India, where the intensity was stepped up to three of these sessions per day with lectures morning and evening. Further commitment meant initiation by Rajneesh – the surrender to him as a disciple and wearing saffron robe with mala. There were no rigorous rules, no dogmas, no negation of life, and above all no suppression of natural instinct. Rather, one was encouraged in deeper self-understanding, self-witnessing, and a joyful accepting oneness with the whole of existence.

Some degree of absorption had set into Rob, Valerie, and even Mary-Ann. The disciples chatted lengthily with them, answering numerous questions until teatime when they departed for London. Behind was left a taped lecture by their Master to which the three listened without delay.

Had Valerie the pick of verbal know-how to describe its effect on her, she would have doubtless chosen that of journalist Bernard Levin writing in The Times after two visits to Rajneesh: "... An effect which seems to bathe the hearer in a refulgent glow of wisdom. His voice is low, smooth, and exceptionally beautiful." What's more, the tape extract they put into play that afternoon enlarged her grasp of the earthbound state as he pointed out a pattern of behaviour to disciples at his feet.

"You will look at me in so many ways, because you will come to me with your dreaming mind which will project. To someone I may look like a friend, and to someone else I may look like an enemy. He will project himself. We create a world around ourselves and everyone lives in his own world. The whole conflict of human society, of human relationship, is between worlds not between persons. And there exists so many worlds, as every individual is a world. And he lives within his world and is closed. This is a sleep. You have around you a filmy enclosure of projections – your ideas, notions, conceptions and interpretations. You are a projector going on and on projecting things which are nowhere, only inside you, and the whole planet becomes a screen. You can never be aware by yourself that you are in a deep sleep. By initiation it is meant that you have surrendered to someone who is awakened."

Although she was dubious about never becoming aware by oneself, and about the idea of passive surrender to anybody, she felt sure of his basic percipience. He had given structure to an outline lately forming in her mind of how afterlife experience begins here. No wonder Frances Banks' discarnate review had noted that "earth existence is a state of living in a thought-world, much restricted and enclosed by the glamorous web of matter." No wonder our John had told of the earthbound cases being "trapped in their sort of thought-replica which they've been unconsciously creating throughout their time on earth". Brian too had spoken of our world being mind-created. Might such percipience by Rajneesh be the mark of one truly "awakened"?

If it had been his sole credential then belief could have paused there, but he was well in her favour already. Aware of a tendency to bottle up guilt she warmed to his theme of "energising negative garbage in us outwards", as those disciples put it. More significantly though, esoteric reading had given her to understand that over the transition period from one Great Age to another, an Avatar or high Adept takes birth to inspire the fresh evolutionary cycle; that such a transition is in progress now toward a cycle wherein eventually the human race will respond to vibrations of another dimension; that the changing Age will demand new methods of development, and that an Avatar is presently working with advanced pupils on a new spiritual technique.

She could hardly therefore resist slotting her picture of Rajneesh into the frame. For all she knew he could indeed be the Avatar himself – known to Buddhists as The Lord Maitreya, to Christians as the Christ, and to Muslims as the Iman Madhi. Why should the calibre of these figures, deified through time and state system, be unrepeatable?

Were Jesus known to have suddenly reappeared in Asia, then presumably Christians would flock to see him – and Valerie in her context felt the same way. Yet up came inevitable problems making a no-go situation. Her ill-health she knew was quite unable to cope with Rajneesh-type, very physical meditation. Travel made her more anxious the further she went from home. Nor could her weak stomach handle Indian food. Moreover, if in spite of frailty she did visit him for a few weeks, what of Peter, The Seven, and our work with them? The odds against her going in the first place at least solved that one.

Then she realised her larger problem, for rescue team-mate Robert lay behind the disciples' approach. He had a most infectious zeal when the fever of pioneering took hold, liable to infect J.M. and myself who were every bit as free and footloose as he. If Robert was smitten he might stir up uncertainty on Friday, even division among us, whereas our need to be unified – especially at the onset of more difficult cases – was vital not only to help them but as psychic protection. What degree we had managed, and our staple alliance with The Seven, must not be endangered no matter how drawn she felt to prospects of a World Teacher.

The issue may smoulder awhile, but she saw that its Robertian threat, which would have to be confronted sooner or later, justified calling upon Philip or whoever was available. So why not grab the initiative now? Here sat Rob Morgan wanting advice, Mary-Ann was likely to be supportive, and Peter was heard returning from his market-gardeners. He was usually happiest to yield then, plants secured. They could form a meditative, prayerful, tight-knit group for our channel to be used in safety, allowing a clear communiqué of The Seven's position before things went any further.

Her auspicious hour found Rob and Mary-Ann agreeing at once. Rob's interest was not in a guru-figure but in a path or system. He had found the Buddhist system of meditation formidable, so had concentrated on thought-control which was no picnic either. The Rajneesh tack of wild purgation therefore had enough appeal to warrant a complete change of path. Mary-Ann was too embroiled in A Levels and a drama course to consider disciplehood, though interested in how The Seven would react if she did. She also alerted her mother that two separate questions were pending.

Back crept the worry which had accrued overnight with Peter suffering his latest in a glut of headaches. Prompt hands-on treatment by Valerie had soothed the symptom but not its cause, nor their ongoing dispute about the nature of that cause and the source of her healing. A headachy malaise he felt after the last rescue session, rather concerning us at the time, had kindled seeds of resentment in him against his colleagues whom he held indirectly responsible. This of course cemented his denial that one of them worked through her in the hands-on treatment as she was wont to believe.

The cause of his headaches was debated by us two "earth guides" but not pinned down. So our morning phone confab had reckoned on a word to Philip or David, maybe sent via directed writing, but sooner if possible than his next dose of rescue cases. That resolve now met Peter when he came in, and played around his cup of tea.

She told him it was an ideal moment for bringing his complaint to The Seven's notice, since Rob "desperately" needed to consult them alongside and would "terribly" appreciate an equal chance while here. One of her voice-to-music tapes was ready to ease away business strain, followed by their favourite TV meal "within an hour or so".

He liked Rob, was in amenable mood, and offered no demur except to remind her of his TV programme. These provisos of his would every so often strike her with the curious paradox of a man essentially felt to be one of us yet was effectively a stranger blown in from the world at large. Nonetheless she led the pace upstairs with an alacrity that clean forgot their minor item of dispute until Chloe the dog tried to join them. It was on the subject of animals, whom Peter was sure could not survive death. Thinking on her feet she decided to present this item first as an entrée, and let discarnate experience have its say.

Peter had given up attempts at meditation. While Rob and Mary-Ann composed themselves she watched him joke mildly with them, tolerate the opening prayer, then recede into himself rather than be a gooseberry to what they were going to do and he was not. When the tape had meandered its tranquil way through ten minutes, dissociation for him was like falling off a log – and off he went.

She had made a point this time of "doing the aura", as she called it, because my protest that such passes should be unnecessary had sounded like mere whitewash.

Her need anyway was to reverse the neglect of the last session and cover herself in face of whoever might oblige tonight. But it was due of course to hearts lifted with her that shortly the feel of David's easeful lodgement, then his trouble-free greeting, brought satisfaction.

"Good evening. It's much better Valerie, very clear. Three of us have come. Are you unhappy about something?"

"Oh yes David. We have a slight situation here which might affect our rescue team as it already has Rob. He wants to ask your advice, and I thought if we knew how you stand on the whole thing it might help. There are also questions to do with Peter's health and the healing which I promised I'd get sorted, but would you mind just settling a simple matter for us before we go into these others?"

"Not at all, if I can."

"You see, Peter will insist that animals can't have a soul and survive death, and he won't believe me when I tell him they do. Little things like this sometimes cause frictions, so I've decided to ask you."

"But there is no question of it Valerie. They could not exist unless the basis of their life was here. All life taking outer form on your earth sheds that form and withdraws to its natural source, its natural state of being in our worlds. To withdraw here after extending part of itself onto your plane is as natural for all life as breathing. Have I not said this to you before, about yourself?"

"Yes you have, in your answer to how I can withdraw properly in sleep. The same process I suppose."

"It differs only in degree. Animal life moves back here in sleep too, the same process in a smaller cycle. They live within their inner form as you do, and their consciousness withdraws from the outer one more frequently."

"In death as well you mean?"

"In the larger cycle, yes. They understand more than you do that their earth body is an outer image. When the image is taken by another creature for food, or when they cannot adapt it to conditions prevailing on earth, they simply shed it. Like us they have to learn by experience, and this evolves their consciousness. They will soon grow another image and try again there, moving constantly in and out of your world."

"We see them as red in tooth and claw don't we?"

"That is only how they appear to you, not the truth of how they are. Their mutual understanding and their motivation is altogether different. Their soul is not at the human level but it is a soul nevertheless which respects and cooperates with its fellow creatures in a way humans overlook. The savagery seen by humans is an appearance created by your attitude and view of form."

"Well that should give him an answer David. What about pet animals though, like dogs and cats?"

"Do you mean those which people have with them here?"

"Yes, from the whole animal kingdom really."

"The animals that people have with them here are not necessarily ones that they had on your plane, but if they wish to be with a pet which they once loved on earth it is possible. Those close to humans often remain with them on passing over, then eventually revert to their own pattern. Not all animals use the earth for their experience, and nor do all humans, but animals who return from your world have their own pattern of things in the same way as we have – for are we not all God's creatures? The evolution of the animal kingdom is such that although the standards set by various animals are not so high as those at our level, there are certain places inhabited almost solely by animals. May I just deviate for a moment?"

"Do, please."

"I wonder if you would tell the Channel that his grandmother is very pleased that he is working with us. She will be able to communicate soon, so if he would like to ask her any questions please have him write them down, and then perhaps you will talk to her for him?"

"Yes he's asked about his grandmother actually."

"This is why I have contacted her. It may help him to believe in us more. She is at the moment regaining her youth, as you know people do, and has been for quite a long time in another hospital here recovering from the serious illness which caused her to come over. She will soon be able to make herself useful, and has lately expressed a strong desire to work with flowers as he does."

"Oh he'll be terribly pleased to know that, because he said how much he'd like to hear of her, and how she's getting on. Now it's my turn to digress David, onto the main situation I spoke of. We've had here all day two young disciples just back from India where they've been learning a meditation technique from one of the Indian gurus called Acharya Rajneesh, and we've been discussing this way of achieving the stillness of meditation. It's a technique which will very quickly get over the slow preliminaries of trying to still the mind. How do you feel about it?"

Since she didn't describe the unusual technique itself, or ascertain whether David knew of it, his being asked how he felt about the general technique of meditation – which is how it came out – may have puzzled him.

"… The same as you do. It is ideal to find the Oneness, in fact the only way." Then perhaps thinking that her real "situation" must hinge on the guru instead he added: "Have you not talked to *him* about this man?"

She recognised the accent on 'him' to mean Philip.

"No we haven't. So you feel that if there was an opportunity of being taught this method, it would be worth Rob going to India?"

"In other words," qualified Rob, "go to one of his meditation camps where one can experiment?"

A clearer gist brought David's answer.

"If you feel it is necessary, you must. May I just say that we are all free. You must achieve what you want to achieve young man. You are your own master. To find that master within you, meditate from where you are, and if it is meant that you should go to this man it will very soon become obvious. Nobody can make you, your inner self, conform or do things that you don't wish to do. Your destiny is mapped before you, and only you can change it from inside. Find that master key within you and unlock the box which holds your path. Discussions with other people may help, but never forget that your life's path has already been planned by your self with your self. Does this help?"

"Yes," said Rob, "I think it does."

"So throughout your life, if you are troubled or perplexed with problems, the answer is there because you set the problems yourself before you incarnated. Everyone ought to remember that no matter what they do for other people, however much they try sincerely to guide, no matter how much they may lead or follow, order or obey, each one has their life set before them by their own choice. None of us has the right to dictate in these matters. Only he, him within us who started our plans, started our lives and set them on course, is in such a position. If we all tried to remember that most important key it would put our problems into perspective, wouldn't it Valerie?"

"Oh it would David, I agree."

"If you wish to go to India young man, by all means go. But I cannot possibly advise you whether to do so or not. It is within yourself. So many whom I talk to in the hospital say to all of us: 'If only I had done that right away instead of listening to other people's dictates.' And the tragedy is that the people giving these dictates were not in a position to do so. They had no right to set themselves up as a rude mentor, because the life they were presuming to guide had already been planned from within. The children I care for here all realise that. Why is it a lesson which takes so many lives to learn?"

"A mass feeling of unworth I think." she offered. "But surely without soul awareness we can't be certain whether we're doing something that is planned or not. I mean it's quite possible to ignore the planned path unwittingly and go off on one's own isn't it?"

"This is what I have said. People do so all the time, life after life, only too glad to let others do their choosing for them. But if you stand outside a block of flats with all the occupants, and you are the only person who has the key to its locked main door, do you spend your time helping them climb perilously in with ropes and ladders, or do you simply say: 'My friends, here is the key' – ? And the key here is meditation. Once they have found it and unlocked the inner self, then they're in aren't they? It's simple. Why take the long way round? Since your friend has asked whether he should or should not go to this man, of whom I personally know very little, then help him find the key to his inner self. Why spend hours discussing, when it's there? None of us can tell him whether to go or not – otherwise we would be part of him."

"Yes," she mused aloud, "meditation is the central key of course. Until we learn that, we have to at least trust ourselves before others. Now I think of it, Brian told us how we are all born with a higher self impetus which we're free to accept or reject. And last session you were saying that when our effort and experience have taught us to receive guidance only from the higher self, then we'll find the Oneness and live eternally there."

"Yes I did, and Brian is right. But prayer is also useful, because if one is receptive to hear the inner voice, then one may pray to the self. Very few do this, yet it is so easy in the silence of one's true being." He then turned back to Rob. "There are many books on the subject, although you should find it quite simple to do if you have sufficient intent on your goal. You may hear your inner voice and be on your way tomorrow – who knows?"

"How do you yourself use meditation to get answers?" asked Rob.

"I find the best way is to sit as you do now, either with music or absolute quiet, picture the problem simply, then leave it and move oneself inward, upward, and then down into receptivity. If one can go through these few stages deeply, then the answer should come. But it is pointless if, when that answer does come, your rationalising ego then has its way with ideas for and against. This is just closing one's eyes and thinking. Meditation for me is letting that crystal clear drop of knowing fall onto the virgin mind with yes or no. This is the aim, and when you have attained it you will know. This will be the way for you. It is a way you can only find for yourself with the help of your true self that is here with us. Start by moving inward and soon you will find that way, with the truth of your life – instead of being led by the desiring mind, that little ego which snatches all your free will for itself. When the two become One, then you achieve what few people have achieved young man. But all the while you are allowing that ego, with its unruly emotions and desires, to lead you into matters which are not of its own plane but of a much higher plane, you are reversing your nature entirely."

Rob was still at his own prior stage however.

"I've been trying first to concentrate, to prevent intruding thought, before taking up meditation itself."

"Then I would concentrate on something of beauty to clear and raise the whole focus, send the question inward as a prayer, and wait openly. If nothing comes from within, there may be an outward sign instead, or it may be of no real consequence either way to your path. In this case the ego is left to decide. What for instance, does the man in India have to offer you?"

"Self-realisation," Valerie proclaimed on impulse.

"But since this is only obtainable within, does it matter where one is outwardly?"

"No," she accepted, and saw the need to be a little more explicit. "It's just the particular technique he offers to release all the tensions, inhibitions, things created by illusion really."

"Is this man a great master?"

"Yes," she heard herself say off the cuff.

"Then surely he could answer preliminary questions while you are in a state of receptivity here."

"Er... I think so, but perhaps not without having made the physical contact first."

"Yet there are thousands of people who have made contact with one of the greatest masters of all time without the need for earthly meeting beforehand, are there not?"

She began to struggle "Yes but it's being able to... forge the first link, and... build on that contact."

"Is it vital to go to Asia to forge this link?"

"No," ceded Rob, "maybe it isn't."

David evidently decided to round off.

"May I just say something? There have been many great masters, as you both must know. Our own divine one, a truly great young man, has no trouble contacting his pupils when they are ready, and I feel that even on earth, in this diverse age in which you are fortunate enough to be born, the matter should be a simple one. So if all else fails, perhaps before you take this long journey you could at least study and contemplate the work of great ones who have spent some time on earth, so that you may recognise the capability of such beings. Those whom I have witnessed from afar walking here with our blessed one are of such obvious radiance and power that, when you are not in a position to behold this, perhaps you should be wary of giving the label of great master to one who may be merely at a higher stage of evolution than yourselves. Wouldn't you think so Valerie?"

"I do," she agreed. "In fact I'm cautious about it myself, feeling reticent over one or two things he's said. I was just concerned to get a reaction from you in case our team become unsettled as well. Because, apart from anything else, meditation is rather difficult for the beginner, and when we wondered whether going to this man might help Rob, I thought they might follow suit – particularly after hearing a lot today that rang true."

"But your team are not beginners. As I believe I once said to Jules, we know you better than you think. He for one will stay loyal to the work for as long as it is asked of him. You need not be concerned there. Your other friends are capably attuned enough to know their path, and will not unsettle your team simply in order to pursue a technique of meditation. They too are strong and stable, otherwise their inner selves would never have assented to join us in such a work. Where answers about a technique are sought, and do not come from within, I think you should refer to Philip."

"Yes alright David. Thanks for what you've given on that. Now can I ask the question on healing?"

"I will get Brian for you".

During the transfer she was able to reflect. At any rate a clear discarnate angle was to hand, which felt gratifying. Even though David knew "very little" of Rajneesh or his method, and could not supply the yes or no she had set out for, he had lifted her perspective in a most categorical way. There was also the small scoop, en passant, that he looked after their intake of children. It might explain those two child-cases who had been slipped into rescue.

More intriguing however was his reference to "our own divine one, a truly great young man", as if he meant a spiritual master. Was this a figure entirely unknown to us, or one of the two completing their seven whom we had yet to meet? Or could it mean Philip? The consistent high regard in which they seemed to hold him, plus his self-disclosures way back, leant her with a thrill to the last possibility.

She thought Brian might tell her when he had finished that health reply. Soon his businesslike manner was in control, briskly remarking on used confines:

"I always get the rough end of the channel don't I!"

"Yes," she sympathised, "although the conditions are quite good at the moment."

"They are, and I've been with you for some while already. I can't stay long though, because we're going to the replantation areas."

"Whatever are they Brian?"

"I thought you might ask me that!" said he, in upbeat mood. "They're areas where new arrivals here have chosen to create their homes, and are having buildings, squares and landscapes created for them. So in order to create a beautiful environment the best of these people and the best of our creators get together and pool their combined thought into solid effect."

"Does everyone focus on the same agreed image then?"

"No, just the best of the creators, who aren't always the most tasteful but the most controlled and effective for that area. We can go and watch though, and it's fascinating to see whole avenues, woods, parkland and lakes being gradually formed. I'd like to describe it all, but I didn't do too well in my last attempt did I?"

"Quite sufficient for us I think Brian. What I was hoping you would actually describe is the healing you do here from your side. I want to settle a personal argument to begin with."

"Right, let's have a practical demonstration shall we? Each of you put a hand into one of the channel's hands and I'll send the power round your circle. Tell me if it gets too hot."

The three followed his suggestion, linking up either side of him. Within twenty seconds, Rob was first to comment.

"... Incredible strength!"

"Now I'll alter the power round," said Brian, and they waited again.

"There's a terrific buzzing!" Valerie exclaimed. "It's like holding an electric wire."

Her loose comparison was understood by the others. Brian let his demonstration rest, sharing a tip from behind the scene.

"Even with good healers on your side the ego is such that they think it is themselves doing the healing, which cuts off a fair amount of our supply in fact."

"Well point taken," she said as everyone sat back, suitably impressed. "But when I try to give Peter some healing, as I did last night, he told me afterwards he thought it was him and me with our minds together doing it, and not you at all. So I'd love you to say something about it that he can hear on tape."

She met a rather bemused response.

"Does he deliberately goad you, do you think Valerie? Because I've talked with him on several occasions over here, and we don't have the differences of opinion that you seem to think we have. However, as long as he feels better, we are not concerned who gets the credit."

"Oh I agree. It's only these headaches he's having. Last night I was a bit worried about him, and asked you to help of course."

"Yes it's always worked well through you from the start, and we are at present correcting this temporary condition. It should soon disappear because it's not too serious a problem, and there's certainly no need for you to worry about it."

"He thinks the rescue work is causing them actually."

"This is partly true. It is a contributory factor. Also his knee is not as it should be, and neither is his chest. The bottom three ribs have bruised cartilages underneath. As I think you realise though, we have been gradually working on all this from the first. There is a slight amount of discomfort still, extending at times into the head, which I know he doesn't mind."

"He says he minds."

"There again you see, he doesn't say that to us."

"No apparently not," she conceded. "It must be his earthly attitude here, the earthly ego, because he told me he felt really ill after that last rescue session, and that you wouldn't like it if you had to go through it all. So I said I'd ask you."

"Well," tendered Brian, "if he's going to listen to this, then I'll say to him – I'm terribly sorry. But your problem is a temporary one, we are trying to alleviate it for you, and meanwhile the degree of discomfort that you have to suffer is little sacrifice for people who have been suffering far more deeply over a longer period of time. I think you are still doing a very good job, and after all, it is what we agreed. Now John just wants a quick word."

When he had withdrawn, the prospect of confronting John so soon after Sunday's debacle brought up a residue of guilt in her. What did he want to say? Immediately she geared herself to a defensive stance, although the incoming signs of his old restored spirit showed it to be unnecessary.

"Hallo Valerie!"

"Ah, um… hullo John. Sorry about your talk session."

"Not at all. It was my fault really."

"I don't think it was you know, because of my sheer forgetting to do the aura."

"Well, tut on you Valerie!" he teased. "But the word is that we'll both have to be more careful in future."

"As the Morgans were new to it I got wrapped up in trying to prepare them you see."

"Yes, they're all saying here that I talked over their heads, but I can't see how that's possible with someone like me! We've got to find our way by trial and error though Valerie, because if I come through and speak straight out like that I tend to go off the subject, and obviously I wouldn't want to confuse anyone. This is why I just wanted to say now that if they could have a few questions already prepared, we could start from there."

"Alright I'll make sure of that next time. Anyway Rob's parents were very impressed – weren't they Rob? He's here at the moment you see."

"Oh good evening. Well so they should be really!" his humour threw back. "Look, I can't stay because Brian wants us to go to this replantation thing with him."

"You're all being dragged off are you?"

"I'm afraid so! Bye for now and God bless."

They closed with a prayer then awaited Peter's return. He was late, which drew banter that he might have gone off spectating too. But Valerie was preoccupied with the answer to his health problem. She felt it had been given in much more prudent terms than the direct one. Brian could have said to him on tape:

'When at the outset, instead of linking with us as agreed, you chose to have dark designs against your wife, you got yourself run over by a tractor. That caused you such injury that its after-extension into the head has made you unnecessarily susceptible to earthbound users. Had you stuck to your spiritual impetus you would not now be feeling ill and getting headaches. You made yourself a constitution tough enough for the job without discomfort, but you've messed it up. Why blame us or the earthbound?'

That Brian had avoided saying this showed restraint perhaps, and in what he did say was evident compassion for those we were trying to help. Yet didn't it also show compassion toward a Peter less real to him than the Peter he knew? The disparity between these two levels of self had become rather noticeable, the inner one not minding and the outer one griping. She herself felt commiseration for the outer one's sense of being reined in to strange work and unpleasant effects. His gripe could have been stronger. He could stop altogether. Might he be enduring it just to safeguard his niche at Ashdene? Then again, he must recall that her original invitation here was weeks before the mediumship began. Their liaison secured him without it. So underneath all the complaint, was his inner impetus prompting him on through ego discomfort for the sake of "people who have been suffering far more deeply"?

She regretted having forgotten to ask whom David meant by "our own divine one", but that would keep. Brian's reply to Peter was likely to be deferred its hearing too, for the complaint had been rhetorical rather than answer-seeking. Any answer might not be one he cared to hear unless it gave immediate relief. As he often found upon his return, seeming minutes away were in fact over an hour, and he scurried down blearily to his TV programme.

Nevertheless she felt grateful that he had spared the time when, forty-eight hours ahead, his returning would land into the effects of our third rescue session. If only she saw the news of his grandmother or Brian's assurance as a potential salve over him then there need be little concern, yet no such hope availed her. By the same token, whilst David's advice on the Rajneesh issue had dispelled her qualms and put Rob in steadier poise, a suspicion lingered that its influence at Ashdene would not evaporate so easily.

★ ★ ★ ★ ★

With the hand of night closing over the sky I stood alone in our Sanctuary, having prepared it for an evening's rescue, and thought of Renée Newbon – who was to join us. I was uncertain why. Presented upon my arrival with this fait accompli, which I was not inclined to query in front of her, I had slipped upstairs nursing an open verdict. The choice of chair arrangement being mine, another was added for our visitor. Meantime my flashback of Philip saying, early on when her name was put forward, that she was "not quite ready because of her emotional state" had come tempered by the fact of his leaving the choice of team solely to Valerie.

Under review my acquaintance with the young woman was shallow, never knowing her depth, but on face value any emotional unfitness was not in the impact she made on me. One-off experience of a healing from her up here, vividly effective through magnetic passes, had seemed from a vivid person alive with energy. She was American, the unselfconscious type, with keen eyes and golden hair.

I wondered if those lengthy courses she underwent at the local College of Psychotherapeutics might profit us in rescue, though was amused to realise that coaxing an unseen, unaware and unwilling patient would be far outside their curriculum. Still, a surer attribute was the aura of clarity she had about her, which some said was the result of a vegetarian diet promoted by Pilgrims health food restaurant, the popular venue run by she and husband Reg in Tunbridge Wells.

Diet aside, clarity of thinking-on-the-spot during rescue was a boon worthy of its hire. Valerie I knew had wanted her in our team from the start, considering her "a strong soul" who could prove "of tremendous help". Thus it occurred to me that on a mere social call she had been grabbed at once. What with both her good self and our articulate Robert Riddell, now heard ascending the stairs chattily together, I dared hope that my shortcomings may be overridden in a productive session.

J.M. followed, then Valerie supportive of Peter who was limping slightly with a bruised knee. My pre-check on his psychic condition had found that despite his ailments he was unaffected, neither worse nor better for receipt of Brian's message and enjoying the extra company tonight. As he plonked himself into the tiny Sanctuary settee his tone was light, his manner easy. Our change of mood evoked in him a deep sigh, acknowledging that the sooner he was gone – more from instinctive flight than embarrassment – the sooner our time would vanish and he could have his way again.

A brief spell of meditation, aimed at stilling us to receive the truer level of self within, preceded. Then my turn with the spoken prayer chose Brian's theme of attunement each to our own "colour" of helpfulness, and an appeal that those colours may work in harmony. If the latter seems too wishful thinking, I was shortly brought down to size. For when, instead of starting off with our first case, we got David coming through, it was to advise against an attitude of mine toward the average rescuee which I had strayed into unawares.

His apt and gently given counsel suggested I avoid talking to them as though they were children. My mode of speech rather than terms used was the inadvisability that I gulped to admit. A quick double-take also saw how it may have put their backs up, although David had not said as much.

"Now, are you ready to start?" he asked.

I looked along the faces to my right. Robert wore an air of aloof purposefulness. Renée's ivory profile was fully intent. J.M.'s youthful passivity gave his "uh-huh", while Valerie held herself in guarded anticipation like me – except mine was about adjusting to the right mode.

"Yes we are."

"Alright then. It's very clear tonight. Don't forget what I said Jules, and that I'm always near."

"No I won't forget. Okay David."

"I'll come and talk with you later."

That was a welcome novelty. For me the feel of him leaving was a bit of a wrench, torn between his context and those he wanted us to rescue from theirs. He did hover within two feet of the channel, maybe seeing in his produce, but I lost touch as another sensation beset me. It smacked of one who was irritable even before I had opened my mouth. My asking for a name first off, purely to innovate, got the response one might expect here from a stranger in the street.

"Why?"

"Well… because we have been asked to help you," I excused myself, "and a way in is to know your name."

Will you help me to move?"

"Yes certainly. Perhaps you could tell us more about yourself and where you want to go."

No answer came, only stricken, frustrated breaths which Robert latched onto:

"You sound very uncomfortable. Are you in pain?"

"No I've just got these… things all over me. You must see them!"

"I'm afraid we can't, it's rather poor light, so you'll have to tell us what happened."

Vexation grew under the reply. "I was just lying here in the wood and these things started crawling all over me. I don't like it any more than you would!"

"Is there anyone else with you?" asked Renée.

"No, of course not."

"I think you'll find there is," Robert said. "But how have you come to be there? Did a tree fall on you or – ?"

"No you can see it didn't. I'm just… here."

"Well we're with you now," I threw in absent-mindedly.

"Oh I'm tickled pink! But I'd just like to move if it's not too much trouble."

The sudden sarcasm jolted me out of figuring that our invalid, believed male, had passed unexpectedly during a nap in some woodland glade. His subconscious mind had registered the event, while his conscious mind associated it with an onset of creepy-crawlies over a dead physical body – without knowing he had left. Could he be verbally encouraged up like our former case in the garden, induced to break his grim attachment without the trouble of explaining? Robert this time skipped both options:

"We've got somebody with us who can help you to move if you'll cooperate with him. Will you? His name is David."

"Why him?"

"Because he works at a hospital and he wants to take you there."

"What's he going to do to me? I don't need a doctor. I just want to get up!"

"Er... it's not the sort of hospital you have in mind. It's only a place where you can rest. This is what you need at the moment. So we want you to go with David. Can you see him?"

"No," was the grudging reply.

"Well he can move you," tried Renée, "if you call him."

"But why must I go to a hospital? I don't like them."

Valerie knew the feeling well.

"It isn't really a hospital," she said. "It's just a lovely house for refreshment and quiet where you'll begin to feel happy again, and to forget all that time in the wood. Everyone's very happy there, getting well and fit. You'll love the experience."

"Hmm... maybe. But I've got to get up first."

My impulse was to at least try the former ploy.

"Right, all you need to do is stretch out your hands. Then you can be pulled up. So reach out will you?"

In hope that David was grasping them we vocalised the fellow upward with a token handlift of the channel as suggestion's artful aid.

Eventually I felt him slump forward through us and out. Whether it meant success was hard to say, but such a heave-ho left us satisfied when no more was heard.

The next candidate was upright – as far as we could tell. He sounded apprehensive about entering a house in front of him, which Valerie thought afterward may have been one deliberately set up by helpers. She had read how they often need to use stagecraft in transmuting any religious diehard through their too-literally-taken belief structures, viz: "In my Father's house are many mansions". If so, this man had stumbled upon the house in ignorance with the feel of its being somehow fateful. Our blank cluelessness at first however was voiced by Robert:

"Why should there be only one house to go into? There are so many."

"There's not. It's that big house. You know it is."

"Do you know someone called David?" popped Renée.

"No… Oh yes I do."

"Well he's asked us to tell you that he can help you."

"Who, David Lloyd?"

"No," said I, "this is a friend of ours, David King. He's with us now."

"And he can actually take you into the house," angled Valerie, drawing Renée's prompt support.

"That's why we're speaking to you, to tell you this. Can you see him?"

"Oh. Which one is he?"

"He's standing here looking at you," lent Robert.

We assumed their meeting of faces, but knew nothing until Renée gave an extra prod:

"If you call him, he'll come towards you."

"I can't shout out like that. It's ridiculous. What's he going to do?"

"He'll take you into the house," said Valerie again, "if that's where you want to go."

"I've nowhere else to go."

"Then just call his name quietly and he'll come to show you in."

"What's inside the house?"

"He'll show you. That's why he wants to take you in."

"Have you called him?" checked Robert.

"I'm not sure if I should. Is it a factory in there?"

"No, not a factory," she returned gently. "It's a very beautiful interior, and you'll get a sumptuous meal of your favourite kind, and hear lovely healing music. Just call him and he'll be by your side immediately. He knows that you have to want it yourself. You're the one who has to ask. So just say, David! – then he'll come and hold your hand."

"I don't want him holding my hand!"

"No don't worry, he needn't. But he will come."

Over the hesitation Renée threw a last bid.

"At least ask him to tell you about the house."

We heard the small voice call him feebly. Moments later, with a "Bye… " its owner left. We never knew whither he had gone, because in bracing ourselves for another case the sudden re-emergence of David and his query drove it out of mind.

"It's alright Jules. Has he hurt himself?"

"The Channel? Yes his knee."

"No this is higher," pointing up at the neck. "It feels strange. Jules we're going to… " he broke off. "Just a minute… " Then, after listening to someone aside: "Yes, right. Our next one is very difficult Jules, and you must help him spiritually."

"We'll try," I said, a bit nervous that he seemed to aim the challenge at me. With it hanging ominously in the air Renée verified her ground.

"Is it okay to ask them to call you?"

"Of course," he whispered before pulling away.

There then erupted, step by step, one of our most formidable cases – that of a priest who suffered guilt from repressed sexual feelings toward his former parishioners. Alarmed to find no apparent change hereafter, his beliefs were now dooming him for eternity.

But to us at the outset he sounded just an inferno of anguish –

doubtless sparked afresh by earth contact – and long short of understanding him it took a while to get any response. From the moment of entry his harsh, pitiable self-torture was groaning and sobbing as we put out our feelers:

"Can you tell us who you are?" put Renée.

Not even a pause acknowledged her.

"Or tell us," I asked, "what you're experiencing? What's going through your mind that causes pain?"

His distress continued, so Robert had a go.

"We've come to help you out of your predicament. Will you let us help?"

Now an imploring note burst through the groans:

"Don't speak to me!"

"Yes we must," said Robert. "We're here to explain. If you listen, your problem will shortly be over. It's not as bad as you think."

"Don't… Don't speak! Don't come near me!"

"Look, can we introduce ourselves at least? We're a little group of people who–"

"Don't!… No don't!"

" – who want to help you," Robert trailed off, blown by the sudden vehemence. My attempt swung in.

"Can you talk to us instead then?"

"I don't want to talk to any of you. Oh I feel so… I mustn't contaminate you. Don't come near me, *please!*"

"Will you tell us something of your problem?" tried Renée. "If you don't want us to speak to you, will you speak to us instead? And we'll listen to you."

At last a sliver of confession came stiffly:

"Oh I've given so many. How *could* I?"

"What exactly have you given?" I enquired.

"Absolutions!"

"Were you a priest?" keyed-in Robert, but the fellow was too full of his mortifications.

"I'm damned! *Damned!* I must stay here for eternity!"

"No you're not," I said. "We've come to free you."

"Oh nobody can do this. You don't understand."

"Yes we do," affirmed Robert. "We have helpers with us, waiting for you. But you must – "

"I know! I know my Book. Don't... *please* don't preach to me! I must pay, for I have sinned. I know I've sinned!"

"But you *have* paid," said Renée. "It's why we've come."

"My child, I know I have. This is *it*! I must stay here".

"No you mustn't!" she urged. "There's someone now waiting to help you away."

"Oh you don't know. I've read. I know. It's my penance, I know it is."

"But you haven't read everything. Otherwise you'd know that you don't have to stay there."

"... It's a halfway stage then. Is that it? I've made my purgatory and I –"

"No," Valerie thrust in. "It isn't a halfway stage. It isn't even purgatory."

"Oh don't!" he cried. "Not more?"

"Look," returned Robert decisively, "we must talk to you. Will you listen to us while we explain?" he paused lacking an answer. "Are you still there?"

One low groan told that he was.

"We will explain. You were obviously a man of the cloth weren't you?"

"Oh don't, it's not fair!"

"Well there's no need to worry about it. Do you know what has happened to you?"

"Of course I know!"

"Yes of course you do, but maybe you don't know everything there is to know. Now let us just explain. We are a group of people on earth, not in your dimension at all. You are – "

"I know where I am! I know what I'm doing here. Please leave me to it."

"But do you know who we are? You must listen. It's most important."

"*Please* don't tell me all this! I know where I am. I don't want to hear about the earth."

"The point is, we've been sent to help you. May we know your name? It's so difficult to talk without – "

"No... No... No."

The priest was adamant, and clearly a full Robert-type lowdown was not going to apply. Renée picked up the traces.

"Can we do anything for you that you would like?"

"Uh... How did you get here?"

"No, you came to us," she answered.

"How did I come to you?"

One hoped she wouldn't tell him that he was using a medium, at which he might explode in horror, though fortunately she had more sense.

"You came because deep inside you recognised that we're friendly and want to help you. But we cannot do so unless you tell us a little about what you are going through. We'd like to hear."

"But it's not possible to do anything. I must... "

"You see, we are here now because we know it *is* possible to do something. We would not be here otherwise. There is someone who's been watching over you, whose name is David. He is also a friend of ours, and he wants to tell you about forgiveness."

"But... he can't give me Absolution can he?"

"He may not be able to give you Absolution but he will show you how you can end this misery you're in – by yourself."

"But it's my purgatory!"

"No you've finished your purgatory. There's no need to do it for ever and ever, because you did not live on earth for ever and ever. It's all over, and he is here to help you see that. He's here to show you how it can be from now on, and he's asked us to tell you that."

"... And where will I go now child?" He spoke with a quick, tortured movement. "Must I shed all this?"

"Yes, don't worry about it any more. You will go with David, and he'll show you the way now. Can you see him there?"

"Tell me more child. Where will we go?"

"He'll take you," said Robert, "into higher astral realms."

"What?" he exclaimed suddenly. "What astral realms? We don't have astral realms!"

An incoming Valerie sidestepped his problem over the word "astral" and ventured a thought of her own.

"Actually I think there's one thing we should say, and this is that I feel you would like to pay for some of the things you've done wrong, and David will show you how you can do so. It isn't that you're going to escape anything, but he'll show you how you can absolve yourself and leave it all behind."

"Ohh… no… I can't. Because I *am* paying aren't I? This *is* my purgatory!"

"No it isn't," said Renée.

"But if I must go through more stages of purgatory I –"

"You don't need to do that," she interrupted. "If you would only let David help you, he will show you what you have to do."

"Which is to help others," sprung up Robert. "This is the most important thing to realise, now that your purgatory is over, that you must devote your time to others."

"But who's telling me it's over?" was the query unheard or ignored as Robert went on:

"… and David is just waiting to show you how. He'll take you to a level which is much more real and relevant to you than being in what you think of as your purgatory. You see, at the moment you're being very selfish, enclosed here on your own, ignoring the real work ahead of you which is to help others."

"Ohh!… Selfish?"

"Yes, because you're far too intelligent a man just to stay where you are."

"But my son, I *must* stay here. It's to His Glory."

"No," insisted Renée, "It's a waste of time for you."

"We need your help," I slid in, with Robert hard by:

"Absolutely," said he. "Instead of wasting your time here in nothingness, wallowing in guilt which gets you nowhere, a man of your calibre must come up and work."

"But are we not equal in the eyes of God?"

"Yes of course, but you have innate abilities and you have insight, which are expressions of Him in you so that you can help yourself and your fellow beings."

"My abilities are nothing compared to His."

"But you can develop them in that new life," Robert persisted, "and turn them to good use in His service. David wants to take you on to a place where he's been working a long time doing just this, and where he needs men like you. By helping others, you see, you will help yourself because it requires you to extend your innate capacity to give, which absolves past error. It's vital for you to realise this, otherwise you will not progress. If you stay in your fixed world nothing will come of you at all. You'll just remain there in all that guilt. It's not necessary."

Yet the priest was not convinced.

"You don't understand. May I tell you?"

"Yes, do tell us," I encouraged.

"… I don't know where to begin."

"Well do try to begin," rose Valerie, attentive. "We'd love to hear."

He did so, in a voice somewhat stricken and painful.

"… My whole life… I was taught to believe that here we would have no form. So do you see that… my sins on earth, which are of the… body… I was sure would not travel with me because I would just be spirit. But now I find that I still have my body… and if I go with your friend and mix with people… then my life will be an eternity of temptation that I… I can't resist."

We sat with bent heads absorbing the full significance of his confession. It seemed to throw quite a pressure upon us, and after we had given our appreciative responses that pressure came to a head as abruptly he wound up – seeing the end of the matter.

"… So may I thank you for trying to help, and say goodbye? I feel I must – "

"Er, before you leave," Robert cut in, "will you promise that you'll go with David?"

He got a petulant reply:

"You don't understand anything do you? I have just this moment explained."

"Yes," Valerie said aside to Robert, "he feels that he's basically going on with people, which means a life of continual temptation you see."

"So goodbye now," the priest satisfied himself, "and thank you again."

At that extremity spurted Renée:

"Just a minute – wait! If you would only let David speak to you, if you would tell him about it, and let him explain to you what is possible over there, you could overcome this problem and –"

"But my child… !"

" – And the feeling about your body will disappear."

"But it's other people's! Don't you understand what I'm saying to you?"

"What we mean though," stressed Robert, "is that you can learn to overcome in yours the temptation of other people's."

"Oh please! I've spent seventy-four years trying to overcome, so don't tell me what I can or can't do!"

We felt as helpless to make any impression as a wave beating against a granite rock. Renée conciliated while our minds cast about in suspense.

"Yes we do understand how difficult it is because many of us here also try to overcome."

"Well imagine being condemned to an eternity of it!" he flung back.

That very idea baffled me, as if alien to life.

"You're not being condemned, just perpetuating –"

"I know, I'm condemning myself," he admitted, my surprise at which let Renée back in.

"You see, David can so easily help you overcome it."

"But how?" In his voice was a stubborn, questioning pain. "How is it possible if I still have my body where the true spirit is now manifesting itself?"

"It is possible," she said, "because in that new state you can do anything you need to do, and David will show you how. We cannot show you because we are not there with you. But he is, and he can explain."

"Yes but you are gathered here to serve. You must have answers?"

"We are gathered here to tell you that David is the one who can help you on that side of life. We can only guide you toward him from earth."

"Just… Just tell me if… my body is still me – for other people have bodies here too. I've seen them."

"Of course," she replied. "But the body there is of a subtler nature, which you can control more easily with your mind."

At this, his voice freshened to spearlike alertness:

"Subtler body!… Control more easily with your mind. Control more easily … " he repeated, husbanding every syllable.

"That's right," said she. "David wants to show you how to use your mind to control this subtler body, not the earthly one. You've shed your earthly one without realising it, because inside was an exact psychological counterpart – more easily affected by your thoughts and feelings but by that same token easier to control once you know how. So you don't have to suffer against the old earth body any more because, if you'll let David show you how, you can realise that you're truly free of it."

"And… And where is this man?"

"He's right nearby, waiting. If you look around, perhaps call him, he will be with you. So will you give him a chance to teach you that?"

"Yes… " was his answer at last, melting into tears.

"Come to him David!" said I, though already aware of a rapid convergence on the channel. We all warmly wished him goodbye and good luck.

"Thank you … so much," he swelled, brimful of emotion. "Do they still say… God Bless you?"

After our most difficult case, those parting words left us unmindful of how they would actually teach him sexual control. But we did suppose his intermediary guide was there to brief him, for David himself was now paying us another visit. He got no rush of enquiries from us, only my vain wish to court his reaction:

"Hallo David. We made it in the end didn't we?"

"Of course you did."

"A very venerable old gentleman," commented Robert.

"But he's been with us for such a long time. I've just come through to clear."

His tone was unusually thin, due no doubt to the channel having got befogged by remorse. We inferred that his presence there was merely to dissolve its oppressive residue – unless it was a precaution too against more complaint from Peter. We said nothing however. Valerie changed cassettes. Robert whispered to Renée in the background. J.M. stayed passive. My focus hung on the channel and David, not least because his company was so peaceable.

If he expected questions but was too modest to invite them, he still seemed preoccupied with the chore – and with someone whom I felt stood beside him. It may have been the same person there as he had consulted before, though my sentience could stretch no further. Then within a short while he broke silence, and much more audibly:

"The people here are coming to you. They are shy."

We were slow taking in this unfamiliar prospect, but Valerie remembered John's little speech where he told of whole communities of people getting stuck near earth together, only dimly knowing they had passed, and some quite unaware. She it was therefore who spoke up.

"Yes, what can we do for them?"

"When they come, talk to them," said David. "Help them out. They are in front of many more."

She now felt positive that our friends had guided part of such a community toward us in order to be kindled by an earthly voice resounding nearer their level. Her moment's recall brought back the pathos of their having no stronger idea than a very humdrum existence with the same surroundings and way of life they had known on earth – at root because of ignorance, feelings of unworthiness, and fear. She had gathered that The Seven would visit these communities, trying to reassure onward any who might be ready to accept their truer being and forge a creative, meaningful direction in life.

"Right," came her assent, "we'll do that David."

He withdrew and we sat there mutely, the rest of us somewhat hesitant. Seconds later one of them arrived, breathing no more than a sigh before Valerie saw her cue to respond.

"What is it? We are here to help you."

"Why is everything so quiet?" asked a mousy voice.

"Does it seem too quiet to you?"

"Yes it's like everybody's waiting for me to say something. He just told me to come in here."

"And what do you think you should say?"

"I don't know. Where's he going to take us then?"

Valerie leaned forward. The eyes she bent on the rescuee were tender, and her few homespun words, given gently and slowly, glowed with conviction.

"He's taking you into a beautiful realm, a land of light, where you will meet all those you loved on earth, where you can learn all kinds of new things and be truly fulfilled. It is the first step that you have to make in your world, which will lead you on and on into ever more glorious worlds. This is your *real* life now, so you needn't fear. There's *nothing* to fear."

"Mmm… "

"Is there anything that worries you about it?"

"Not really. But we must listen now. He's calling us to listen."

"Yes alright, you do that."

Our visitor pulled out, and David reinstalled himself. As he began to talk we caught on that he was using the channel's voice to reach those who had been drawn.

"… I am speaking to you all. For many of you here, your

surroundings, your realisation of a continued life are sufficient. You have crossed the great divide, and just being here may seem satisfaction enough. You have seen and spoken to several of us today who, I must admit, appear rather as if we are trying to sell you something – a better plan, a better ideal, a better life. And another transition after so short a time may seem too much to ask. But we *are* in a position to help you still further.

"Where we are going to take you may not be Nirvana, may not be Paradise as you think of it, but we do want you to come with us because we know in our hearts that we are bringing you further inwards to the Oneness and Love of God. It is, as our earthly sister has said, a step nearer the Light for all of you. Coming here, for some of you, may have seemed like being shepherded. Yet it was done with love to show that there are those on both sides of the veil who are ready and willing to help you. We would give you all we have, all we are, which is love. Nothing bad can be sold to you when it's packaged in love. If my hands were big enough I would carry all of you.

"So come with us! Leave your familiar surroundings. Leave those old familiar patterns that are once more becoming dear to you – before it's impossible for you to leave, before you are caught and trapped once again. Come with me! Come out of the darkness and into Light! Oh God... at this moment we offer ourselves to all that You stand for. We give ourselves up to the symbolism that You showed us, so that as we pass from one world into the next Your Strength may give us strength. Today these people need the courage and help that comes from Your Eternal Overflowing Love. We're walking into Your Light, Lord. We're coming. Come with me people! COME WITH ME!"

And so saying he was gone. Our momentum of regard carried on through the silence he left behind. Each of us had tried thoughtwise to back up his prayerful call, and it still kept us immobile, like an array of statues concentratedly posed.

In due course, as I registered not a discarnate but Peter himself docking in, we closed the session. He bore no obvious ill-effect, was even flippant about our odd huddle round his settee – though Valerie and I did exchange glances. Tacitly we felt that his colleagues, with David coming in "to clear" and lighter caseload, were tempering the wind to their shorn lamb – who went back down among his flowers.

The success or otherwise of David's speech was never known. But on our way downstairs, interest was already being shown by Robert and Renée in the idea of whole communities being earthbound – which interest prompted Valerie to oblige. She produced those two tapes where it was mentioned, and once everyone had a meal on their lap we listened to the relevant bits.

Discussion followed over why the earthly ego should become trapped in such numbers, sometimes *all* unaware of having passed. Finally we likened the ego to a spotlight thrown onstage by its source lamp, the true astral self, whose trouble was often that the ignorant ego spotlight got caught up within the mass cultural belief playing on its stage. This belief told the spotlight that it was the whole source lamp. On its return therefore to the source it hung about in the theatre stalls, so to speak, instead of becoming the lamp again.

Renée suggested we heard part of a talk – of which she knew we had a recording – where her teacher Ronald Beesley commented on the problem. He was an avuncular and highly gifted luminary much respected at Ashdene. His skilful insight into healing, his profound intuitive knowledge and outlook with diagnostic ability once compared to that of Edgar Cayce, had drawn a cosmopolitan stream of students to his Centre on a hill amongst woodland near Speldhurst, our neighbouring village. He had featured Valerie as the subject of auric diagnosis for his book, The Robe of Many Colours, and she in turn had painted his portrait. Close encounters of this kind had led her to trust his integrity.

So she was happy to search out his talk for us, and with the tape in play we gave keener ear to what he might say of those thousands who pass every day into "the fourth dimension". We heard him speak with quiet dignity and assurance of consciousness as a fourth-dimensional force operating through physical matter, of true higher plane life where hell-creating fears and negative beliefs are outgrown. Soon we were reminded that his emphasis was on raising consciousness above ego level to link with one's fourth-dimensional self while still here – and bridge earthly factors which bind.

"… Once we can get over the fears of the survival factor, then we can set to work on the knowledge area. The complaint of most on the other side is that the human material which comes up from earth is so ignorant, it is so kindergarten, it is still so steeped in its traditional ideas of God and the Universe that they almost all have to relearn at kindergarten stage the simple lessons of evolution, growth and development. Earth itself is a school, a college, a place of learning. It shouldn't be wasted. But it packs people's minds with third-dimensional knowledge, making them so intellectually isolated and insulated that the fourth dimension cannot communicate freely.

"So it is this bridge of knowledge that desperately needs to be spread through our society and social structure – that of the spiritual nature of man. What is this curtain that seems to come down when we are born, that seems to cut us off, if you like, from the source? This at first is a protection, a necessary protection for the life to start clean and fresh, uncontaminated with memories, a new page unprinted. Then, unfortunately, it is swamped in all sorts of traditions – the idea that we shall be rewarded with eternal life and be saved from damnation. When they wake up on the other side none of this applies, and they find themselves right back in school again. Who sold them the idea of cheap salvation? Who was it that made faith do the homework and the person do nothing at all? Once we enter into an awareness of our fourth-dimensional being we begin to see the truth that we are the workmen, the sculptors of our selves."

★ ★ ★ ★ ★

There were no chats with The Seven that ensuing week, and contact via the writing was shut down until Betty returned from holiday. It frustrated me because in the light of Renée's success with the priest I wanted to query why Philip had thought her emotionally unready for rescue work. After all, she had taken a very active and capable part and received due tribute for coming upon what the priest needed to know. Maybe finding this in each case was the key, which above par she had seized in our most difficult case yet. Someone had made a bid that she should join us, though it got lost in the undergrowth of tactics speculation. Not until afterward, when we had dispersed and I was alone with Valerie, did I myself bring it up – to find her way ahead of me. Her invite had been for that express purpose, yet she was pursuing a policy of "wait and see" which my youth failed to grasp.

Robert had barely mentioned the Rajneesh issue, maybe for a similar wait-and-see reason. His post-rescue reply when offered feedback complete with David's reaction was: "Mustn't mix our drinks." He wore the parturient smile of one who had sown a seed and knew better than to dig the thing up again. While Valerie was glad of this, its manner somehow compounded her unease with his opposite approach to rescue.

She did accept that hers, using heart rather than head, was often erratic. But his pedestrian tour round whys and wherefores from each rescuee, she felt, was diffusing the process. Of course one had to probe. Only his emphasis niggled. It had begun to try her patience, and a crack was appearing in their team relationship. My stance lay between them, anxious to repair the crack because above all it would weaken what unity we had as protection in the work.

A taut lull hung over our week then, uneventful yet unsorted. The latest rescue session had shown a variable element creeping in, which jerked us up from some degree of complacency. But whether any of us faced the likelihood that our work, sooner or later, could carry us into much lower realms is hard to say. We were too motley a crew to reassemble outside work sessions. Every Friday's speculation about tactics, which got nowhere, envisaged no serious change. After confab we stayed in our same ruts, never applying ourselves to the logic that murkier levels could throw up a murkier challenge.

By the time we sat again the next Friday our mood had altered only because of that new variable element, for otherwise we were expecting a normal enough run. With everyone seated I drew the Sanctuary curtains on a clear night. But inside, because of my effort to overcome disappointment at Renée's absence, less heed was paid to the atmosphere building up around us. It felt as thick as pea soup.

We would learn someday from Brian of those conditions into which the etheric force-field of our channel, like a radio set, had tonight been tuned. Unbeknown to us, we were in at the deep end, sinking down through a dark, dank, misty strata of existence, grey with slime and having no vegetation, littered about with caves, dug-outs or other primitive dwellings. Any pleasanter memory of earth is but a far off dream compared to this starkness, out of which stronger wills draw perverted sense by ruling the weaker ones in a constant dominion of fear.

As yet oblivious of it ourselves, owing to David and Brian's inability at that wavelength to use the channel, we became mystified by three cases who flitted in and out, too timid even to speak much. An impression began forming that they were afraid of reprisals for association outside the herd, which then led us to suspect where we might have landed. Not until one more had slunk eerily in to peek at us and flitted off again, did another's animal-like curiosity give us a change to engage.

Quite how we appeared to the poor creature from that subhuman level must be left to the imagination. But his full blending with the channel must have triggered echoes of earth memory, and soon we reckoned it was a young man who, awoken that the life he had come to know was not absolute, spoke at last with a sort of craven tenseness, almost against his will.

"… There *are* different places, aren't there?"

"Oh many, definitely," assured Valerie, with Robert qualifying in a flash.

"We know of places where there are beautiful beaches with sea-shells, and all kinds of lovely plants growing near the sea. There's blue water, warmth and sunshine."

"And nice people," laid on Valerie, "to talk to."

"But they wouldn't like *me*."

"Oh they would!" she coaxed. "They're longing to meet you actually. In fact they've asked us to come and fetch you."

"Will we play football on the beach?"

"Yes of course," said Robert. "There are some very colourful beach balls, splendid ones."

"I can remember being brown."

"Suntans! My word, yes. So we'd like to take you there, you see, because you're a friend of ours now. It's a simple step for you. You'll remember things as they used to be."

"I . . .I had a dog."

"What sort of dog, and what was his name?"

"Lars. Can't remember the sort they called him. But there really are these different places aren't there?"

"Of course there are."

"So you've no need," Valerie enjoined, "to stay where you are at all."

" – I must go, quickly!" was gasped in fear, which Robert mistook for an eager readiness:

"And one day we'll all meet on the beach, alright?"

"Ahh… ahhh!" The lad seemed to founder, as if being pulled or dragged down. J.M. voiced his suspicion.

"He's gone back to the wrong place, not where we were talking about."

"No I thought not." acknowledged Valerie. "He was frightened of someone".

And that someone was close behind. A rather sordid viscous sensation filtered into the channel. I felt homed-in upon, fixed under its gaze. Far from sure of our capacity to rescue this intruder, whom one assumed to have snatched our lad, I muttered my most ambiguous "hullo" – to be met with a distinctly oily response:

"Good evening. I think that I could help you in your work that you are so generously devoting your time and effort to. If I stay here I might come in useful."

"And your name is?"

"My name is John… Smith. If you would care to direct these people towards me, I think we could form a very good team."

"On the other hand Smith… " I geared up.

" – Thank you for listening. It is a pleasure to have you with us."

"We don't want you here," said my overrider.

"I'm afraid I'm going to stay!" The mouth twitched in a brief sneer.

"Well we won't take any notice of you."

As he stole away without answering I had a hunch that he nevertheless grinned sinisterly, and my mind took stock of whether he could wreak serious mischief through the session. At core though, this depended pretty much on his willpower versus ours with David and Brian's, plus that of rescuees in wanting to get free. Valerie was considering their will particularly in the light of a statement by Ralph Waldo Trine; "One need remain in no hell longer than he himself chooses to; and the moment he chooses not to remain longer, not all the powers in the universe can prevent him from leaving it."

But perhaps Smith was less keen to retain our next fugitive. A cacophony of discomfort exploded over us, where for guttural choking, rasping and asthmatic spluttering the subject was barely able to speak. My first thought was to gird the sufferer in some immediate sense of security.

"Hallo, you're okay with us now. Do you know where you are?"

"… Eh?… oh… yes I'm… uhh!… uhh."

"Alright then, I'm Jules and this is Valerie, Robert and John – four of us around you helping. Can you hear?"

"Oggh!… I… I… di-i-ed. I've go-got… uhh."

"Don't worry, we're listening. Yes?"

"I'm… dro-dropp-ing… in two… uh… pie-ces! I am… le-le-lep… oh. Go away"!

"You were a leper?"

"A-Am! Don't… tou-touch."

"But you're not infectious and we're giving you healing to release this condition. It's coming into you now."

"Ogghh!… No… do-don't… touch… me!"

"In just a few minutes you'll be clear of it. It's all going, all drifting off you."

"Yes," spoke up Valerie, "you're gradually being healed at this moment. Do you feel different already?"

"Do-don't! Don't… touch… ohhh!"

"You're being healed," said she, "cleansed. It's going from you, and very soon you'll feel better."

The sounds of sufferance dwindled at least.

"… I'm… uh… ti-red."

"Yes that's fine. It's because of the healing."

"Take him David!" I cued, in the fond belief that languor was a sufficient go-ahead for him to dart forward quickly. Our confines were abuzz with invisible action. If he succeeded it would have been not only in spite of Smith but under another insidious nose which then poked into the channel. Distinct from his grinning forerunner, this one's unsavouriness felt cold, dry and hard.

With my reluctant "Good evening" I did wonder whether each Friday night the same predators lurked, whatever our plane of rescue or theirs of origin.

"Have you seen us before?"

"Yes," was the chill utterance, followed up by Robert in uncertainty:

"Have we spoken to you before?"

"No. But I am a doctor who may be able to help you this evening, since you seem to be in my area."

One could scarcely misunderstand the intent to beguile, nor evade the impression of menace which lay behind this otherwise ordinary statement.

"And in what way," I enquired, "do you think you could help us?"

"You may call on me to take the people you are trying to heal into my hospital if you wish."

"How do you treat them?"

"We have many ways of treating them during their recuperation phase."

"But what do you use to treat them?" I pressed.

"The latest hospitalisation methods."

A sincerity as transparent as glass was also as brittle I thought, not even bending toward a method of which we would approve. I gave up in favour of a clue to his actual stage of progress.

"Are you usually in this area?"

"I have sp-ent much time here," he replied with an odd trip on the tongue.

"You seem troubled."

"I have no... trouble. Remember to call on me when you need a patient looking after."

"What's your name?"

"Doc-tor Jones."

I gave the team a raised-eyes look. His naivete in still believing us dupes, and his failure in seeing how insalubriously he came across might have struck Robert.

"Thank you Doctor Jones. We'll call you if ever we're in need of your particular kind of help. Meanwhile I think we'd better let some more patients through."

The rascal sloped off, and within seconds I picked up a refreshingly welcome, if surprising visitor. It was one of The Seven, John in fact, who arrived concernedly.

Though greeted with light enthusiasm, in answer his tones were serious:

"Hallo Jules. I've come with all of our group because you need a great deal of support. Your efforts are being thwarted, and you must be very careful."

"Yes we do seem to be getting an influx of phoneys here!" I twinkled. He went on, sober as a judge.

"The clue to remember is that they have little recall of earth names. They always use very common names Jules. We are all with you now, but trust no one except Brian or David who are nearest the channel. God Bless."

He left without further ado, his message clear. From it we

construed that other intruders may be trickier to spot, more dangerous, and that he had been sent expressly to assure us of our supported ground. His solemnity in warning of our efforts being "thwarted" made me doubt whether the leper was rescued after all. But now a third escapee was hanging onto the channel as their lifeline, struggling tooth and nail to clamber "up" out of what sounded like herdish hands.I lent our connivance.

"Okay, you're coming into safety with us."

"Uh… I'm nearly up… nearly there. Oh it's so hot!"

"It's very cool here," said Robert, "so come with us into the shade."

"Ohhh no!… Can't you see?"

"Can't we see what? I asked.

"I… uh… keep coming up… uh… and… being pulled down!"

Wishing we had given proper thought to these haul-up contingencies I grabbed the handiest thing in our world that might raise his or her thought-level by association – one of the shop's cut roses from a vase at my elbow.

"Well you're coming up for good now."

"Ohh can't you see I'm going down? Help!"

"No hold onto me. Here's something you haven't had for a long time. Smell this and imagine a lovely rose garden. Isn't it gorgeous? So up you come. Let it draw you. Come on!"

Everyone joined in the encouragement – hearts, minds and voices stretching out to our nursling until at length he heaved a sigh of relief.

"And I don't have to go back?"

"No," I promised, "you won't ever have to go back."

"Well done," congratulated Robert. "It's good to have you with us. Just relax now."

"And I really don't have to go back?" An almost unbelieving wonderment quivered there.

"No, not ever," I reaffirmed.

"What do I have to do?"

"Nothing except go with our friend David and have a rest. After that you can do whatever you like."

"I'd like to remember me. Can I do that? I want to remember me."

"Yes you'll remember who you are alright. It's just that you've had a bad time and need to convalesce first – okay? So do you see a man in the light here?"

"Umm... what? Yes he's making me... feel... sleepy. I've wanted to meet people for... so long and... now I don't know... what... to say... "

David had moved closer to the channel, seeming then to draw round behind, and soon our valiant sleepyhead was gone. I saw no reason to believe that my rose contributed anything. While we awaited developments I figured that as a ploy it may have been aimed at the wrong person, fallen short, and become transcended by our vocal encouragement. Earth voices always beefed up a channel occupant. We were not going to get off lightly with that success however.

In the middle of whispered exchange with the others a sudden sickening dizziness assailed me, one which was recognised, given a moment to collect myself, as coming not from within but without. Some noxious figure had steered in upon us, undetected till their aura reached my senses. The channel's mouth had straightened to a stern, inflexible line, so hard it looked cruel. I seized both the wrists in case of physical attack, at once receiving a brief but sharp image of extremely long, very dirty fingernails. Their owner, with a suppressed violence the more intense for being under restraint, boomed his outrage in a dead, flat and toneless voice:

"THIS IS MY PLACE. YOU ARE DISTURBING MY FRIENDS. YOU ARE UPSETTING THE HAPPINESS OF MY PEOPLE!"

Rancour veritably oozed from him. It tore at us, and clutched Valerie in an iron grip of fear. Yet she dared to respond first:

"Are you happy yourself?"

"I am, because my friends are."

Her nonplus brought me rallying:

"But they're not happy at all are they? And you have to feel so in yourself to set an example surely. You're not a sheep are you? You can't be happy just because others are."

"I have all I need. Leave this place! We don't want you. Why do you interfere with us?"

"Simply because your so-called friends are so miserable, and you must be too. If you really were happy you'd ask us to join in wouldn't you?"

"And why," queried J.M., "are the ones we've spoken to so hot and uncomfortable?"

There was a perceptible flinch. Our contender's voice hardened slightly:

"Because of the allocations. Why don't you leave us?"

"Well", said Robert, "we've only just arrived, and I must say you don't sound at all happy. Perhaps we can liven things up a bit."

But this was ignored in pique at the wrists being held.

"Let go of me!"

"No I won't. It'll help you get the picture."

"You see," Robert angled, "we'd like to talk to you about your happy place."

"It's no good because I have to follow instructions," was the reply, squirming against my hands as Robert tried to propitiate:

"Now come along. Just relax and talk to us."

"Then... uh... why do you need force?"

This measure of mine to protect the team in general, and Valerie in particular who sat directly facing him, must have slackened a degree at that question – for like lightning he managed to wrench one arm free and lash out wildly so that I had to duck. Pandemonium then ensued as we three males, six-footers all, piled in to quell the flailing, snapping firebrand.

Valerie had shunted back hastily with her chair and gone into the corner by her altar lamp. To her it felt as though Horror personified had lunged towards us. She shrank inside, only to remember in relative safety that it was nothing of the sort – just a man more frightened than she, frightened of us and of life.

A minute later we held him fast again. Robert pursued a one-sided conversation about philosophic stance, J.M. issued decrees for peace and love, while I was unclear whether we should be rescuing the fellow or pushing him off. In either event, once he was calm enough to hear how intransigent we were he slunk away exhausted. Our intransigence of course was partly because we were unable to "leave" his "place" anyway.

Oddly, challenging him with the fact that we sat in a cottage room on earth never occurred to me. Nor would we apply it further ahead to a similar encounter, even during the full dialogue which Robert eventually won from such a person. Within my recall it failed to come up between-times as a ploy. Unpreparedness and sheer loose thinking were two reasons. Another lay with the affective sensation, often intense from the rescuees' world, of being enwrapped, almost sharing in that weird ghetto of theirs which shut out the rest of existence.

But although the impact of physical truth on our intruder could have proved interesting as a challenge, possibly a shock if believed, in hindsight it looked an unlikely leverage against his clannish will to remain despot. The priest was not uplifted by Renée explaining that he had come to us rather than us to him. His life was saved when she told him what he especially needed to know.

Tonight, whatever that despot's special need, his pull-out let David and Brian step into the breach right away – and we got the impression of Peter having to be rushed back early. Their hive of movement thereabouts suggested a group protectiveness until he was secure, plus healing in which Valerie and I joined. Naturally our urge was to take as much out of the dreaded effect as we could, albeit nowhere near enough.

On his return our close proximity at the task rather startled him, a surprise overlaid by the headache and wave of nausea he met. I did feel for him, waking from some bewildered dream perhaps into the miasma of bodily discomfort, faces, and spent drama – a drama in which he felt not even a spectator. His clothes were dishevelled, his hair awkwardly awry, his wrists sore. Ad hoc my choice of first-aid was humour, knowing his brand well. It liked to tease Valerie's innocence, customarily with the double-entendre, and I knew her term for discarnate intruders amused him no end. Little prompting from me had her newsflash the main feature.

"Oh we've had Wandering Willys all over the place tonight darl', absolutely crawling with them!"

It worked. His face spread into indulgent glee.

"Really?" he chuckled. "You've had quite an orgy then have you?"

Her flicker of protest amused him also, he towing her along on his string the while we unscrambled ourselves into the shift downstairs.

His headache was aspirined, his nausea abated, but of course my device of humour wore off too. After supper I found him broody in the shop, tying bouquets, mildly contentious to extract from me what had happened. I gave a dilute precis. Yet one could tell beneath his frowns how much further the rude awakening out of trance this time had fuelled his resentment. It was abristle nearer the surface. Indeed together with the issues of Robert versus Valerie and of Rajneesh, which had not by a long chalk run their course, it would play its role in the upheaval slowly brewing.

CHAPTER EIGHT

A CONSCIOUSNESS OF CHANGE

April had already given place to May, and we were amid the fresh luxuriances of summer. Nothing at Ashdene looked suggestive of change because the usual trend was itself ever in flux over some new metaphysical book, zealous character, or potential approach. Swollen now was the tide of New-Agers who made us their listening post. But behind all this our affiliation with The Seven seemed evergreen, original, abidingly maverick, and we forgot that life with them as a group must also have its seasons.

On ground level meanwhile Peter absorbed himself root and branch in the prosperity of his flower shop, evidence of which often overflowed into the library, even through to the Snug where his trail of floral snippets would find him perched on the settee arm twining a garland with deft fingers, laughing with Valerie as he worked. Her studio having been forfeited to him, she did her work up at the Sanctuary window, easel and brushes being cleared away every time for that room's true purpose.

It was a purpose to which she felt more disposed than to her canvas nowadays, as mentioned in her lone talk with David, and she might not have been painting at all if he hadn't offered to try inspiring her with "landscapes of foreign origin". The trouble was that she felt no such inspiration. I counselled patience. Unlike herself he was an amateur painter. Like us he was fallibly human. Nor might he have the influential skill of Orlando through the writing.

One evening however provided a chance to talk it over with him. She had spent much of Sunday at her altar table composing the latest meditation tape, which by teatime was ready to be tested out on Mary-Ann. They enjoyed their togetherness these two, mute or otherwise, as they did under the tape's playback and afterward discussing its merits. At that point Peter had edged upstairs in the hope of showing them his most avant-garde bridal bouquet yet. His search for them below had let Chloe out, and when to her scratches they opened the Sanctuary door that bouquet got him admittance too. None saw how conducive the atmosphere had become to his trance proneness.

Having got high praise for the handiwork, his lesser interest in their own doings started to dissociate him – the aroma of grain incense, the faint purl of residual music first closing ears, then eyes, where he had tarried on a chair by the window. Not that Valerie was taken aback by any means. What did give her a jolt was the spontaneous arrival of Philip taking an opportunity to check on our welfare, whether for example there were any problems or questions about the rescue work.

Faced with this now rare personal visit, her list of questions gone astray, she muddled through the ones which came to mind, they being carefully answered from the perspective that was always his. No sooner had he withdrawn than a glance down at her recorder showed the tape to have jammed early on – thirty minutes worth of answers lost and her memory of them unsound because she had been relying on the tape.

The blow clouded her interaction with David who followed him. Changing tapes she tried to recoup her loss by asking similar questions, then gave it up after getting dissimilar answers. Such a mood put their artistic alliance altogether out of mind, and neither she nor David brought up the subject. His sole intent anyway was to express gratitude for our efforts at rescue so far, sharing with us news of various success cases since they had reached the hospital. He wanted to emphasize that many of these had been bystanders drawn by having heard or watched even one our numerous failures enough to recognize their own position and seek help.

A few, of whom Valerie pressed him to speak in particular, were children. He described, "rather bashfully", she said, the play-areas specially created to imbue healing encouragement, how also he comforted them with an introduction to the actual storybook characters of earth. These were the thought-forms of their earthly creators, he explained, each originally a blueprint which generations of children has sustained with their ready belief and delight in imagination. "A lesson for us all", he added significantly.

Later she had pondered on it, the way we sustain and reinforce borrowed images, beliefs, concepts which as a result become part of our projected world for good or ill wherever we are. So, belief in non-entities will give them elemental life. Belief in conscious entities, including fellow humans, boosts their consciousness – hence the effect of prayer.

But under her nose lay also a small physical lesson. I was in Surrey that weekend, en famille with a close ladyfriend, and was greeted back next evening into general bereavement over both tapes' demise, not just that one. Her recording level had been set far too low throughout. With barely a sentence audible we sat till midnight straining to interpret the distant blur of sounds. Peter himself took an occasional turn, his ear pinned hard against the speaker to catch what he could "about the children," he said.

Actually he would have preferred to hear some reply from Philip or David to a private appeal of his, which Valerie was keen to tell me about once he had gone to bed. She had an episode to relate. On Saturday afternoon the art buyer from Liberty's London store was due to pick her up for their regular chat at Binns Tearoom in Tunbridge Wells. While she waited, Peter whisked off on a short delivery of plants, his return from which half an hour later to an empty house assumed her to have left. Unknown to him however, the engagement had been postponed by telephone and Valerie had resorted to her garden, where she knelt tending a plant beneath the shop's extensive rear windows.

Since that section of wall was of wood and glass, like old garage doors, Peter's resumed activity at his workbench could be well heard.

But just as she made to pop up in playful surprise at the glass he started speaking – to a customer she thought at first. Then the names David and Philip were accented, and she froze.

Evidently thinking himself alone, and in their presence, he had decided to confront them on his own terms. "Any sort of proof" which would convince him of their separate existence was being asked in exchange for his fidelity to the work. If they were souls, he pleaded aloud, why couldn't they make themselves more real to him? If they were real, why couldn't they materialise in front of him and show it?

Whatever else he said was given respectful distance as she tiptoed to a far corner of the garden. There, with her embarrassed sense of intrusion worn off, she could hardly help reviewing this young man's personal lot – isolated in bewilderment and uncertainty upon her artist's stool, within the little shop she had lent him, the house in which she had allowed him a home. Not even the convictions of its habituées pertained to him, yet they rolled like waves around his island self. Apart from his truer soul nature known to The Seven, the self whom she might have caught in that portrait, he was a worldly persona who may never feel quite comfortable with us or them. How much could he stomach before the feeling reared up in revolt? And what then?

He soon spotted her through the window and strode out to learn of her adjusted appointment. She kept silent about the eavesdrop of course, waiting to see if he would guard his new initiative or declare it. In fact he guarded it until their bedtime drink when a desire to know his chances told all. The actual deal she sidestepped, assuring him only that a sincere thought of his in their direction should reach them at once due to their working partnership. The higher the thought, the better chance of reaching them.

Her latter proviso was added because she already knew of his rudimental faith in them as play-figures who may grant him certain benefits, either applied for jokingly or "as a test". One of those asked – not without result I gather – was in search of rare flora to fill a bouquet. Another was that an elderly customer might be treated with a visit from her nephew. However virtuous or puerile some were, and in spite of her knowing a number of sensitives who would decry such behavior as a lowering abuse of privilege, she saw the beginnings of a faith which was raiseable. At least his attitude was healthier than friction with The Seven, on which borderline he hovered sometimes.

He had not yet visited my class in Broadwater Down, a prospect which was shortly to come up during our next talk with John. My original idea had been only that Peter visit, not allow trance control as John had in mind, so I had since become hesitant. The last thing I wanted was for Peter to feel coerced, exploited in any way, most of all during his period of resentment. Although this had cooled, the outlook was fair but fragile. Extra demands on his faculty, in my view, were therefore at a higher premium than ever. I hadn't foreseen the potential usefulness of my class to our work. Nor did I suspect how serviceable was my small flat to the ongoing plan, for being out of Ashdene's range it was cherished as a haven of retreat.

Where Waterdown Forest spread high onto the southern edge of Tunbridge Wells, a broad avenue thickly lined with trees ran along its crest for a mile. Nicknamed Millionaire's Mile from the wealth which had set great Victorian mansions sedately apart behind rhododendrons on either side, Broadwater Down's former eminence had long been divided into flats, of which mine was among the smallest and rented at £4.7s.6d a week. But I was very proud of it. After my succession of bisky bedsits downtown I had sped up the hill in 1968 to attain at last somewhere worthier to call a home, more nigh woods and fields reminiscent of boyhood.

Number 21, hidden by foliage cloistering the drive, was of modest size, mellow brick, gabled-Victorian-vicarage style, having my self-contained garden flat tucked away on one rear corner. A tall redwood towered over it paternally. Holly and laurel bid welcome at its white entrance door with lamp, patio beside. The hallway, bathroom off, ended neatly where three doors met. I would often stand here looking round into my cosy bedroom, sunny kitchen, and large square sitting room, coal fire aglow. The former rooms shared their own lean-to roof, dwarfed by that sitting room which was a high-ceilinged part of the main house. Its great latticed window took up almost one wall. I had acquired a few old armchairs, dotted about the threadbare carpet, and these humbly served my class as would boxes in a ballroom.

The half-dozen or so class members, all young, were J.M.'s peers to whom he resorted after each episode with us. In our company he was unestablished, atypical. In theirs he enjoyed camaraderie, hobnobbing round my meagre hearth. Via him they learned of Ashene's events, over a social gulf which kept either group from meeting. Yet the gulf didn't prevent seeds of new development crossing back to Broadwater.

In class he and I, with some of the others, had been accustomed to the occasional "presence" alongside which we reckoned was the goodly ministration of a helper or two. Then, both at the same moment, we had become aware of John landing between us. His singular vibrance, now registered three miles outside the channel in this very separate milieu, was odd to apprehend. But over two weeks, while we got used to his and an unknown colleague's impromptu visits with their cheery, buoyant feel, J.M. realised that his cooperation was being sought.

Each would take turn moving in close, as if to gauge their measure of welcome, then withdraw again to resume their support of our meditation. On the fifth trial J.M. made the conscious decision to "let go", and experienced the unknown colleague blending – until a subliminal part of him pulled back into the body. Whoever was blending retreated like they had just been stung. His report of it to me later was done in private. He said it felt a private thing. As far as we knew the class was unaware, and we both believed this incident might disturb them. So pending consultation with John through his normal channel we agreed not to speak of it.

Our following class session however produced the kind of anomaly least bargained for. One member had invited Ellie, a student nurse from London who shared their lodging house. She was a happy-go-lucky young blonde in a print dress, found most attractive by the predominantly male company, though her being too young for my taste had me almost forget she was there while we started our regular drill.

John and colleague were late arriving that night. The wait had unduly bothered me. When they did come, such was my relief to have them behind us that I gave short shrift to a class member's report of inner sight, not connecting it. He had glimpsed a sunny, smiling young man with fair hair and blue eyes under a broad-brimmed felt hat tipped back on his head, its cord visible beneath his chin. Images of various sorts are common in these circles, frequently exotic or outré, and I served the stock guideline to "note and leave" without another thought.

What drew my full attention happened ten minutes on. A stuffiness arose, an invisible congestion of the air more like that of Ashdene Sanctuary on rescue night than this clear room. Moreover, opposite us, near floor level, a low mumbling was heard. Heads turned towards the fireplace where our female guest had last been seen perched petitely on a footstool. Hitherto she had insisted that the position would be unintrusive, but now her diminutive figure looked as if flung against the chimney breast like a doll in some Victorian nursery.

Collapsed inwards with long blonde curls cascading into her lap, she was in danger of slipping sidelong down to the grate. Its imminence, plus the apparent gibberish pouring from her, made me voice directives to the class and hasten across to pull her upright. As I did so the screen of hair parted over sounds which became recognisable, and my heart sank. They were the initial attempts at speech of a bod who was brassily expecting us to trace his relatives up North with the news that he was "not dead".

His uncongenial feel had me wonder if those relatives would find it happy news, though the thought was bitten back. For here was a very human need, however misplaced or unwanted by me. As kindly as possible therefore I stopped his supply of details to explain why first the chances of their belief in his message were slim, how he had opened the young lady to unwarranted danger from many whose motives were not so innocent, and that in everybody's best interest he must leave her body immediately and ask our helpers to show him an appropriate way.

He was disconcerted, since he could see neither a young lady nor a helper, and questioned whether I was quite right in the head. Thus my further explanations were equally passed off as "moonshine". But his stay had come under threat from others waiting behind him, particularly when he refused to leave. A scrimmage ensued in which he disappeared altogether, sunk amid jostling rivals for "the magic seat", as one who finally took over called it. He enjoyed the experience, held it a "terrific lark", and decided he was going to sit tight. No longer in any mood to bandy words I managed to dispatch him, if rather roughly, after a brief tussle of wills. Ellie's safe realignment met faces that gaped at her in commiseration.

The mishap had shaken them. They were cautious now about our Ashdene work, nodding sagely while I advised her not to sit passive with any group unless sure of special guidance or until she had learned how best to protect herself. She felt in too shocked a state to argue, relieved at not being deemed certifiable after having undergone a phantasmagoria which she was not keen to repeat. Nor was I keen to have another trance subject on my hands. The class wound up with healing treatment, soothing and restoring her nervous system for their exodus home. She was then cosseted among them, and J.M. was silent.

I could imagine John and colleague's view of her plight, but exactly why they should wish to enlist J.M. was obscure. Two days later at Ashdene, when Valerie and I were in the Sanctuary perusing the newest writing answers, I had a private hope of comment on it from Orlando. None was found, disappointingly, most of their dialogue having a higher focus. Yet in random moments while she went off downstairs I chanced across a note scribbled down the side of one page. It recorded that he had shown himself to Betty's inner vision as a "fair-haired young man broadly smiling under a Spanish-type sombrero hat tilted onto the back of his head". The similarity to my student's glimpse within the same hour was remarkable. I heard Valerie bring Peter up, and contained myself.

It was the same two days since their tape of Philip and David had jammed, albeit with David's "lesson" re the effectiveness of prayer held in mind. So we had arranged to spend time centering positively on those numerous rescue failures. Peter was not a passionate volunteer of course but hated to be alone, as he would otherwise have been that evening. Given the consolation of more direct involvement with the work, prayer to him fell far short, especially for meaningless names on a list. Yet we believed he was thinking The Seven might prove themselves real to him if he toed the line a bit.

Having settled into our usual places we were quite tranquil, the atmosphere crystalline even. Presently, to faint strains of the Tallis Motet, Valerie read out each name or description with spans of a minute while they were colour-bathed in hues of tenderness, healing, expansion and joy – then showered through with blessings of the sincerest love we could muster.

How much Peter was able to join in we never knew, but he had evidently lost consciousness by the time the music closed over our final patient. Naturally we expected this. Our sole uncertainty was whether he could leave the body with a caretaker or stay close in one of his cat-naps, for not every such exit was trance. On occasion he tended to awake from these naps blandly assuming the channel had been occupied, whereas in fact we had just let him doze in obvious sleep, trustful that one of The Seven stood guard.

But sleep was not obvious tonight. Neither could we be sure who was on duty until our most familiar stalwart began anchoring in. Valerie set her tape to record and I smiled in greeting:

"Hello, is that you David?"

"Yes", said he. "Some of the others are here too. The conditions this evening are excellent. Perhaps never again will we have to struggle. We especially treasure the rays you have given out. They have an earth quality which is vital to us because of its direct effect on the lost ones."

"That's great. So our ray quality hit the mark?"

"Yes, its lower vibration blends into them better than ours. They feel it keenly. We wish more on your plane would realise this. Is there anything I can help you with?"

A rehash of his last talk would have suited Valerie.

"Oh David it was terribly upsetting that the tape-recorder went wrong on Sunday night, because we didn't record all you said."

"You mustn't be upset. I was just explaining about the children and thanking you in a small way for your work in the rescues."

"It's only that Peter was very interested to hear about the children and I wasn't able to quote you."

"He could remember more himself if he tried, unless the subconscious has erased it. Early patterns of resistance die hard. However we don't consider this a fault, simply a reaction. I will say it all again for you at a later date if you wish, and if he still does not remember."

"That would be marvellous if you could," she glowed, as though nothing was further from her mind. "Now is there anything to report David? I mean, since the conditions are so good we don't want to waste these opportunities."

"Our work is more important than our talks, but I will of course always come to you both."

Sadly we did waste the opportunity and others ahead. A whole range of questions should have surfaced, like practical advice on prayer, rescue tactics, and how to identify David better for the rescue. My stumbling-block was made up of inhibition, lack of clear thinking, and not writing down questions. So a mere desultory check floated off the top of my head.

"You plan to come through and explain before the cases – is that right?"

"It's right, yet it isn't always possible."

Valerie's own check was worth an extra look I felt.

"And you said to talk to you much more than we do during the work didn't you?"

"Yes, then I can guide you into formulating your ideas."

What on earth though, we could say to him during it had me baffled as she sped forward into the art matter.

"Oh, that reminds me. I don't want to make too much of this, but I have tried to tune into you when I'm painting. Is there something I should do that I'm not doing? When I tune in, for instance, should I be more positive?"

"It may help if you think over again my suggestion about perspectives. And do you forget the trouble I have usually had coming through to you in this room because of all the people?"

"No, I see."

"Do you think then it is wise to paint here?"

"Well I suppose not, except that it's the one space left for me to paint in now. Downstairs has become so hectic."

"I understand, but till tonight it has been difficult enough using this open channel because of all the others who wish to do so. You can therefore imagine the extra trouble I'm having with yourself."

"I'm glad I asked then. Would my bedroom be alright?"

"We can try, although your house is fast becoming a meeting place on several levels. I'm sorry that I have failed you in this. I am giving it my attention."

"Maybe if we went out into the countryside we'd be unlikely to get anyone around us would we?"

"Very few I imagine."

"Well I'll start going out again and see if I can receive you there."

"I will try." He paused, turning to me: "Jules… "

"Yes?"

"… just a moment." He was listening aside. Then: "John wants to talk to you. So I'll say goodnight, and bless you dear friends for all you have done."

He moved out with customary caution. Never having become quite as adjusted as his pals to the processes of entrance and exit, he still took longer than any of them over a manoeuvre seemingly considered delicate each way. Yet between the lines of a shy taciturnity we read that he enjoyed being with us. The feeling was mutual, if unexpressed because we didn't fully acknowledge its extent at the time. It was hindsight which saw how, co-worker and friend, he had earned a unique place in our hearts without even knowing what he looked like.

We could have talked on, happily appreciative of his mien, were not John champing at the bit nearby. One could feel him there, eager as an Ascot stallion for the starting box. At the drop of his colleague's last thread of control he slid in, sitting the channel up with lifted head and that boyish, somewhat sardonic trace of a grin:

"I thought he was never going to go!" came the chipper tune. "How are you Jules and Valerie?"

"Very well John," she responded cheerily.

"I wish I could help you with your painting, but I don't think I'd be much good. I'd probably put you off it for life!"

"Well Peter often asks you to do things for him."

"Oh I know he does. I have a go, but some of them are a bit steep."

"He has faith in you actually. He's always saying, I'll have a word with John."

"So it seems. I think he's going to have to rely on me a lot more in the future."

"How do you mean?" I perked up.

"I mean in the work we've got to do, Jules."

"Oh I see. Now could you brief me on what's been happening at my Broadwater class?"

"Well we've been guided to one of your groups Jules, because the Golden Ones have asked us to see if we can bring it into the general effort. The other group you teach wouldn't gain from the experience we don't think, and hasn't the same rapport. It's the one your John (J.M.) is in that we've been concentrating on recently, and he's the person we have in mind. The problem is that although I've been trying, and Orlando has been trying, it's a feeling of release which he doesn't yet have – the final consent. You know?"

"I do, yes."

"And unless he's prepared to give that willing consent we can't do it Jules. So what we could do is try and get Peter to come along with you as a boost on one or two occasions. If we succeed, you must ask him to sit on (J.M.'s) left, with yourself on the right, and maybe the blending will make it easier. Do you think so?"

"Yes that sounds feasible. You hope then to enlist his trance potential for what? Not rescue surely?"

"Oh no. At least not in the way the channel works. That needs a lot of planning as I think I said once before, and a toughness which is quite rare. No what we have in mind, if we get the permission, is just Orlando and I coming through to try and communicate with people in distress who are attracted by the light you all create. I watched David do it that time and learned a lot. So I thought we could have a go, you see. I'll have a word with Peter when he leaves us tonight and put it to him if you like."

"Okay, but I'm concerned about the rest of the class John. They're not keen on this idea of trance work of any kind at the moment because of the debacle when Ellie joined us one night."

"I know."

"Can you say anything about that?"

"Yes. The young lady allowed people through without any self-control, and neither I nor Orlando were able to help you as we would normally. We were outnumbered, and when she ignorantly gave way to those opportunists we only had the power to support you from your side. It's strange isn't it, that we're having to work to earn your friend's trust because we couldn't work with the young lady's immediate sort. It has to be a surrender from strength not weakness as I think you know, or we'd end up with a situation even more difficult than this channel. If you could keep your group as before, without anyone who lays themselves open like that, then it's a situation we can easily protect. I can be with you, and Orlando would be the control."

"Yes. Unfortunately the class have been rather put off, concluding it's safer on their road of meditation. Now I realise you're not expecting them to give that up, as any appeal to the lost ones would only take a short time, but they see it in black and white terms. Is it just a matter of explaining to them do you think?"

"To be really serious for a moment Jules, you're right about our only needing a short time, but if their meditation takes them away from the soul and compassion for fellow human beings in distress it's not meditation is it? Their souls know what's best for each of them, and personal superstitions, with you as with us, count for nothing. There are moments, as you and Valerie know, when I maybe lose my patience or fool around, but … the sheer joy of helping almost brings me to tears at times. It's all guided from a much higher source that knows the will of these young people, and if that's what they wish then I'm really but a piece of the honeycomb Jules."

Beside my sharing his ground, the catch of emotion it caused in his voice held me off with respect – a gap filled by Valerie:

"Actually if you wanted two rescue sessions a week our Friday team could have another one here, supposing that's what the Golden Ones want too."

"They wish it that we have as many as possible. I think the reason for choosing Jules' class is because there is an aura there of calmness and peace, whereas in this, shall we say, time-honoured place it might become increasingly difficult to draw people. The wrong types, the people who we can't reach, will go anywhere they see a chance. It's the others we need new territory for, so they'll have room enough to see the help that deep down they really want. Are you with me?"

"Oh absolutely, yes," she said.

"But if I seem more serious than usual I don't mean to sound as if you're being ordered or anything. It's obviously up to you, although we know very well that you both understand these things."

Nevertheless her left-out feeling persevered:

"Would you like me to come to this other one?"

"If you really feel you'd like to, by all means. What would be ideal though, is for each of you to run your own. The main group effort would still be based here with this channel in its present way of working, and the new one could try our different way. Then the two might spring into four, or even more."

"Except we'd have to find mediums," she stickled.

"We almost have two already," said he. "But an earth group which totally believes in the power of thought and is united can bring about tremendous results on our side without a medium you see. Through the ones we have, cases can be accepted by you and then sent out for your sub-groups to concentrate on."

"Gosh that's a point. Yes, without a medium."

"Like you were doing tonight. I heard David thank you for that, and explain about it. Those people will definitely have been helped, I assure you. It's so obvious from where we are, however vague it sounds to you, and I can only add my own thanks."

His endorsement fell good on the ear, but for me his vision of sub-groups was unrealistic.

"The thing is John, where are the people with true will to take part in these groups? My Broadwater lot aren't even primed yet."

"We'll talk to them when we get through, and as the momentum starts it'll attract others. I think some of these are part of Us actually Jules, although don't quote me because I don't know yet."

"Okay," I granted. "We'll see how everything goes."

On a finalizing indraw of breath his tone changed.

"Well it's a very serious mood tonight isn't it! What have you been doing with yourselves?"

My shallow answer, "assimilating events around us", was from thinking of an event behind us which Valerie had erased off the rescue tape. I brought it up.

"There's one small query John, now you're here. The other night at rescue somebody extra came into control with an ominous message apparently for me. They said I was due for an emotional upheaval. You didn't hear this did you?"

"No, I don't normally go right down to where your rescues are. It sounds very much like the Auntie Edie's of our world. I'll see, but I don't think any of us want this sort of nonsense. Who was with you, David?"

"Yes," said Valerie. "When I asked him about it on Sunday he told us that someone had got in between the rescue cases, and he himself was so concerned with the next case he didn't take any notice of what they were saying."

"No, he wouldn't. He's very anti the Aunties!"

Having got the picture I reverted to worthier input.

"So what do you get up to during our work John?"

"Oh I'm usually positioned well to the rear! I'm by the hospital actually. I take people on when David brings them, and then sometimes I'm allowed to help him and Brian afterwards with the healing. By the way, there's a chum of mine standing here who you haven't been properly introduced to yet. I've warbled on too long, and I know he'd slip away without a word if we let him. So I'll hand you over for a bit shall I?"

Agreeing, we hung on intrigued as he left the channel in limbo. Five of The Seven were thus far known to us, one of whom we had still not spoken with direct, and it was this one's gradual take-over which presently gained a twinkle of recognition from Valerie. Call it logical surmise, an obvious guess, feminine intuition, or the flavor of one who has stood at her shoulder every week, but she cottoned onto him soonest:

"Well I never! I do believe it's … Yes it is, after all this time!"

"Do you know me Valerie?" asked a fine silvery voice.

"Of course. It's you Orlando isn't it!"

"Yes I… imagined he would put me in the hot seat before long, although it's awfully nice being able to speak to you both like this."

"And now," she thrilled, "you can tell us something about yourself at last. We hardly know anything do we?"

"No, I must seem the dormant character to you."

"But really quite active perhaps?" I suggested.

"As far as possible with John around! I'm afraid I'm rather less impassioned about things than he is, but he's right that speaking through the channel now will be good practice and let's hope we make a worth-while team for you Jules."

"At Broadwater you mean? Oh I don't see why not. You two should suit us very well, with plenty of scope once their fears are allayed."

"… Could you wait a moment? … Yes … John says he won't be coming back, but he's going to give you both an identical message. This is a little habit of his. He wants you to tell him what the message was next time he speaks to you."

"Okay," said I unexcitedly, assuming there was a point to it. "We'll try to be receptive. Maybe he's testing us for rescue inspiration."

"Anyway Orlando," she skipped on, "you quite enjoy doing the writing do you?"

"Yes I do it through several people. Unfortunately they think that I am their guide."

"You couldn't write through me without Betty though could you?" was asked in wistful tone.

"I'd find that very difficult I think."

"Quite how it works always baffles me," she said. "I don't suppose you could explain?"

"Yes, it's a technique of moving certain parts of your nervous system through your minds. Whereas now I am in almost complete control, those of you who do writing aren't able to allow us in to the same degree. So we work indirectly by prompting parts of your sub-conscious and motor-nerve impulses to get our thoughts through. Those you will accept, that is. In a way you are writing down your own thoughts, yet they are really ours."

"I understand. Gosh it's marvelous having this opportunity. I did hope we'd actually speak to you one day. Now, what were you in your last life – because Orlando's not an English name is it?"

"I came from a family of actors. That's why the name is a bit strange, but it helped when I joined the profession myself."

"And were you successful as an actor?"

"No I'm afraid I wasn't."

"Did the life get you down then?"

"Not particularly, because I had certain financial arrangements made for me which allowed more luxurious resting periods than my contemporaries."

"Are you still wearing that hat Orlando?" I fished.

"… Oh the sombrero you mean. No I only put that on for a while recently to cheer up any of you who could see. You all look so sombre sometimes. It belonged to a role I once played."

Roughly inferring both glimpses to have been of him, my thought went to his present role.

"Do you work full time with John?"

"Frequently now. We make a rather good team, which I believe is why we were designated together by our Golden Ones. While I am less forceful than he is, I understand him."

This rekindled in Valerie a question long overdue.

"I wonder Orlando why we never hear of women among you. Aren't there any who have become guides or at least reached some attainment in the group?"

"But of course! Who else do you speak to among us?"

"We just know you, John, David, Brian and Philip."

"Yes well we are only a few, a small handful from a large team who can't all come through for practical reasons. As I believe you have found, most people very near earth blend into the channel easily without even knowing it. But from a subtler level we not only have to make a conscious effort to contract ourselves down to the channel, we are also more restricted in the range of types that his subconscious can accept. Although it is flexible, it will mostly take those at a lower stage than us, otherwise we wouldn't be able to do the work. So only a few of us, male or female, but who on the whole tend to be his male colleagues, can blend in with ease or find it necessary to make the effort at all."

"Oh. I don't think we realized there were so many of you. We thought, or I did, that there were just seven."

"No, we seven are the ones who chose to work with you on earth because of our affinity with you both, and with the Channel. It's a small but very important part of a larger group enterprise in which you are also engaged at a deeper level."

"And do I meet and talk with women workers there?"

"Oh yes, with both sexes, because like us you go by individuality not the form brought from earth. This is where we know you best, and it's why I'm afraid we tend to forget that your earthly mind will only admit those of us who speak in the channel, although I did think that David was letting through some of the ladies."

"He has in the rescue, not to talk as guides or helpers like yourself."

"We're not guides of course, but I do understand what you mean. Maybe I could arrange for you to speak with one of the ladies if you like."

"Yes please Orlando. That would be marvellous."

"We'll see what can be done. I must go soon."

"What will you do when you go?"

"The first thing I shall do is make plain to John that I did get his message right, probably several times! Then I shall rejoin the group at the hospital, and maybe when I've finished my work I'll go for a walk. We have many beautiful rivers here. One of my chief pleasures is walking along them, following their course, and I explore as far as I can. But it can be rather discouraging sometimes because in order to explore I have to know where I am imagining myself to go, to some extent, and can end up in the duller areas of our world if I'm not careful. You probably don't understand."

"Yes I do, completely."

"If all three of us were now to close our eyes and imagine ourselves at the Taj Mahal, the joint view could be relatively ordinary because our minds might not be developed enough to capture its beauty and grandeur – and my mind is not yet used to imagining the heights of our world to the extent necessary in order to go there. See?"

"Like on this level," she equated "we have to conceive a plan before being able to carry it out?"

"Yes, because earth is only a denser version of the same law. Its denseness allows your feet to go almost anywhere, but what you appreciate depends on what you are doesn't it? The people there come from all of our worlds, and each person only sees from the level of their own world."

"So those who use their imaginations a great deal here, is this a tremendous help to them when they go back to you? After all, everything there is governed much more acutely by thought, and if you can't think a thing you can't have it can you?"

"Not unless you're helped, which is the very predicament of our lost ones. Thousands stay down in earth-like conditions because they have never broadened their minds or outlooks while there. What they think they want is always physical, so when they eventually drift any higher their minds either become panic-stricken or fade into sleep. They can't take any more, and the rest is unconscious until they awake back on earth as if for the first time."

"Meanwhile," I commented, "they've told some spiritualist medium that nobody reincarnates."

"Oh I imagine they would if they got the chance. But if we can get them to our hospital we can help them to adjust consciously, and offer them a wider experience to take back with them when they go." His speech had begun to weaken, halting him. "Wait a minute ... I'm not sure what's happening but ... I can't use the ... voice as well."

"I expect it's the power," she said, "which probably has become weaker by now. Don't worry Orlando, you must come and speak to us again whenever you can."

He was reduced to whispering: "Yes I will. And ... do please remember us ... if you are in need."

"Thank you. It's been wonderful talking like this. We've learned quite a lot from what you've said tonight."

"I pray ... the blessings of our Eternal Ones will grace your ... lives ... forever. God bless you both."

"And you Orlando."

"Goodbye."

Leaving was less easy for him, but he made short work of it. I liked the fluent, lightsome way he came across, and his clear-cut feel. Valerie's own impression looked a tad wet-eyed.

"Oh he's such a lovely, pure person," she summed up, and blew her nose. Meeting him after so long raised the appreciation level perhaps.

Our returning Peter thought she was distressed until we put him straight with the context of who Orlando was. His whim then bounded away through a string of mental associations which loosened us into laughter as we packed up. If, before his return, he had in fact been asked by John to boost J.M. at my class, his outer ego showed no sign. We kept the item aside, tacitly knowing better than to push our luck with him on top of a trouble-free session. It was his world therefore that we happily and amusedly shared during supper, TV, and chitchat.

Most evoked at these times was the odd core harmony between us, indulgent of him or not, arguing or distant, a harmony which ran under our incompatible outer selves. He had retired when Valerie drew attention to it. She felt that its axis must be the group soul. I shrugged my shoulders, feigning an objective stance yet secretly like-minded. Still too shy to lay bare my earliest experience of "Us", I veered off onto her query about lack of females among The Seven.

They had spent their earthly years in a society where men were thrown together more, I mooted, in schools, universities, workplaces, pubs and clubs. So maybe for The Seven this influence carried over to some extent as a handy basis of their discarnate teamwork. But what of the final two unknown figures in that team? No one had described them as male, she said, or mentioned them at all. Come to think of it, they were a complete blank spot. The two us stared at each other, and in virtual unison wailed: "We should have asked Orlando!"

★ ★ ★ ★ ★

Friday's rescue proved hauntingly memorable. Had we got an action preview of it, while waiting overlong in suspense for its start, we would have been unsettled to say the least. As things were, Valerie, J.M. and myself sat before a vacant channel, conscious only that Robert was sunning himself in South Africa and that nowadays the habitat of our work was changeful, besides being testier each session.

To boost morale I reflected aloud on Orlando and John's emphasis that our work did much more than free people out of their earthbound trap into the big wide reality beyond. It gave them a golden opportunity of guidance to the level where they could realise their true adult self and regain perspective for their entire future anywhere.

"Mmm… quite a thought," murmured Valerie, attention still on the channel which at last showed David's slow entry. "Ah yes," she smiled, "he said he'd prepare us first whenever possible."

In her opening dialogue with him, hard to hear on tape, she expressed concern to avoid another shemozzle with lower types. Volume level was raised however as he told us that there would be no violent cases for four weeks.

"Tonight you will be at the waterside," he said.

By itself obviously the locale had little meaning. His pregnant pause led me to assume he expected some reaction from us.

"We're ready David, unless you want to say more."

"I know that you are puzzled," he spoke up. "But you see, many of those who need our help form themselves into groups here. Out of the endless stream of humanity which every day passes over to our world there are quite a number who band together, unconsciously creating the same surrounding which they were used to on earth. This is the kind of situation which we intend to visit with you. So you will be talking to bands of people. Will that be alright?"

"Er … yes," was my slightly thrown reply, " I should think so. We'll see what we can do."

"You'll have to do something about the head Jules."

I put a cushion behind it. "Is that better?"

"Excellent."

"Could you tell us more," pressed Valerie, "about the waterside?"

"Yes. Often people come across here in bands as a result of what you would call disasters for instance, not realizing that they have left your earth. So they find themselves in surroundings which conform to their expectations. Others who might have passed singly out of similar surroundings on earth are then attracted, and reinforce the illusion in which the whole group continue to exist. I was a long time coming to you tonight because we were impressing the images of such an area on the channel's subconscious for reasons that will become clear to you during your rescue. We are going to be dealing with people who are intelligent but isolated."

Valerie and J.M. were mute, both giving me a nod.

"Do you think," I asked, "that the method we've used so far… um… "

"Will still suffice for these people? Yes it may, providing you remember to break their problem down to the basics and work it out from there. Brian will be with you."

"Okay then."

"God bless," he said gently, and withdrew.

In a few moments someone coasted into the channel. I felt we were being ignored and put forth a "Hallo?" – which brought nothing. Valerie made her own bid:

"We'd like to have a talk with you if we may."

But she hadn't expected one with brisk Australians.

"It'll hev ter be very short," flashed the brogue.

"Why is that?" I enquired.

"'Cos we're all going on holiday."

"May I ask where?"

"Oh we're gonna try an' git down ter the south of France, then cruise the Mediterranean for a while."

" I see. What's this place we're in now called?"

"This place, young man, is called Pegwell."

"Ah that's it," I fudged. "You'll have to forgive us I'm afraid because we're from a different state of existence."

My dropped hint probably meant nothing at all save that of a nutcase to be glossed over.

"Were you planning to speak to Bill? He'll be back in a tick. He's just gone to load all the beer 'n stuff on board."

"So meanwhile may we ask who you are?"

"I'm Doris."

"And what do you have to do to get the boat ready?" It was irrelevant, just stalling for time to think.

"Oh all the general foodstuffs, gettin' it stowed. Takes a whole lot of planning a trip like ours y'know."

"Yes I should think so. How long have you been doing this sort of thing?"

But Doris moved off for hubbie to deal with us.

"Right," said a businesslike tone, "how long hev we bin doin' what sort o' thing?"

"I mean living at the waterside here."

"Ooh quite a spell, weeks I think. Yeah it must be. Doris knows better'n me 'cos she keeps the log."

"We're talking to Bill now are we?" asked Valerie.

"Yea that's me."

"And who do you think you're talking to Bill?"

"Well aren't you sightseers? We always hev some down here."

"Do you know where we've come from?" I followed up.

"Speak agin an' I'll tell yer."

I repeated the question and he replied at once:

Oh with that accent you're Pommies aren't yer?"

"Yes we're from Tunbridge Wells in Kent, England."

"Kent? We've just bin through there, an' I think we went through Tunbridge Wells too, but I can't be sure. Where's that, in the middle of Kent?"

"No it's at the Western end."

"Well we've bin all over," he gloried, and sidelong to Doris: "Isn't that where ... yeah didn't we look at a boat up there somewhere?" Then back to me: "What's the river you've got runnin' through your territory son?"

Under sufferance I threw him the sole boating river known to me in our district, five miles away from us.

"The Medway flows through Tonbridge."

"Didn't we go down the Medway Doris?"

It felt as if they were doing things all this time, bobbing in and out of the channel's radius because it was ours. Doris bobbed in again.

"I think we did 'cos we went though Canterbury remember. Is that in Kent?" And at my verification: "Well we can't fiddle around here all day."

"Hang on!" I called. "There's something you need to know, and that we have to tell you. Do you realize you're in Kent right now?"

"Yeah 'course we do. This is Pegwell Bay isn't it?"

I had never heard of the place, not knowing far East Kent where it is, and stuck to my weak tactic.

"No you're near Tunbridge Wells."

She sniggered. "I think you'd better talk ter Bill. He does the navigating!"

"It's true. That's where we are right now."

Anxiety had beset me. I was at a loss, fumbling along in hope of extrication by the others. Such a state of mind, with Doris and Bill swapping to and fro, made me insensible of the latest swap to Bill:

"... Now, what's this you're saying?"

"I'm saying that we know we're here but you only imagine you're there, and what I mean is ... "

" – I'm not too sure you know what you mean sonny! Well it's been nice talking to yer."

"Could we talk to Bill then?"

"I *am* Bill! I know my old woman's not too hot looking, but she doesn't look anything like me!"

"You see, the reason we made the mistake," I took up, clutching at a straw, "is that there's a medium between you and us. You are both invisible to us, talking through somebody else's body."

"You bin drinkin' too much o' that pommie brew son!"

"No I don't drink."

"Well maybe you *should* be drinkin' some o' that brew!"

"But what I say is happening now. You're ... "

He had walked off. My sideways glance saw Valerie shaking her head slowly at the floor and J.M. raising his eyes to heaven. Within seconds, in came Doris.

"I've just fixed us a beer. Can I offer you one? We'll just hev a quickie, then Bill says we'd better be off."

"No wait," said Valerie. "We must have a word before you go."

I assumed her "word" was an idea until she held back, looking at me unfortunately. How one wished that Robert or Renée could launch away instead. My initiative had gone, my thoughts were feathery, and my lips were speaking almost before I had figured out what to say.

"We've got something to explain. Do you know what happens when people die?"

"When people what?"

"Die! They leave the old body like a butterfly from a chrysalis, and you… "

" – Look I really don't go much for this Jehovah Witness stuff."

"No it isn't that. We're not like them."

"Well I've read my Bible and I know all about that. Bill doesn't go too much for it either, so it's no good trying to talk to him about it. He thinks it's all a load o' cod, and he makes the decisions. All he's interested in is booze and sex."

"Yes I'm sure. But you see we've been talking to some people who have died and you're … "

" – You've bin talkin' to them y'say?"

"Yes and … "

" – Like sort of, er … spiritualists? My Auntie used to do that. You mean with the glass 'n alphabet?"

"No we have a trance channel where … "

"Oh my Aunt Elsie used to do that back home. She was slightly daffy! I reckon you'd better see Bill if you want a donation to your Church young man."

"We don't want donations, but you two in particular should be interested because … "

"I might be interested if I was living here, but we've really gotta get this trip goin' y'know."

"The point is that it's your very situation."

She had moved off however, and my feeble entreaty floated in mid-air with Bill bobbing in:

"I think you'd better let Doris git on with our stores, and we'll talk about this when we come back. Hey, is that one of your mates there? Looks to me like he's comin' over to hev a word anyway. Come ter think of it we've had that young feller on board here once or twice."

"Yes but the point is … " I began to stutter.

"He seems pretty anxious to talk to you son. So maybe I should leave you in private.

"Okay."

My sense of abysmal failure now rose at the prospect of having to confront David or Brian. I felt browned off too, as a recognisable aura came into the channel.

"Jules? Good evening, it's me Brian. Hallo Valerie, how do you feel?" he asked of her poor health.

"Much better thank you".

"You haven't come for healing recently."

"No I don't like to ask the Channel."

"I don't suppose he'd mind. Well Jules, do you understand what's happening here?"

"Yes but it's a job holding their attention."

"I'm surprised you haven't got on to the nub of it yet," he said, stirring my blood. "There's no need to fluster you see, because they've been supposedly going off on this trip of theirs for some while. All the boating enthusiasts are here, and they're absolutely convinced that they're going off together. I can't get anywhere at all with them. They can see I'm not interested in boats so I thought they might pay more attention to strangers, hoping that you might also come up with some bright ideas Jules. Perhaps your best chance of communication is with the wife. If you could lead in about boats, even."

Why he thought I might have any idea at all of how to rescue these people was never clear. But sparing him my main impulse, which was to give up and leave them there, I queried his choice of Doris as target:

"With the wife?"

"Mrs Winters, yes."

"Would she listen though? She hardly has so far."

"No but she is more receptive than the husband."

"Well alright Brian, we'll have another talk with her, although I can't see any better way to get through than facing them directly with the truth."

"Yes," agreed Valerie. "Surely the only thing is to give them a tremendous shock, be absolutely blunt to them."

"That might cause a riot down here Valerie!"

"Would that be so bad?" said I with relish.

"No, perhaps at least it would get them out of their inertia."

"But it might be the only way Brian," she stressed. "I mean, otherwise it seems hopeless!"

"Well I'll leave that up to you. It may be a good idea because the longer you delay the more they'll get tired of your attentions. You see, to them I'm just someone who's always hanging around, as part of their illusion which they've grown used to . So I can't do it at all."

"Who are we to them, then?" asked J.M.

"You seem like tourists who have wandered onto the quayside, and the quality of your earth voices has a closer ring to them. Maybe you could adopt some sort of authoritative pose, as local police or something. If you want to discuss it I'll keep the channel open, or I can come again if you need me."

He was certainly being flexible in his support, we noted, possibly because they were such a diehard case. That idea for us to adopt an authoritative pose might have proved very effective had it been suggested rather earlier, but in our view we risked their disbelief if we now posed as police or customs officers – tempting though it was. We could lose face and our chances of rescue. Our resolve therefore was to re-open parley with the subject of boats, then thrust the hair-raising truth at them.

A little after Brian had gone I sensed Doris sidling in. It seemed to me that she had grown bored with the tedious round of stowage, becoming curious about this new bevy of strangers in confab at her waterside, and perhaps also wondering how Brian was connected with us:

"He's a nice young man isn't he?"

"Yes he is Mrs Winters," I said. "It is Mrs Winters isn't it?"

"Yes, he told you then. A friend of yours is he? I must say he's very polite. He never calls me Doris or him Bill."

"He says he doesn't know much about boats," put J.M.

"He knows sod all about boats!" Are you keen sailors? I've never seen you down here before."

"Well," came my shuffle, "I don't do a great deal of sailing but I like it when I get the chance."

"Trouble is, yer don't hev too much freedom of the waters here do yer? Back home, me and Bill used to sail all the time. We used to hev the most beautiful trips. That's where he proposed to me, on the boat. He always said afterwards that I had no option in gettin' away!"

An opening was there via the freedom aspect, for we could have offered them wide open scope if they followed Brian. Yet I missed it, wholly bent on our goal and uncertain how to introduce the naked truth ad lib:

"Mrs Winters, we have something to tell you. It's about what we do."

"I'm not sure I know what you do."

My hasty outline, of our efforts through the channel in helping "those who have passed over", only got so far before she interrupted:

" – Oh I don't know if I can get Bill to, but I'd quite like ter come along to it. My mum and dad hev passed over. Can I talk to them?"

"Yes you can, far easier than you think, but... "

" – Bill's the problem though really, 'cos he won't like me doin' anything like that."

"But we were doing it, you see, when suddenly you two came through. You're talking through the medium now. Do you realize that you're what the world calls dead?"

Doris was not shaken in the way one would hope, for my rendering had instead caused lively alarm:

"Bill? … Do you hear what this young man's sayin' about you?" She shot out of the channel, whereupon seconds later an apprised and irritated Bill shot in:

"Look young fellah, I don't wanna start any fights here but these people round us on the quay are much plainer than you are. So I think you must retract that statement and admit that you're the one who's slightly strange!"

"But the reason you can see these others more plainly," I put to him, "is because they've also passed over. We haven't. We're still on earth, and to us you're talking through our medium. This is how we can hear you."

"… You just wait one minute while I tell Doris to go up and git us some more kerosene, 'cos you 'n I hev gotta hev a talk about this. Just … just wait will yer?"

His over-reaction, as I saw it, was from a basic doubt which had been brought up again by his seeing us less clearly. Here was no average dismissiveness but a frightened dig-in of heels because their living state was punctuated by other irregularities which aroused suspicion, unease. Things were not precisely the same, not all they should be, whilst in the main they appeared as solid as before. An inner recognition was being fervently denied by an outer belief in death.

Perhaps their actual trip to the Mediterranean had met with sudden disaster halfway, the shock of it so violent as to numb them both through their death exit. Unable then to face the disaster, their minds reverted to halcyon days at that waterside before they set out, joining others of similar state. If they felt wholly alive, bodily intact, how could they be "dead"? All doubt was thus suppressed, the irregularities assigned to imagination, alcohol or failing eyesight. So when forced to face it head on Bill felt he had to lock horns like a stag with the rival truth, the threat of death to his safe world and wife.

He quickly returned:

"Now what's all this about sonny? What are you trying to tell me?"

"The fact that the earth world thinks you're dead because your physical body died, but … "

" – If we was dead we'd be here with Doris's Ma and Pa, and she'd know anyway 'cos she's bin hung up on all that spiritualist business a long time. How come we don't see them if we're supposed to be dead eh? Tell me that!"

"Because it was so smooth you didn't realize, and you've shut yourselves in a dream world. Her relations will be waiting somewhere outside it, maybe with your father and mother too."

"Yeah well Pa's got a long way ter come 'cos he's right down in Brunswick Bay and I'm not plannin' ter go back there for three or four years."

"Brian could take Doris to her parents though," said Valerie.

"Her parents are dead, I told yer. She was brought up by an aunt."

"Don't you have any relatives who've passed on?"

"Do I have any who've died y'mean? Well yes, we all have. But I don't see what that's gotta do with this conversation, such as it is, and frankly I don't have the time to stand here arguing. I don't wanna be rude to you, 'cos this is your country an' all that, but Doris is coming back so I think I'll say g'night."

"Hold on Bill," I tried. "There are people ashore who particularly want to speak to you because they've seen a way of helping you, and our friend Brian knows where they are. So if you go with him you can ... "

"What that other young fellah? He never mentioned it before." There must have been a loud splash close by. "Anyway sounds like he's jumped off the quay!"

I took the thought but stumbled on:

"And they've also died you see. It's just a matter of going to them for proof of what we're telling you."

"I really think you'd better go and discuss this business with someone else, 'cos I can't have Doris getting all worked up over it again. I reckon if yer wanna come down to one of the get-togethers we put on here you're very welcome, but we hev ter be off."

"Can we speak to Doris a moment first?"

My request fell on deaf ears as he left, though Doris did pop in with a nervous appeal:

"I've gotta say goodnight to you now 'cos Bill really wants ter git on, an' we're havin' some folks over to dinner later so I'd better see you again young man. Don't stay around. Bill gets very ugly if he's riled. I think you sort of upset 'im somehow."

"Well sorry, but if you can please just remember our message that you have all passed over and are in the afterlife, you... "

" – So what's happened to my mum and dad? They've passed on and I haven't seen them!"

"You will if you go with Brian, I promise."

"… You wait right here young man. Don't go away now!"

We stared at our knees in silence, daring to suspect a possible breakthrough. When Doris came back she was furtive:

"Listen, Bill's gone off for a few things we need fer tonight, so you tell me what you gotta say very fast. I wanna know about my mum and dad."

"They'll be there somewhere Doris." I said, "waiting to greet you maybe."

"You mean somewhere right here?"

"No, not exactly here. You see when people pass on suddenly without realizing it like you have, all they find around them is what they expected to find before, so it is in fact a dream-replica of the world they were in before. This is why all you continue to see is the waterside. Come outside that dream by going with Brian and I expect you'll find your parents."

"So you tell me how Bill and I died."

"I don't know, but … "

"Well if you don't know I'm sure I don't!"

"Brian will know that. It must have happened very quickly, and you've suppressed the event because it was unpleasant. But you really are talking to us through someone else's body right now. I promise you that's what we're looking at."

"I reckon you'd better look again young man, 'cos you've got it wrong. I'm on holiday, and my parents are in heaven. I saw them die. I didn't see Bill die."

"Look you can easily prove what I say by … "

" – I don't think I wanna prove what you say. I don't wanna be dead, an' it's no use talking any more about this 'cos Bill's coming back an' as you can see he doesn't look too happy at me still natterin' ter you. So I'm gonna say goodnight very quickly okay? I really must go."

And she went. I was part relieved and part regretful over having pursued that confrontational tack. At least it had left them with the truth, which might sink in one day providing a signpost via Brian. Then again, his idea of an authoritative pose may have been their saviour for all we know. J.M. pointed out our dual lesson from use of the tack. We had seen just how fixed the earthbound could be in their dream, and also how different they were in reaction to someone thus approached on earth who most likely would never even bother to argue with us. Only because Doris and Bill's version of Pegwell Bay had a dreamlike quality did they feel the need to defend it.

We expected Brian to come through, but instead a further waterside denizen emerged – tepidly austere, giving us the once-over for several seconds without a comment. As my mood backed off to let Valerie take the cue she got response to her polite "Good Evening?"

"Good evening Madam."

"Are you a boating enthusiast?" she opened casually.

"Yes".

"And have you been here long?"

"I've had her tied up for about six months now, I should think," answered a middle class English voice.

"You don't intend to sail off anywhere then?"

"Oh the wife and I are thinking about a little cruise around the coastline for relaxation, but we haven't decided yet."

"So are you happy where you are, fairly contented with your life?"

"Damn weather gets on my nerves a bit!"

"Why, is it always rainy and cold here?"

"It has been since that lot moored up next to us."

"You think that has something to do with it do you?"

"Not the type y'know, to be on these yachts, not the type at all. We get all sorts on the water nowadays."

"Yes, dreadful isn't it? So what do you do most of the time, you and your wife? Do you read, or … ?"

"I'm not sure I should be answering these questions. They seem rather personal."

"I only wondered out of interest. We're new here," she said, which sufficed him for now.

"I play bridge."

"You find others to play with you then?"

"Yes we play with the Williams's up at the club a couple of nights."

"Do you ever see a young man around called Brian?"

"I see lots of young men, but I don't know their names so I never speak to them. Hooligans most of them. Damned hooligans! You know they cut up a boat last week?"

"Did they?"

"Smashed the bottom right out of it."

"Heavens, that doesn't sound too good."

" I told you. This is the sort of element one gets here these days."

"Well you get them everywhere don't you, not just here. You must forgive me for asking these questions, but there is a good reason for asking them."

"Some sort of survey is it?"

"No I'll explain later why we're talking to you, but perhaps in the meantime you could tell us what interests you most could you?"

"Well let's see … cricket, bowls, and bridge at the Club. I like a game of bridge, and the odd glass of Scotch. Still got an eye for the young ladies! Do a lot of sailing y'know … A lot of sailing."

"Have you ever wondered what life's all about?"

"You can't tell me what life's all about. I served up front in '44."

"Pretty horrifying was it?"

"That soon shows you what it's all about."

"But did it ever make you wonder … "

" – It made me wonder a lot of things. Death and destruction. Not worth it y'know, not worth it. But they'll do it again. I'm always telling Margaret they will. Aren't I dear?"

There was a minor juxtaposition as the lighter, feminine air of his wife blended in. She was keener to unearth the background to these questions and asked Valerie to reiterate, which was duly done:

"Yes, what I meant to ask was if either of you had ever thought seriously about matters such as life after death, and whether you believe in continued life – that there is no death. Have you ever thought about such things?"

"Not much I'm afraid," said Margaret. "My thoughts go mostly into entertaining I have to say, which we do quite a lot. Then of course there's the bridge party twice a week and that does rather … I've spoken to you before haven't I?"

"No you've never spoken to me before."

"But somebody from your organisation came along before. Aren't you from the Witnesses?"

"No we've come to tell you something important, hoping that we can explain it without you becoming too upset."

"Oh. Sounds frightfully ominous! It isn't about the newspaper delivery then, because we haven't had any delivery for a long time and I've been thinking I must pop along to find out what's happened."

"Is there anything else you don't have nowadays?"

"Well at home I used to have a great deal of help, but it's so difficult now when one can't trust a girl to come regularly any more. I have to do it all myself you see. With life on the boat though it's not such a worry because it's more a question of mucking in, so to speak – you know, the way one does!"

"Otherwise you're quite happy are you?"

"Yes I suppose so. I must say I never thought I'd end my days on the wide blue yonder! But things have settled down and I'm fairly happy to do so now."

"I'm glad," Valerie went along, delicately steering closer to the wind. "Can you remember … er, or rather, can you tell me anything about your life, perhaps going back a little way?"

"Well I don't … Is this … Are you doing a survey?"

"No it's not that at all."

"A thesis then is it? You're doing a thesis?"

"No, not that either. But you can be sure we're only asking these questions for a very good reason, as you're both intelligent people whom we've been sent to help."

"You're not from the Party are you? Because we have paid our subscription, and anyway my husband deals with all that side. So perhaps you should be talking to him."

"We're not from the Party, no. We're just helping people to understand things."

"What sort of things?"

"Well, difficult things that they find hard to accept, and we felt you might be able to, just as easily as your husband. There are three of us here – John, Jules, and I'm Valerie. You're Margaret I believe?"

"Yes that's right. Good evening." She acknowledged, and her eyes must have wandered to the dark little portable on Valerie's lap. "Oh I say, is that a camera you've got there? I'm not the sort of person who wants to be splashed all over the daily papers you know."

"We're not reporters," said J.M., "nothing like it."

"Very well then, although some of these questions are quite personal. If you want to come on board please do, but I'm not terribly sure we want all of you."

"No," Valerie drew in again, "We're more concerned to find out whether in fact you've ever heard of people speaking through mediums."

"Well I've come across it of course."

"And that people who are commonly supposed to have died haven't at all?"

"Yes, one has read this sort of thing. I didn't take much notice of it at the time, but as one gets older one begins to hope there's something in it. My husband isn't a great believer. He always says that he doesn't have to go to Church on Sundays to be a good Christian. I go along with that, but we always watch anything we can see on Sundays, and we were actually regular churchgoers when the children were young. You're from a religious organisation are you?"

I winced inside at this, but Valerie used it to drop a subtle hint:

"You might say so. We're trying to help people understand that they have in fact reached another life – while we're still on earth."

"Yes I suppose we're rather fortunate really," was the unhearing response, "because no one knows what's beyond, and … are you Spiritualists by any chance?"

"In a way perhaps, but … "

" – I can give you a cheque if that's what you want. I'll have to ask my husband though. He says I'm terribly easily led!"

Not hearing our refusals either she left in search of her spouse, who shortly sped back at the double. By the sound of him we had been taken for some new religious crusading group:

"Now what's going on here? I don't want you people getting the wrong idea. My wife and I are just as much Christians as anybody else. And what's all this tape nonsense?"

He had spotted Valerie's check of the microphone. The male in me rose defensively, beginning an explanation which he cut off:

" – I don't want to make a scene but this is private property and you are guests here!"

"We respect that," I said.

"Yes … well, I'd like to have that tape before you go if you don't mind."

"You shall have it," was my attempt to blunt him.

"So what is it exactly that you want?"

What I wanted at that moment was for the whole boating bunch to float off into their "blue-yonder". But no way was I going to let Valerie bear the brunt of his posture. Feeling bull-headed I began to charge at him with the hoary truth, careless of how he caught it:

"Right we'll tell you. We were talking to your wife about people who don't realize they have died, and who we try to help adjust, and you're… "

" – You mean you talk to people who are dead? I've never heard such a damn load of nonsense! The people you really ought to be speaking to are that lot over there. They're the kind who dabble in all that ouija-board malarkey."

"But they don't understand at all. You see, we talk to such people through a medium, and you're one of them right now."

"Oh this is damn stupid!" he snapped. "I don't know why I'm even bothering to … "

"… It seems like that to you only because you're in a world much like the old one, which is in fact created by your mind. It's why you haven't seen your children recently," I added gambling.

"Absolute balderdash! I haven't seen them because they're away. I know where the children are jolly well. Could see them tomorrow if I wanted to."

"Where do you think they are then?"

"The eldest boy's up at Cambridge, his brother is hitch-hiking round Europe somewhere, and the girl – she's married."

"Why haven't you seen them for so long?"

"We often don't. We prefer staying down here rather than go through all the bustle and fuss of London, or wherever it is they want us to meet them. It's too much for us now at our age, charging up there. And Margaret's much happier down on the boat."

"Okay," I ceded, "but the fact remains that you're speaking to us from the afterlife through someone else's body. However ridiculous or unbelievable it may sound, I swear that this is the truth."

"Yes well I'm afraid I have to be getting on. If you'd like to leave an envelope we'll see that you're alright and you can pick it up later in the week."

"We don't want money. We're telling you because … "

" – You're trying to tell me I'm dead are you?"

"I'm saying that you're not of course, but that the world here thinks you are."

In my slapdash mood I overlooked how ambiguous was the choice of phrase. He rounded on it predictably:

"Then let the world think that, young man. I'm not, so there! I've never been one for caring what the world thinks. If I was, phuh… I'd… "

He was distracted by Valerie's reaching behind me to pick up her vase of mixed flowers with a will.

"We could prove it to you actually, because I've got some flowers here."

"Oh that'll make a change," he said. We haven't had any around for some time."

Living in mental environs where boating and water were the significant factors his experience of flora would have been nil, or of very feeble replicas since that was all they needed to be. Fresh garden blooms introduced by us therefore were likely to stand out with crisp realism and vividness in a few minds whose imagination might value yet had "not developed enough to recapture beauty", as phrased by Orlando. So now from Valerie's bunch thrust into prominence the rank flood of colour and scent which assailed our yachtsman had him breathtaken:

"How extraordinary! But how … ? Surely it's … "

"These are on earth," she declared, then remembered having put beneath her seat cushion another possible ploy. It was Peter's evening paper, sneaked up from downstairs. In a wink she had it out, unfolded, and presented to him:

"Also look at the date on this paper. I don't know when you passed over, but it's 1972 now."

The closed eyes of our channel did little to diminish swivelling attention upon where she pointed. Struck momentarily dumb over the page, that bent head became like one cast in stone.

"Good God!" was sputtered. "Where did you get this?"

Her voice had the unrelenting quality of the fact with which she confronted him: "Perhaps it will prove to you that we are on earth, whereas you have actually passed over into a new phase of living."

He seemed stupefied, in a daze before able to reply:

"… But you must tell … I think you should show … "

"Yes there's nothing to worry about. Our friend Brian will take you on to beautiful areas where you'll be perfectly happy, and where others too are leading wonderful fulfilling lives. Because really there is no death. It's a continued life of ever-widening consciousness, and you've only passed into a phase near earth without realising it you see."

While still trying to ingest his, his mind raced.

"I wonder, er … Can I take the boat with me?"

"You can take whatever you like. We'll call Brian and he'll guide you to delightful places where you can sail effortlessly wherever you wish – once you've adjusted to your new life and learned how."

"What about the rain?"

"Ah well that's because you've not yet passed over properly, and haven't yet reached those places. If you go with Brian you'll find yourself in far lovelier, brighter surroundings where it need never rain, and you'll be doing marvelous things with all sorts of interesting people who've also passed, you see. No one ever dies really."

"I do believe you now Madam."

"Thank you very much. Right we'll call Brian."

As she did so, one more concern niggled in him:

"Look, I … I'd like you to explain this to Margaret. I'm no good at explanations. I think you'd do very well. You will talk to her won't you? We perhaps never had the … um… intimacy we ought to have had. We get on well, mind you. But I don't know if I can say it to her the way you've put it to me."

"Alright," agreed Valerie, "We'll try to do it as nicely and tactfully as we can."

"I'll send her over and then, um… go for a stroll."

"Yes you do that, and find Brian while we talk."

Remaining very shaken he left. We were unsure if Margaret would need the same articles of proof, but our newspaper was retrieved to give room for the gentle showdown promised.

Her return had a shiftiness, as though after noticing the husband's condition she was fearful of how things had gone between us. From the original flower-bunch however, one bloom lay in the channel's lap, over which Valerie greeted her:

"Hallo Margaret. We'd like another word with you."

"Hallo." Then in astonishment: "Gosh what's this?"

"A flower from earth. Do you recognize it?"

"Of course – it's a tulip, one of my favorites! How did you know?"

"Well we've brought it specially for you."

"Beautiful! I can hardly believe it! We haven't seen flowers like this for so long I was beginning to think… " and she faltered. "Have you had a row with him?"

"No," said Valerie, "we've been explaining something to your husband which we're now going to explain to you, feeling you'll understand. This flower is from earth, and the reason you haven't seen them for so long is because you've both passed on somehow into a sort of mirage-world which is not yet the true heaven. There you will find much more beautiful flowers than this if you go and look. Your husband has fully accepted this now, and has asked us to tell you."

Moments elapsed at revelation given weight no doubt by the thunderstruck look of him as he came away, his having "fully accepted this", and our tulip phenomenon – itself an unexpectedness which she couldn't altogether take on board.

"But I haven't seen them here!"

"No because you haven't realised where you are yet. You and your husband actually died, and as your life continued your old idea of it did too. But that's why it's not the true afterlife, only a temporary dream you've made with the others there. So you must go on."

Margaret hung in the balance, probably retracing to herself the awful clues to this change which she had slurred over, the loose ends disregarded since an odd juncture far back – an event freakish and horrific followed by eerie calm. Whether it had been an explosion in the boat or other tragedy at sea, she was brought with jolt to the present:

"… And I'm still with him."

"Yes you're still with him and you'll … "

" – Forever?"

"Yes, forever in heaven."

"There's to be no release?"

"Of course there is! You're both going to feel much happier now."

"My dear I've felt unhappy since the day of our marriage," she confessed.

Now Valerie got the jolt: "Have you?"

"He's very domineering you see, and he's always had his way with the children. In a sense I'd hoped for some sort of release. But if what you say is true, I … "

" – Yes wait. I think you will find your release Margaret because…"

" – But we must have been here for so long and I haven't, have I?"

Still befuddled, she got Valerie's patient reissue:

"That's because you never realised all that time where you were. Now that you do realize, you can be taken into wider spheres, freer opportunities, and not with him at all if that's how you'd prefer it."

We could have pointed to marriage being only "till death us do part". Not that anyway the vow took much account of Margaret's timorousness.

"How shall I tell him though? I've never had the courage to face up to him before."

"You don't have to. Everything will be arranged for you now. In that world you only stay with those who are truly close, whom you really want to be near. You've just continued with him for the time being because you hadn't completely passed over. Do you understand?" She waited. "Margaret?"

"Yes… yes I do understand. But I don't quite know how he's going to be told. He's so headstrong."

"Brian will tell him. He's very experienced in this sort of thing. It's all going to be fine, I promise you Margaret. You'll really be able to enjoy yourself now in complete release, doing all the things you always wanted to do."

"And I won't have to see this wretched boat ever again?"

"No, never, if you don't want to."

"Who is this man you're talking about?"

"See for yourself. Brian would you come now please?"

We hoped he had finished with the husband and was ready for her. A long thirty seconds went by, she growing doubtful:

"… I don't think anybody's … Ah. Gosh is that him?"

"It must be. I knew he'd come if we asked."

Whatever was beheld seemed to inspire confidence.

"Give me your hand!" she said to Valerie. "Thank you my dear. This has meant such a lot to me."

"I'm glad Margaret, and wish you a marvellous life."

Her liberation dropped our tulip to the floor.

Fancying as we did that Brian would take her high enough to show the difference, then hand her on and return for comment, we waited – aware of the session's timely end. Valerie asked aloud to have a word with him, but it was David who came through instead:

"You'll have to make to do with me I'm afraid because Brian's busy."

"Oh David," she said, "it seems we did manage to rescue those two after all."

"Yes, you did very well."

"Now during our conversation Margaret mentioned that she had in fact read something along these lines at one time in her life, and yet one of you told us that reading should make it easier for them to be rescued."

"That's right, it can do sometimes. But where there is an overriding influence like her husband, this can stretch far over here if allowed to."

I had intended a protest at David or Brian over their not preparing us sufficiently, prior to the former couple. Valerie's unqualified success with the latter couple however, made such protest look to me like a weak excuse for my incompetence. So I just tried to draw David's opinion.

"Pity we couldn't help the Australians. In their case that trip and the boat were dominant I suppose."

His answer had a forgivingly practical ring.

"So you can see how difficult our task is with these ordinary everyday people. Violent ones, of the kind you had before, are often easier. Thank you so much for this evening's work my friends. You'll have to stop now because the side of his head is getting painful. Perhaps you could do some spot healing."

Though not in the mood I gave passive assent and he wove his way out quietly again. We were preparing to heal when another entry was sensed which was not that of our patient. I went on immediate alert until Brian's savour became plain.

"It's alright Jules. Did you want to speak to me before you go?"

Valerie reiterated her query:

"Yes it was about Margaret not being easily helped even though she had read beforehand."

"Oh I don't believe she had read anything worthwhile. I think she was merely referring to the fact that she's read of those spiritualist-type organisations."

"That sounds more like it," I concurred. "Sorry about the failure tonight Brian. It must have been frustrating for you too."

"You didn't altogether fail. It was fifty per cent success. You succeeded where David and I had tried for ages. I'm just going to need five minutes quiet to deal with this head Jules, so bear with me would you?" We'll take it in a curve here, and here, okay?."

Thus, with our trio clustered around Peter's form in the stillness of the Sanctuary, a distinctive and taxing rescue session was left to endure long upon our minds. Its failure, embraced by me as my own, made any confidence I had gained at rescue feel sunk in Pegwell Bay that night.

Every alternative method I dreamed up of handling the Australian couple – like to say we were customs officers after contraband and that they must go off with Brian for questioning – appeared more expedient, my actual attempt looking all the sillier. So much did I bludgeon myself over it, keeping a low profile whenever 'The Waterside' entered our conversation, that I never thought to ask David if we could have another chance with them.

Whilst Peter returned complaint-free he was later fascinated by this particular caseload, and part of me squirmed over his focus on it. I felt as though he almost enjoyed my discomfiture in a turn of tables from where he had previously seen himself the loser.

That part of me, quite unvoiced, felt indignant because his basic attitude first off had made himself loser, and because I myself didn't feel cut out either for rescue or tending his mediumship. Nor had I wanted these roles anyway. I rebelled inwardly. But my rebellion was soon to be outshone by his.

★ ★ ★ ★ ★

The more ignorant people are, the greater their distrust of that to which they are unaccustomed. Though we had tried to keep our work secret for Peter's sake, it was well nigh impossible to fend off from the door of Ashdene that hydra-headed monster of gossip, and it appeared we had drawn its fangs. Formerly we had been amused at the likelihood of village tittle-tattle. Yet Valerie's fifty-five years were long enough to know that even along the fringe of one's acquaintance can lurk those sufficiently narrow and censorious to undermine a labour of love – with the best moral intention of course.

One of our less frequent droppers-in at that period was Kenneth Carter, who numbered among her artistic circle locally. An oil painter like herself, affable, and living in the Sussex village of Chelwood Gate, he reminded me of an owlish, tweed-jacketed, boys' prep-school teacher, perhaps in his thirties, of medium build and height but rather far off medium in his sympathies.

Kenneth was inclined to dwell on obscure significances such as the recurring event of number nine in his life, which theme, during a lift home he once gave me courtesy of his Morris Minor, made the journey seem longer tha it was. On another occasion, in Ashdene's forecourt after an evening with us, I observed him remark out of his car window to Robert that he had come there "with nothing and left with a loaf". The loaf I believe had been given him by Robert, who was seen to blink cluelessly.

For us however, Kenneth reached his quirkiest point after he joined the obscure Baha'i sect. At least it was obscure in our eclectic range. Beyond their small, neat notices in newsagents' windows we knew next to nothing about them, for while we found no quarrel with their stance we had never linked its eddy with the new wave of knowledge affluent around us. Theirs had the look of a generalized view, a profession of belief in "the oneness of mankind and abolition of religious prejudice" – thought by us to be naïve but innocuous until they shattered our oneness with a Kenneth-led religious prejudice against Peter's mediumship.

That word 'obscure' sprung to mind throughout the whole business. It all mushroomed from his phone call to Peter, true content unknown because Peter's version of events tended to be the one that he thought was most agreeable, which meant that it often deviated a fair distance from the facts. His version got translated through Valerie to me. But what came across to both of us was that in the phone call Peter had obviously heard support at last for his underlying resentment of the work, and had decided to play on this welcome support with a vengeance.

Kenneth himself, we gathered, had somehow heard of the mediumship per se and discussed it among his Baha'i associates as a dreadful road to ruin – like discussing the telephone as ruinous in itself regardless of user or usage. Whether they were aware of our usage and its background we had no idea, though to us such minds were unlikely to have considered that far. They would think that any usage solely and automatically brought in the nastiest element and might hamper or arrest spiritual progress should one so much as lift the receiver.

Maybe we ought to have been prepared for this level of superstition, but we were not. I had forgotten the existence of such notions, and Valerie was dumbfounded from having thought Kenneth more intelligent. For us mediumship had never been an issue on its own, any more than was the telephone. It was just a perfectly natural means of talking with friends who lived on a higher sphere and lately with those on a lower one who needed their help. We took it for granted that the key factor was user and usage, determining how every phone call went in common sense terms.

We could only suppose Kenneth & Co. to be fearful of it under the usual materialistic assumption. If one assumes body and self are the same thing, then trance control will seem in theory like an invasion of the self. In practice Peter knew he was separate, but our summit meeting with him found he was firmly entrenched in two main arguments from them – which I thought were a cover-up for their basic fear. One of these concerned his soul-path "going the spiritual mile". The other dug up his worry about The Seven and their rescue cases being mere "submerged facets" of his personality.

I suggested he ask himself if the latter worry was perhaps rather far-fetched considering how many facets were involved. If it only applied to some, then which ones? Why these? And what of the rest? Furthermore he had to account for the fact that The Seven, and even their cases, demonstrated both corroboration and enlargement of existing discarnate knowledge received through a prolific number of independent channels over a century – knowledge which would take any student years to assimilate let alone express in that form. As an eight year student myself of such knowledge I told him how in my ears they could very easily have slipped up somewhere, but never had. Did he think his "facets" were genned up enough to seem faultless and well coordinated in so way-out a specialist area?

Psychical research, I added, had found no causal relationship between trance controls and cases of multiple personality. I offered him a look through case material where working psychiatrists had noted the distinction between them. For my part, study of multiple personality records plus sentient experience felt his controls to be distinct individuals, or I would not have gone this far with him. Yet it was a complex area. If he distrusted my judgment we could arrange a chat with College of Psychic Studies President Paul Beard, who had integrity, fairness and venerable insight into the subject. How did that grab him?

Not a lot. In him was fixity, a stiff deadness, as when Valerie had first broken the news of his seven colleagues. The minimal response he gave sounded to me as if he was after a face-saving device to cop out, not an unravelling. My suspicions of this had perhaps given an unintended edge to my tone in an otherwise sympathetic manner toward him, so Valerie switched tack. She thought his intention was to assert his independence, a freedom she had never in the first place taken from him. There was no need, she said, to bandy other people's dogmas for his freedom. He was free already.

It won nothing from his attitude. Instead we got thrown back at us the fixed idea he held of our having imposed a "heavy religious trip" on him by way of his role as medium. He argued that she was speaking of "freakdom not freedom". His sense of freakdom in the mediumship included all our "stuff" about raising oneself spiritually through deep meditation techniques, personal growth aids, knowledge of inner levels, and extending self in unconditional service to others via rescue work. "Going the spiritual mile", he called it.

Here of course he was getting nearer Valerie's nub, and doubtless he reckoned it would put her on the spot when he told her that the whole thrust was "not in the least necessary, according to religious sources" – by which was meant Kenneth, we construed. Provided one lived a blameless life, he said, worshipped God in faith, observed chastity and decency, obeyed the laws of one's country, then one's progress was surely heaven bound. With true faith, knowledge became superfluous. Mediumship was not a way to God, and he must relinquish it in order to be "saved".

At the absurd notion of our ever thinking mediumship a "way to God" she burst into laughter, then checked herself. His brows were knit. For a moment she had thought he was pulling her leg about "worship" and "chastity" and "faith". Coming from him these churchy morals were only tenable in that light, and had taken the sting out of his intended blow. Yet she saw that he was serious, miffed at not understanding the weakness of his case before her. She also saw him bringing the reluctant role he played among us to a head.

It was down to brass tacks therefore. Gently she reminded him that finding a way to God or practising mediumship was not our concern as a rescue team, him included. We had agreed to do the work on a purely secular basis because it had been offered us and felt imperative. He must appreciate this fact in his own agreeing. He should well know too that we were not concerned with, or interested in his religious sources. We were not even Spiritualists. We were basically a mixed bag of free-spirited, independent types much like him, using his ability to release earthbound people into a fuller life of their choice. Each individual, as Brian had said, *is* their own path "to the Oneness", and David had testified how injurious it can be for another to dictate in such matters.

None of us, she went on to say, were dictating to him. We were his fellow workers, as were The Seven, each on our chosen path and merely offering him information received through his own mouth from one of his inner colleagues. It implied that before birth he had given himself the facility not just to channel those who need help but also to shift his focus of identity to a more harmonised level of self which would transform his life beneficially. He didn't need to be "saved". He had prearranged his psychic constitution as a door with the key of love and acceptance in its lock, and he could open it whenever he wished to see there was no problem.

The scowl on his face made her speed up those last words for fear he might interrupt and miss their point with an old gripe or some new one. It turned out to be both. His win-or-lose attitude still claimed to feel dictated to, imposed upon, and by the sound of him had not expected rebuttal along such grass-root lines – which unsettled him anew. He defied her plea for a team discussion, where he would be outnumbered four to one.

His next objection, presumably also supplied him by Kenneth, was to us like a fusty and decrepit tombstone with weeds growing out of it – the one about holding discarnates back by communicating with them. She felt lowered, ashamed almost, at having to tell him what he must see perfectly well. Our contact was encouraging people on, not holding them back. As far for the Seven being communicated with, it was they who chose to do so with us, she reminded him, and the reason was not cosy chats in the parlour but of work which would evolve them on through practice of the love and compassion they extended toward "the lost ones". She quoted Ronald Beesley as saying how one progresses in the invisible world to the degree that one helps the world below one to progress. She had also read of discarnates stressing the fact, and quoted: "If we work through you we can evolve ourselves." She understood the work to require an extending of the self and therefore a growth of the self. Our chance of growth was also involved, she laid before him decisively.

He was unhearing however. The charity of his eyes and mouth

struggled hapless against the frown, with which he drew from his pocket a piece of paper. On it was a list of questions he wanted putting to Philip. Valerie's worried, pained stare at him as he handed it over was for me a mark of how serious she felt this dig-in of heels to be. One dared not ask what would happen if Philip's answers proved unsatisfactory. She disappeared upstairs to "beam" that man from her altar table, maybe clutching too at his early tender: "If you should need comfort at any time, please come to this place and wait for me."

Meanwhile my brief was to clear remaining doubts in Peter about "holding back the dead", and allay any other fears. I explained that Kenneth and Co. evidently had no grasp of normal mediumship let alone our special set-up. Had they even the most basic knowledge they would know the two reasons why any discarnate is held back, though nobody could be so held against their will. One reason was from selfish grief of the bereaved relative, and the other was frustrated discarnate attempts to contact the relative who had been warned on earth that they are holding back "the dead" by communicating. I added rather tactlessly that he was holding himself back from his inner nature if he refused to help them.

He rankled, accusing me of "intellectual babble" – which gave neither of us confidence while I went into a charge now made that the work put him in danger of "permanent possession.". According to case studies, I said, possession was normally due to ignorance on both sides in the unaware secular world. He himself by contrast had knowledge all around him. He always had discarnate sentries on hand, plus two earth guides, and was especially looked after because of the high pressure work we were doing. Should an intruder try full possession we were able to dislodge them. The only loophole left was his state of mind at present, which our information said was a good deal lower than he had planned it to be. Persistent fear tends to attract its object, as does love. He had the chief safeguard in his hands. By reversing his state of mind and looking to his higher self access, prearranged for true strength during the work, he could fill in that loophole.

I was failing to realise that none of the aforesaid would wash with him. My own mistaken belief was in thinking that an attitude was alterable simply by the correct information. I had no idea of how else to handle Peter, but facts were not his ball game. His mode opposite me, which had gradually become one of indifference, was developing into one of resistance. He got up from his settee and paced the room like he was ready for flight.

I tried to finish off by arguing that Kenneth & Co. could hardly know their ground since such restrictive beliefs must prevent them from exploring it. Hence every kind of untested precept is dragged in to excuse their fear or doubt, to make it sound knowledgeable when it is nothing of the sort, conjuring up bugbears which have no foundation in fact and are utterly disproved by experience. They were superstitions he was borrowing from I counselled him, and a superstition – as our cultured Langton neighbour Idries Shah defined it – is an emotional attitude toward a lie.

This won no mollified smile either of course. Tit for tat, he brought forth an old Victorian slur from Kenneth that afterlife accounts were too materialistic to be believed and must be due to subconscious imagination. Curiously I had often found that slur bundled in alongside those others, as though part of a standard package dealt out by sectarians to the infidel. My answer appraised him of an afterlife whose lower spheres were full of materialists from earth creating a world out of their subconscious imagination. Materialism's belief that only physical matter is real, and that all else arises therefrom, automatically conditions many passing over to extend their livingscape in a replicate earthly mould. But it is this same view which from earth pours scorn on afterlife accounts for portraying a materialistic scene. It has created that which it criticises.

Even the popular accounts of less earthbound life, I argued, still reflect the materialistic need of men and women in transition. True realities await them further on. But as Orlando pointed out, to go there requires a growth or enlargement of consciousness. Peter's channelling of David and Brian had featured glimpses of these levels which tallied with reports. If he thought such specific corroboration just came from his subconscious mind then seasoned researchers would like to know how. Again he was offered the chance of discussing his problems with one of them and again he paid no heed.

The counterblast I got was of wishful thinking and bias on my part, in fact on everyone's part who swallowed a heaven-world either too materialistic or "too ideal" for sensible belief. They would all be biased against him. In defence I explained that soul-realised discarnate minds together on their own level are bound to generate a relatively "ideal" world as compared with earth experience where diverse levels of mind abrade. Here on earth the ego-mind level is predominant, with mere shadows of the ideal, whereas higher degrees of consciousness find an increasingly truer actuality. If he had never seen a bouquet, but merely its shadow on the wall, he might think the true bouquet too ideal. Instead it would simply be more real. Anyway we were not "against" him, I protested, just trying to help resolve his queries. Didn't our answers satisfy him?

He had stopped pacing and now stood, thumbs in his jean pockets, near my settee, his gaze fixed out of the window. At my challenge he looked down upon me with frustration, sighed and turned for the door. He declared his intention to follow the Baha'is, with their easier, undemanding creed, and live an ordinary life. Their disapproval of mediumship suited him, he said, whoever was right, because he wanted the free prospect of not having doubt round his neck like a halter. So that was the end of the argument, and of his channelling. We would have to find somebody else to do our "dirty work". He had to finish some "proper" work in the shop. If I felt like coming through for company I must leave my "stuff" behind and be with him "in the real world".

These decisions were spoken sideward at me, his hand on the doorknob, before he strode out leaving the door open. My head hung low. I had now lost us the Channel himself. Was he really going to join those Baha'is? Peter? It sounded as absurd as Valerie joining the Salvation Army, bless them. Had she guessed his intent? If so her mind must be full of Philip's earliest warning: "He's going to leave, you know, and forget all this, unless we ... "

"Keep him on the path?" she had asked at the time, bringing Philip's reply: "In a way, but you mustn't stress this Valerie, because he doesn't know whether he wants it or not." At last then, he had made up his mind. Had we stressed it? I supposed we had. So The Seven must be on red alert. Suddenly that reminder of his list of questions for Philip jumped me up to call after him. It was evident on his face that he had forgotten, with a certain awkwardness. His rally was to tell me there was no longer any point, but I asked if he could at least give them a chance to answer him like he had us.

Back came the complaint of their nil response to his cri de coeur for proof, which to him meant their lack of credibility as separate people. So saying he strode on into the shop. Yet I saw he was a trifle conscience-stricken. My plea descended to the personal. What about us, his friends? Was its significance in our hearts of no account either? Valerie was waiting up there. She would feel the cut-off most. Might we not be allowed one last sitting, and say goodbye to The Seven?

Grudgingly Peter relented. An about-turn later, our entry upstairs met Valerie's long, earnestful look at both of us – one which nodded to me, lingered on him. She sat in her Mendlesham chair at the altar, his list of questions to hand. I have no recall of dialogue between them, only of how disconsolate she seemed, the sparkle gone from her eyes. Peter went straight to his settee, where he found himself with the incommodious task of oblivion and desired to be through with it as quickly as possible.

She switched on our background theme, the Adagietto from Mahler's fifth, while I took my position nearest him. Joining us in her lower drawn-up chair, she brought the list with her portable. Peter's lids were closed. We said nothing, nor made visual contact. The sole sounds were of our music, her brief tape-loading, and those of a storm which had begun its determined assault on Langton.

I think she and I prayed like we had never prayed before. When at length I came to my senses, Peter's body was limp and motionless, head down onto his chest, mouth open. I threw a side glance at Valerie who didn't return it. Though she was partly noticing the ingress of someone taking up control before us, her demeanor was abstracted as the channel's head raised a little. We knew it was David. The list was gently pressed into my hand. I greeted him and got to the point.

"We're sorry it has to be like this but … Peter is wanting to know a few things from you."

"Yes I know," answered David in grave voice.

"Do you know what the questions are, or do you want me to ask them?"

"Please wait, because *he* is going to speak with you this evening."

"Okay David." We understood whom was meant.

"But first of all," he continued, "we have somebody from outside our group who perhaps can allay the suspicions of the Channel. He is with John, unfortunately refusing to acknowledge us and too violent to be allowed in to speak   himself. He was, however, a close friend of Valerie's."

"Good Lord!" said she, stirred to herself again. "What, this violent person's a close friend?"

"He was. And we have from him certain data which will help to convince Peter. You need to remember April 13th 1965 onwards, a man called Ben."

"Oh Ben!"

"Does this mean anything to you?"

"It does. He was a doctor."

"His wife was called Clare," came the prompt.

"That's right. What happened there, then?"

"You know about it I think."

"Well I haven't seen him for a long time. Is he with you now?"

"No," said David. "But his associate is, whom you knew also, and who says that you came between them. I don't want to know if this is true or not. It is your own personal life. But if this means anything to you, then you will know we have the right person."

"Yes it's certainly the right person, and he did have a wife called Clare, but I didn't think I meant a great deal to him I must say. Anyway this should be enough to convince Peter."

"He did not love you?"

"No, not really love me."

"But you were together?"

"Yes I knew him for a while."

"And did you love him?"

"I think I did love him, yes. He was a wonderful … " She halted, unable of description.

"So the seeds were there," concluded David, "and you know of whom we talk."

"Yes. But this violent person is who, then?"

"We have no name."

"I see. Well I probably didn't realise what was going on at the time."

"April 1965," he prompted once more.

"Yes that's when I met Ben. Thank you so much David. Let's hope this will help."

"Now *he* will be with you."

At that promise I could feel her light up beside me. It had been long since I myself had spoken with Philip, tracing back to when our team had first gathered and he had said a little for Robert's benefit on his "some sort of small promotion" to a higher level earned from the work. He had said it without pride, in almost prosaic terms, which may be why I forgot to bear the shift of consciousness in mind.

So presently, after David's slow disengagement, I was unprepared for a rapid rise in atmospheric intensity not experienced before – as if the whole volume of the room was expanding from within itself. Measure by measure, rarefaction had me breathless to such a degree that offhand I assumed it to be independent, and not from the same source which elevated our channel to full seated height, head up. But the leaven was recognisably Philip as he took absolute control:

"I empty the room of all wrongdoers, and negative thought," he affirmed. "We need peace."

Seconds on, my breach of it was wobbly:

"Philip … the Channel has some questions for you."

"I know."

"Do you want me to ask each one in turn or what?"

"It is not necessary."

"Go ahead when you're ready then."

If he had not heard Peter express his questions physically he would have felt them all volleyed at him emotionally. I never looked at the list, which afterward disappeared back into Valerie's hands. One can surmise however that it was based more or less exactly on those put to us. The compact answer Philip gave certainly typified that of a senior discarnate, who looks from the opposite end of the telescope so to speak, and this sedate, upright figure in front of us started with somewhat wearied knowingness on the charge that he might be just a facet of Peter's own psyche.

"The first words I am tempted to use are these," rang out languorously. "That if he should look upon himself, he would realise that by writing questions to himself he is either a fool or he ignores you thus. They seem to me to explain a great deal about this young man's psychological make-up. The ego is very strong here. Used in a certain way, he knows that it can affect the personalities around him. And so his chasing after clouds is not necessarily for his own knowledge, but to put attention upon himself.

"Throughout your centuries, such questions as he asks have been asked by, not hundreds, not thousands, but millions of men. They are asked in fear and wilful ignorance. They are asked because men wish so much to disprove the afterlife. Subconsciously they know that, were it true, they would surely be creating for themselves a greater hell than they could ever imagine. If everybody in your world could listen to us, and if they could realise the valuable work that you – and indeed my whole group – perform, would there be war? Would there be killing and torture? None of these things would occur because of man's knowing that the hell he is creating upon his plane will surely go with him.

"In the Channel's case it is not wholly this which prompts him to ask his questions. It is partly so, and partly because the mind is a sieve. Old knowledge clings to the outside, but further knowledge added to this goes to the holes at the bottom and drops through. Those people who feel that it is not necessary to go through what the Channel has called the spiritual mile are putting themselves above reality. They are the ones of whom all our higher plane hospitals are full, the teaching homes are full. Their lives are not wasted because they are leading them in a Christian way, the way that they feel they should lead them. But they are going to repeat themselves.

"The work which you do, as I have said before, is invaluable. As personalities there, it is your reason for being together – nothing more and nothing less. In the beginning I also told you of the hard times you were to encounter. Then, you thought that it was from the beings whom you were going to help. But it is from the beings on your plane. Within a very short time, even the people amongst you who are called your friends will start doubting you. This of course is part of your chosen path, so designed that you may help lift your whole group through the spheres. You have both been with me. You both feel me next to you now. We shall all be together. When our task is completed, the next step will be available to us.

"At present the love of you both sustains me here. Slowly this body that surrounds me is soaking up your good thoughts. This Channel does need your help, but more than that he needs your ardent prayers. I must not stay much longer because my presence may be harmful after a certain time and is tiring for him. If you have a question please ask it."

"Well," Valerie mustered herself, "there's one other question bothering him, which we do know the answer to, but maybe it's best heard from you. He feels that to be a channel is holding him back spiritually."

"The only thing that will hold him back spiritually is his own ego in asking such questions. This is his job. It is what he has elected to do. Another of his questions concerns my statement on predestiny, which he should reflect to himself. He has chosen this work and he knows it."

"Is there any particular way we can help him?" she pressed. "I mean it seems very difficult to do so."

"I don't want you to help him in any physical or material way. But when you are helping him in love and prayer you are helping each other and us. We need our whole group to uplift its thoughts. My dear ones, when you have done that, then we may all move on. If you wish to use a simile from your plane, think of us all as a jig-saw. Without one piece we are not complete. So you must all help the pieces to fit, and form the complete picture. And then it can be moved."

She remembered their chat alone together in April when he had spoken of the group soul imprint.

"Yes, even you can't rise beyond a certain point until the rest of us have risen so far, can you?"

"Because I am part of you. You must not think of me as separate. We are all of The One."

"Er, while you're here Philip," I put in, "since we're recording your answers and Peter will be hearing them later on, is there anything you'd like to emphasise to him direct?"

"It is not necessary. I shall be with him when he listens. And now this power fades. I must wish you ... Yes, you may breathe again Jules! God bless you both my dear children."

"Thank you so much for coming," said Valerie, more grateful than her words. "May love be with you always."

"And with you," he returned in a whisper.

Long after he had gone we were still conscious of his transcendent atmosphere, embodying a kinship which it seemed nothing would now shake. Away went every shadow of my own rebellion over the waterside foul-up. I felt raised of spirit, aware that I could do my best as well as my worst. Valerie sounded in similar heart. Moments before Peter came back she laid a hand on my arm. "Let's just do what we can Julie-boy, and leave the rest up to him."

★ ★ ★ ★ ★

Peter's mood too was found changed after he got up from the session. In it was no basic change of resolve, but between the lines of his much softened interplay with us he appeared to realise that he had made himself look the dupe of opinion and the shuttlecock of ignorant minds. Maybe it was the impact of Philip's attitude on his subconscious. Anyway our easing of relationship brought tears into Valerie's eyes. They were automatic. She could do nothing about them but blink them away.

Although supper then pulled us down to the mundane, she and I were not wholly there. Something Philip had said of Peter was occupying our minds. We should have asked for qualification of the statement: "He has chosen this work and he knows it." Did he, the *earth* Peter *know* it? Why otherwise was the pronoun "he" used when our subject was the earthly level of him rather than the astral level? Perhaps at some stage over these months his ego itself had since grown aware, remembered his pledge with The Seven. If so, ongoing reluctance would hardly want to disclose it. Or did Philip mean semi-conscious knowledge, the kind one holds without letting oneself be aware of it? Knowledge which causes shame, psychologists say, can be hidden or cancelled out by fear of experiencing that shame. The subject knows all along, but ego-protection affects not to know involuntarily.

Nonetheless we had no wish to put either surmise directly to the test, for our prime concern was to manoeuvre a hearing of the tape without treading on his toes. As it happened, the three of us were still so heavy with the issue that to speak of anything else rang false, and by the time coffee was served he gave in to the situation of his own accord. "I might as well hear what's on your tape then," was the signal which hastened Valerie's finger to the button.

One might have thought, by the way he eyed her machine, that it was a scorpion poised to attack. But soon he was hearing of her erstwhile love affair, and his taut facial muscles relaxed around the scent of intrigue. To bring extra-marital romance within Peter's ken, especially of *her* past, was to bring it to a haven of piquant welcome where it would be stripped and inflated out of all proportion. So the evidential point of it was alas lost under his eagerness to probe her for particulars. He would have stopped the tape if she hadn't kept him in check. Any lowdown on it all was suppliable later, she ruled, insistent that he hear Philip.

To delay such gratification was not easy for him. His mischievous grin over her narrowed only as he heard Philip speak of him in less than radiant terms. His head lowered. One hand palmed up and down the nape of his neck, while a slight flush appeared on his cheeks. I was put in mind of the day when he came back from a haircut embarrassed by the result. Now as then, we felt it prudent not to scan him meantime, averting our gaze. When I looked once more, near the tape's end, he had a touch of that old rigidity across his face, and Valerie switched off the machine.

His attitude was no longer exactly mutinous, the scale of active opposition toned down, yet he didn't accept the value of answers given – treating them with disdainful sufferance. The chief complaint to wriggle from him called into question Philip's "waving the big stick of predestiny", which he said was reminiscent of his father going on at him over "a proper career". If he had free will, why could he not alter his chosen destiny? Did we honestly believe that one's fate was predestined for life?

I affirmed that we honestly did not. He could alter his destiny anytime, but for true effectiveness this had to be rearranged via the inner part of him which had set the former choice into motion – like our body has to breathe in deep before we can most effectively breathe out. At that however his blank face made me start afresh. I thought an analogy from his business world might mean more to him, as far as it went.

His chosen deal to supply all the flower decoration for a wedding involves a substantial agreement first with those concerned. He has agreed to supply goods and talent for his own benefit as well as that of the main figures and the guests. He signs a contract to carry this out at a particular place and time. Of course he can change his mind, break contract and go somewhere else, but it will obviously be far less convenient to do so because the arrangement will not be already there for him. He would have to start again from scratch with new people, time and place before it can be effective.

On a life plan scale, Philip's originally stating that "it's all been arranged for him", then referring to "predestiny", were integral with each other, I said. Everything was in place, set up ahead of time for his particular personality to fulfill itself through the work he had booked to do, which was probably meant to fan out in his own creative ways. His true self had agreed with soul companions to apply its personality talents along that route designed for it, the one he could safely follow to achieve the best effect.

Valerie lent me support here, quoting a discarnate teacher's guidance: "Fourth-dimensional planning acts into your three-dimensional world with care, precise economy, and no wastage of energy. In this way you are contained, part of a wider pattern, and must be prepared to trust, knowing that you are never quite tried beyond your strength." She also threw in bits of David's counsel to Rob Morgan: "Never forget that your life's path has already been planned by your self with your self. Your destiny is mapped before you, and only you can change it from inside." To do this one had to find "the master key within" which is attunement to one's inner self.

Undeterred by Peter's raised eyebrows, she told him that no one was waving any big stick. He could swan off and ignore the planned path if he wishes. We were not trying to curb his free will but advising him, as friends, of the most practical course which apparently he had set himself from a higher vantage. He could do as little or as much of the work as he preferred. We would never cast him out if he chose to do none at all. His home at Ashdene was not conditional on the work but on the friendship underway before it started. We just maintained like David that in matters of a higher plane the truth of his life was to be found within him, and not from the ego alone.

Through this he sat staring at the empty dishes of our supper, half-listening as would a small boy determined not to be outdone. There *had* been, I noticed, a slight rise with her assurance of his place at Ashdene, yet he seemed generally confused by a welter of credo altogether new to his ears. Unease in result had him piling the crockery while he told us he felt safer with himself rather than subservient to "some fabled alter ego". All the same, he would think about what we had said. I feared he merely meant to get us off his back, which was understandable.

I prompted him about David's evidence. It had to be prised apart from the affair aspect, but he agreed again to chew the token over on his own. Otherwise our "philosophy", he was sorry to say, had not altered his scruples about the mediumship, and if ever he did choose to continue he still wanted "a good long break for the time being". Perhaps Valerie saw the guilt in his not meeting our eyes as he spoke, because she reached out and squeezed his hand:

"It's alright darl', don't worry."

With a sheepish smile he moved behind us into the kitchen, put down the crockery and paused.

"By the way Val, can I keep chickens down near the shed?"

She looked round at me in amazement. We both turned to see him grinning cheekily, and the sheer nerve of it released our tension into laughter.

The days passed relatively smoothly, Valerie and I bearing our disappointment. Had we taken a resentful attitude toward Peter it would have been as difficult as to resent the spontaneous advances of a young puppy, now that his bonhomie had picked up. But we did feel displaced, out of joint when not anticipating contact with The Seven and rescue work on Friday. Nor did we know whether the crisis was alleviated or just delayed in a wholesale nose-dive.

Robert and J.M. were soon informed of the stoppage and turned up anyway for a summary confab on it, part of which Valerie recorded.

"I suppose it's predictable," opined Robert, "that in such an open house our Channel would get nobbled by cultish intruders at some time or another, projecting their jaundiced beliefs into a field they know nothing about. The level of miscomprehension makes one think of those astral bullies, except it's had worse effect! Kenneth's an odd, mixed-up cove. He means well but his curiosity is easily satisfied by his imagination. So we must see them in perspective as we do the earthbound, and have patience with Peter. He'll probably simmer down if left alone for a while."

"Yes I agree," said J.M. "We have to go easy, take it on the chin because our work is up against the same kind of hang-ups and misunderstanding that you'll find over any project outside the conventional frame. Humour and centredness are important, knowing that ripples on the surface can't affect the depths. I think he'll see-saw back again, if only from feeling awkward in the gap. Or The Seven might try chats with him during sleep-life."

Not long afterward Kenneth and two of his Baha'i associates dropped in unannounced. My arrival that evening found them perched upright along Valerie's settee like an owl and two sparrows, regarded coolly by her long leonine silhouette opposite. The glance she cast at me seemed to say: "Well they just came. I couldn't really turn them away could I?" Indeed she could not. My mild courtesy toward Kenneth, who then introduced his little army, had a sinking expectance of battle. On the other hand they were both unexpectedly young, tame-looking, vulnerable, quite contrary to the busybody mould. Whilst I was a young twenty-four they appeared younger, a pair of diminutive raven-haired girls – a Baha'i version of those Mormon youth-missionaries I thought.

The outcome was also something of an anti-climax. Mediumship I gathered had again been the core of their offensive, even if now their expressions told me it was her mature adamance, with the dignity of a duchess, which muted them. She was rounding off with the fact that Peter had heard the Baha'i view and he had heard ours, so we felt he should be left alone to make up his own mind, as should we be to follow our choice of path.

On their issue, her use of the heart may well have reached them where my heady blast never could. Little else is recalled thereafter, except my spoonful about something esoteric, its drift since forgotten, which attracted eager enquiry from the girls. A vague image of them, perfectly pleasant, asking questions on the human aura, fades without memory of them leaving – or of Kenneth having said a word.

★ ★ ★ ★ ★

In a corner of Ashdene's old white-walled garden, tucked around the shedside nook, there appeared a frame of chicken wire. Next to materialise was a sturdy henhouse and two meal sacks. Then across my early morning ponder upstairs broke, "Cock-a-doodle-doo!" followed by a carillon of clucking. I opened the Sanctuary window to meet Peter's prideful beam at me from below:

"Langton used to have a night life till someone shot the owl," he wagged. "Now it's got a crack o'dawn life. Brought them over from Chid," by which he meant his village of Chiddingstone.

He had absorbed himself in rustic busyness. For a week or two the ply of his hoe and cluck of hens would rise clearly on the summer air, mingled with our chink of teacups. All the more rum was it therefore, during such an afternoon, for Valerie to find him in his Sanctuary seat, upright, eyes closed, and insensible.

Baffled, she sat with him awhile, anticipating trance control. But when none took place she became mindful of that comatose state into which he had first fallen long ago. At the time, he had awakened after ten minutes, though ten was now twenty and she called me up from the garden. I tried de-mesmerising passes and other gentle means without result. To me, his state resembled the paralysis widely experienced before projection of the astral body. I kept this to myself because unsure, hearing Valerie already on the phone to Dr Hicks.

Half an hour later, patient unchanged, her anxiety had risen beside the doctor-figure who loomed large and arbitrary in that small, private sanctum of ours, his worldly bag plonked on the settee. As he began to examine Peter's body I felt superfluous and went downstairs. In due course Hicks descended, Valerie behind, she showing him out amid muffled exchange. Her return to me made a shrug of shoulders. Peter had been medicated and lugged dopily onto his bed. His condition was given a psychiatric-sounding label which eluded her, prognosis full recovery in an hour or so.

Within the hour his footfall was heard on the stair, and a bewildered face made entrance. He told us that he felt okay, if groggy. We bade him sit for a cuppa, over which he traced back to the random whim of mending Valerie's altar lamp base as she had frequently asked of him. In search of his dropped screwdriver he had grown dizzy, taken to the nearest seat, and undergone "that tunnel experience" of yore. He had no recall of the Doctor, or of going to bed. Our fill-in saw him disconcerted, though used as he was to sudden oblivion it bore less weight than his urge gardenwards again.

Valerie and I agreed on a writing session to check this event out. The indispensable Betty was keen of response, and the next afternoon her hand was conjoined with Valerie's upon their Sanctuary writing pad in wait for Orlando. He was longer arriving than usual, but gave immediate answer to their enquiry:

"Do not be concerned. Channel asked here for inner tuition. Ego coined its own excuse. Earth form given temporary shield against lost ones."

"You mean the paralysis?"

"Yes."

"So you're trying to negotiate with him perhaps?"

"Refer above."

"Do you want us to do anything?"

"Please pray in love as advised."

"What do you think of his absorption in chickens?"

"Excellent and meant for him. Much else is self-planned for his earthly enjoyment. Please encourage, and have faith that all is working for the good. He needs this time of renewal."

"We tried hard," said Valerie, "to answer his objections to the work, and told him we supported his freedom if he didn't do it. Should we lean more on him though?"

"Pressure not advisable. Love and trust. Show him your support for his enjoyment too. Group now waiting for me. Will explain anon. Blessings to you."

He had gone before they could lay down their pen. If The Seven were up to something, thought Valerie, she had no idea what it might be, and nor did I in examining those answers later. Our only conclusions were that Peter should be shown our sincere encouragement, and that during his "time of renewal" he needed to "feel himself outside us", as Valerie put it, "so he could come in again of his own free will". She was unprepared though, when the same week he asked to join her in meditation.

He had assumed this to be the whole purpose of her daily sojourns in the Sanctuary, whereas they were half devoted to prayer for the earthbound. Expecting a fair number would be present she told him of her concern for his security, but he dismissed it all cavalier-fashion. Nothing of the kind was going to happen now he had "got on top of the situation", and was in a better state to "find the master key within", ran his surprise announcement, using her quote. The fact that nothing happened in his most recent header was proof wasn't it? This time no blackout either. Once his chickens were put to bed he would join her up there and stay conscious.

She dared not refute him, despite there being nobody to sit with her in support. Maybe his stimulant came from the "inner tuition", or maybe he sought artlessly to change his path from within. At least David or Brian would be alert to the situation and stand on guard, she comforted herself, setting off upstairs. They might even make use of it. Another element was unthought-of however until she had waited some time in readiness for him.

He called from the garden to report a spot of chicken trouble, pending which she should start without him, so she did. Sounds below of a chicken-chase round the foliage were drowned by her music tape. It rolled on, she taking upliftment and giving her compassionate thoughts to all those who are lost. This form of work was her preferred one, and she applied herself heartily. But toward his own aim Peter slid into position rather breathless, dog-tired, with much of its impetus gone, she read between a few unempathic words. Her effort at prayer continued silently, the last round over him. By that time he was out for the count.

Having already turned her altar chair to half face him, she was soon bracing to meet full-on the attempt of someone at control. In the circumstance, and not recognizing any mannerism, she felt a spasm of unease. Then the head lifted and a quiet, modest tone named itself as

"John Wheeler". He was apologetic, saying how intrusive he felt, partly because he had heard her urging people away to higher guidance. He had feared he might be unwelcome.

Sure of his bona fide she grabbed her trim portable, which was always primed, switched it on and moved into the closer chair to reassure him.

"Well I didn't pray that you shouldn't be here John. I prayed that you should all be loved, and blessed, and healed."

"Your thoughts are a great blessing to me," he said. "They affect us more acutely than you know. I ought not to be here anyway, but I so much wanted to thank you for what you have done."

"Oh good!" Her pleasure was evident. "I did it because I thought there would be some here who would be helped by it. What else should you be doing then John?"

"Teaching."

"Who do you teach?"

"I teach the young children."

"Oh you do? Still, perhaps it's nice to have a little rest here, and I'm glad you did."

"I nearly went without talking. There are quite a number here who have listened, but often they can't use the channel. So it seemed a good idea to try and thank you on their behalf too. Do you have a brother?"

"Yes I have."

"Was he in the Services?"

"He was never strictly in the Wartime Services, no. He was killed when he was twenty-two, at the beginning of the War."

"He told me he was a cadet."

"I think he was in the O.T.C. that was all. Is he alright?"

"Yes. He said he's watched the Channel react to you sometimes in the same way he himself used to, and that you were always saying, don't y'know, too much."

"Oh gosh yes, I'd forgotten all about that phase. My mother has often asked me to find out how he is, and I had thought of broaching it at some point but … "

"Is this person really your brother? Quite a few here want to talk you see, and would use the slightest knowledge as an excuse."

"That's a thought. So it might not be him."

"No I think this man merely wishes to come in."

"Actually I don't think he did react to me like the Channel because he and I weren't close enough. In fact we weren't close at all, and we hadn't even seen each other for a number of years before he passed on."

"Do you talk to any of your relations through here?"

"No I don't ever. There isn't anyone close who's gone on. I've sat with professional clairvoyants who refer vaguely to some distant aunt, but like a lot of people I don't find this useful or significant. It's much more worthwhile to talk personally with someone like yourself who works over there, or to try and help people who are genuinely in need of comfort and right direction. This is why I prayed just now. It was for the bewildered ones I felt were here, and who might be comforted by the music or the words."

"It was your rays of thought which comforted most."

"So when I come up to do meditation, which I try to do every day, and then pray for those gathered who might be listening, they really do benefit from this do they?"

"Oh yes it helps them a great deal. If you could see how your compassion moves out of your aura like waves of sunshine to disperse their fog and warm them, you'd be surprised. Your recognition of their presence is also reassuring to them, because they are mostly ignored by people on earth and this creates much bad feeling."

"I suppose it must. They don't always need to come through and talk then?"

"Not always. But it helps the ones who can, and the ones for whom it's the only recourse because they are so unaware. Different people have different needs. I enjoyed the words of your meditation, particularly the reference to the lotus."

"Peter didn't hear much of it I suppose, although he was the one who asked to do meditation this evening."

"Your brother?"

"No this Peter – the Channel."

"Oh is his name Peter too? I'm sorry."

"Yes. And do you know the other young men who work with him – with the Channel Peter I mean?"

"I know two of them."

"They've been doing the rescue work with us, David and Brian that is."

"Yes, I help the children under David. But it's a very large community here and I don't know everyone."

"Orlando said there was a large number of you, and you're not one we've spoken to before."

"No, but I'm not troubled. One rarely has the chance to speak, and they let me come in this time."

"Is there anything else you'd like to talk to me about, now that you're in the channel?"

"Tell me about yourself."

"Ah well, there's such a lot really. I don't know what you'd like me to go into. It's so difficult telling people about oneself."

"It's more difficult from over here because in our world we very often see and hear things concerning your plane which you might not accept. Some of the things we would tell you I fear would be ridiculed there."

"Yes on earth generally perhaps. But most people we talk to have a glimmer of understanding, so they're unlikely to ridicule."

"There is something from what we see which I could tell you. It's about a great deal of trouble on your plane between peoples in the East."

"And this is sort of ahead in the year 2000 is it?"

"No at the end of this month."

"Gosh, and it's going to involve England?"

"No, in the East."

"Oh. Is there anything else? There must be many things I'm sure, not necessarily about the earth but about personal things I mean. It must be awkward for you though, because I find it so from this side. One can't see you or your reactions properly, like talking to a complete stranger over the phone here. One knows you're there, and yet it's awkward trying to relate with you, if you see what I mean."

"Yes it's the same for us, because we see you in such a different way. I don't know how to even begin explaining that. David suggested I just answer your questions."

"Well, are you happy?"

"Ohh!" he breathed. "I wish I could think of a word to describe my state of happiness to you. Terribly happy will do."

"Good. I'm so glad after all the rescuees we get."

"Please do not judge by those. There are many who are happy here."

"You've no wish to incarnate back on earth?"

"No, although I've been here a great many years now."

"So there's no pressing necessity to incarnate?"

"Necessity but not pressing. Perhaps I will, but I must talk first."

"Yes you have to decide, before you do incarnate, the sort of life which will suit you best in order to exercise your soul's potential don't you?"

"Yes."

"It's no good coming without a plan, because you can lead such a wasted life."

"I'm afraid many do. But I must leave now. I've been here long enough."

"Alright John. Well it's been lovely talking to you."

"I'm sorry about your brother."

"Yes. Maybe it isn't him who's there."

"You see, you must be wary of charlatans here as on earth. They'll use any trick to get through to you, which is quite natural because they are very desperate people who haven't yet grown up in our worlds."

"Yes I know. Anyway I'm glad that the meditation tape was pleasant for everybody, and that it comforted some of them."

"It was truly beautiful. Thank you."

"Now the Channel will come back straightaway will he? No desperate people will slip in?"

"No, our friends have drawn around to protect. I think he is among them. God bless you for all you have done."

"Thanks, and give my love to the children."

In her wait she acknowledged that whilst outwardly their chat had amounted to nothing much, John Wheeler's feedback to her prayer effort, given with sincerity and from eye witness, was an inward boon. She had been heartened to learn how direct was the impact on those near, underlining a onetime discarnate statement: "We are naked to every impact of thought." Moreover during this purdah of ours from The Seven, tonight's humble exchange had seemed to her as salient and unexpected as a song in prison.

Not until Peter had woken sheepish over his lapse did she click that no reference had been made to the stoppage. She herself had become too absorbed with what John Wheeler was saying, and the novelty of him, to ask. If he knew that our work was on hold perhaps he was not inclined to comment from his outer position, beside prior advice just to answer her questions. Had one of The Seven shown up instead, her interview would no doubt have centred round Peter. She told him about the mention of her brother, which aroused his curiosity enough to hear the whole tape and drift away afterward looking thoughtful – more impressed than he let her know.

So our much-argued interworld mission was still left in the air above Ashdene, where it hovered laden but passive with an inscrutable element. If John Wheeler could use the channel why not his senior colleagues? Was Peter's subconscious blocking them? Surely they could have passed her a message anyway? All we had was Orlando's message, part luminous, part mysterious: "Channel asked here for inner tuition ... all working to the good ... group now waiting for me. Will explain anon." What inner tuition? What to explain? Nor had he ever ended in such a strange, opaque key. Valerie stood now at the Sanctuary window, seeing through it in symbolic form the erratic light of a stormy summer evening.

★ ★ ★ ★ ★

Often it can be the less obvious factors, rather than those directly in our sight, which spark off required change. David had hoped to impress Peter with their accuracy on Valerie's '65 affair, failing which he may have allowed John Wheeler's use of the channel just to bridge our gap a bit. We thought it unlikely however that he calculated its produce. The fact was that Peter had been quite taken by the hearsay of Valerie's brother, and placed much credence on the whole Wheeler communication. He said that it came across as humanly natural to him, having a casual "more real" openness.

It leant him to the possibility of contact with his late grandmother, whose welfare interested him. David's message about her, since conveyed by us, that "she will be able to communicate soon" and that we could put his written questions, promptly outclassed his Baha'i sympathies along with the "master keys" aim. As one who drops the pebbles he has been holding once he finds a ruby in his grasp, Peter now substituted Granny whom he had known round the farm inglenook.

Upon an evening therefore which Valerie and I had set aside to pray for him as advised, he joined us in the Sanctuary to supply her channel. Whether he saw the irony of it compared to our last session together, this time handing Valerie a list of questions to prove rather than disprove, I cannot say. The dead cert is that when he handed them over he was blissfully unaware of his mistake in assuming one may "call up" any chosen discarnate to order.

Nor were we about to enlighten him. Apart from not wishing to dampen his positive spirit we had in mind David's hope that contact with her "might help him to believe in us more", and Valerie had sent a quick beam to signal readiness if the lady was available. Besides, our aim of concentrated prayer, with him its innocent subject, not only made his presence useful but was also some degree of shield against intruders. With regard to anyone else we kept an open mind.

In the event, not our three open minds put together could have conceived what was shortly to happen. My first sense of it was an eerie preternatural stillness transcending the Sanctuary kind. Its immanence was felt despite our music tape, peculiarly interior as well as exterior, near and remote at the same time. There was no sense of its having crept in, just of its already-being. Paradoxical to be sure. I examined Peter who had long gone with a will. But my side peek at Valerie saw her eyes and mouth wide, seeming awed. She closed her eyes and opened them again twice. I did so myself to perceive that, with them closed, the stillness became an incredible quality of light – yet one whose wholesale brilliance was, by nature, not light at all.

Its quality I realised was expanding not in itself but with my own gradual acceptance of it as supercharged energy – a gigantic dynamism over-within-around us, pure and tranquil, personal yet impersonal, investing us to an extent that I found a tad scary. The dynamism was stretching me beyond my unison glimpse months ago into a much broader aware-state, like going up in a glass-walled lift out of all mental paradigms. One translatable aspect was my grasp of everything everywhere as immense, creative goodness, and that apparent evil is the same goodness temporarily distorted by the unevolved ignorance of its seed units. Such imbuement would serve me well.

There and then, as though laid back in place by a gentle giant, I was restored to physical focus. The murk of the Sanctuary had become electric. Valerie was staring fixedly at Peter's form. It bore no mark of its owner, or of familiar control, or of any earthbound type, except that the head had risen. Something about it was untouchable and unfathomable. We held fast, riveted by an absence of anyone we recognized, which was also a definite presence.

"What's going on?" she whispered to me.

I was stuck for an answer. Never had my varied medium-filled years been so flummoxed. Call me slow, but I failed to connect my inner experience with who was there. It had seemed too vast for embodiment in our channel. She had timidly switched on her recorder when of a sudden the presence spoke:

"CEASE ALL NOISE. THERE MUST BE SILENCE."

We gaped until she found tongue:

"Is the recorder too much noise?"

"IT IS NOT PART OF US."

From a long quietude the presence spoke again.

"WE ARE MOULDED TOGETHER. I AM THE VOICE OF YOUR COLLECTIVE CONSCIOUSNESS. THE POWER YOU FEEL THROUGH ME YOU WILL FEEL WHEN YOU JOIN ONE OF OURS. WE MAY NOT BE ALIGNED IF ONE PIECE IS MISSING. WE MUST BLOSSOM. AS A COLLECTIVE FORCE WE MUST BLOSSOM. I AM ALL OF YOU. I AM YOUR SEVENTH, THE EMOTIONAL BEING OF YOU ALL. IN YOUR HIGHER STATE I KNOW YOU ALL, BECAUSE I AM."

The delivery stopped. Its source lingered, then let go of the channel. Under her breath Valerie said "Gosh", and dumbly my wits struggled to contain this as an objective experience. Was it so improbable?

There followed several minutes lull with no exchange between us, just a waiting for what would happen next. Eventually we recognised David's slow engagement. He broke silence without greeting, and in subdued tone, leaving us to realise that the others were with him.

"We have had far to come, Jules and Valerie. It's an effort this evening."

"I'm sorry, is it the channel's condition?" I asked.

"No it is not your fault. We have been with Us. We have been a long way. We must restart the group."

"Do you mean people-wise if the Channel restarts?"

"Yes."

"So you want a much stabler, harmonised team here in place of the hasty assemblage we started with?"

"Yes, but now you will know them."

"I see. At least I think I do."

My assumption was that he meant people whom we would "know" inwardly as having agreed, prebirth maybe, to join us. Of course it put a question mark over our existing team-mates. I asked if he could say more but he shifted away without an answer.

Another silence ensued until, barely recognisable, Brian trailed in. Valerie was now hungrier for facts:

"What's going on Brian? Can you tell us?"

"The room is so full. It's difficult."

"We gather it isn't a channel problem," I said.

"The channel is perfectly flexible, but full of dark rays. We have been to Us. We know what we must do. There are to be five in your group. There are two yet to come."

From the arithmetic Valerie figured one departure.

"Can you say if Robert is meant to come back?"

"Please don't treat me as different to yourselves. You must know. You have been told."

He sighed and retreated. Evidently they were in shock, call it spiritual shock, from their journey of consciousness to the group soul nucleus and the greater perspective on how their plan was going, as well as from their downturn back to base camp and then further to us. Brian's emotion at seeing the actuality so far, I took it, had muddled ourselves on their level with our ego on earth, unable to believe we had stayed ignorant.

Next to drift in was a very mind-blown John, who greeted me as usual by name though feebly. My reply half joked over the change in him.

"Hallo John. It is John isn't it?"

"Yes … 'fraid so."

"You sound awful old chap."

"We have been with our Selves, and it's difficult to come through to you. We must not play. We have such a short time. We must use the time well. We depend on each other so much. Nothing must be wasted."

"Okay, we won't press you into saying any more. It must be hard for you."

He left, with uncharacteristic relief I thought. Valerie had muttered a, "Yes", on each statement he made, while I was wondering what precisely lay behind them. Out of nowhere however a sudden reflux of The Presence overshadowed my thinking.

"GATHER UNTO ME, FOR YOU WILL BE LIFTED. THE TIME IS SHORT. WE MUST FINISH ALL THAT REMAINS. WE RISE AS ONE. GOD BLESS US."

It sounded like an utterance made for more than us two. The room was certainly full, as Brian had said, and I knew it was not the fullness of a rescue night. Maybe other group soul members were there, at levels to which that call had more context than it did to us.

The Presence faded out of our awareness by degrees, like the decrescendo of some major symphony, and soon another of The Seven was on his way through.

"Good evening Jules. It's Orlando. Good evening Valerie. It's very full isn't it!"

"Yes it is," I agreed, "and a very rum session."

He had last said that the group was now waiting for him, at which time they must have been setting out. So here he was returned, and communicative too.

"We must help each other. You don't understand. We all now understand. We have been to The Record ... our thought processes."

"The Akashic Record?" asked Valerie.

"No our path record. We must try to work together. It's so black in here. We've come a long way to you."

"If there's anything we should know Orlando," I pressed, "you will tell us won't you?"

"Two of the original people are not here," said he.

We both misconstrued him:

"Well Robert's on holiday."

"And Renée couldn't stay because ... "

"Oh I don't mean those two. We're all linked. When you meet them you will know. We have so little time. We depend on each other."

"We'll do all we can," promised Valerie.

"We will help you. We have more serious work to do. We must stop using the channel for frivolous communication. If you could see ... Oh, if you could see what we have seen! But we're advised not to talk."

The reason for that, it occurred to us, was to avoid prejudicing our free-will choices. Valerie set aside her disappointment.

"We'll try to redouble our prayer effort."

"You will be told how we can progress."

"Good," said I. "Alright Orlando, thank you."

He floated off summarily with that distrait air the colleagues shared tonight. Of the five we knew, only Philip hadn't come, and for him Valerie wore a look of hopefulness. But instead a little character unknown to me popped in. He had an innocent feel, which put my intent to close the session on hold.

"Hello!" he chirped. "I bet you can't guess who this is!"

Valerie did so in a trice, however, as being one of the children nurtured by David and John Wheeler. On that afternoon when the tape had broken down he had tagged along behind David and chatted briefly with her. She remembered his name too.

"Harry?"

"Yes!" he glowed. "I've just come to say hello."

"How are you?"

"We're all fed up. David isn't here."

"He was here earlier," I marked.

"Everybody's gone," was the moping reply.

"Where to?" asked Valerie.

"I can't tell you, but it's always nasty when they've had to go there because they're always so strict when they come back." He then whispered excitedly: "Shall I take you somewhere? We're not really supposed to go though."

"Describe it to us Harry," she prompted, without realising he was already set in concentrative mode. Thirty seconds or so went by till her expectance ran out. "He's gone."

"No I'm not. I was just taking us there. It's a very strange place. Lots of hills. On the hills are those boxes ... houses ... and there are very strange people that live in them. We're not supposed to come here on our own. Do you want to speak to some of them?"

"What do you think Jules?" she conferred.

"I'm reluctant without David's guidance."

"But I can do it!" cried the lad indignantly.

"Perhaps we shouldn't Harry," came her check, "without David saying yes."

"Ohh!" he winged. "I'm going then. You won't do anything I want to do!"

Once he was out I summoned Peter, though got no inkling of him. Surely by now he must be ready and waiting? Within a short space not he but David was back:

"Jules?"

"Hullo David."

"You must cease. Listen to what we have said and please discuss it. Our journey has made it difficult for us to speak. We will do so again in the next few days when we have assimilated what we have seen and are able to share something of it with you. The Channel will be informed as to when. Please don't encourage Harry and the children, and please don't think too harshly of us for we are all shaken. Our love goes with you as always. God bless you."

Taking this in I lost the chance to mention our need of Peter, but reckoned David must be aware and gone to fetch him. While we hung on, a woman worker from their hospital came through saying that Orlando had arranged it. She introduced herself as Frances, and queried my asking her to be brief:

"Why?"

"Sorry, it's only that David wants us to stop. We have a lot to discuss."

"I was just listening to you and then we all had to move when he came. He's so large isn't he! John said I could come after they had. He hasn't been around for some time, and we've missed him."

Valerie took over as the one promised this visit:

"Can you tell us something about yourself Frances?"

"I help by taking people for walks in the grounds and that sort of thing. I used to be a nurse you see. It was so different there. I do see all the mistakes I made though. We don't have to see them if we don't want to."

"But you do eventually?"

"Yes it makes my work with John and David happier."

"In the sort of hospital or rehabilitation centre?"

"Yes, and … "

Peter's sudden inrush cut the interview. Dopily he muttered the words "nasty shock", I imagined from his fast reentry or collision with Frances. Otherwise he didn't say much, appearing spaced-out. I gave him a drink of water and had to help him downstairs, where not much was said either. Normally we might have been anxious that he would ask after his grandmother whose contact he had gone up there to supply, but in fact we had forgotten about her. More surprising was that he hadn't mentioned it. His list of questions to her remained on the altar table, unnoticed by any of us.

He did ask who had come through. We named the four distrait colleagues, at which he gave a slow nod and gazed out of the window with unobservant eyes, his customary animation still suspended, saying he could now believe in them more – without saying why. Our leave-him-alone policy left his reason alone. We felt he needed his own digestion of experience clear of our account, so talk was kept to the mundane. After a quiet supper he jumped up, almost himself again, in recollection of his chickens and went into the garden.

Straightaway we fell to discussing what exactly could have turned him. Valerie put her bet on the Presence or another discarnate meet-up, while I opted for a general fusion of effect on his subconscious and actually experiencing himself among those assembled.

We switched from there to the session's effect on ourselves. By and large Valerie's inner sentience fitted mine, though heartful instead of heedful. It prompted me at last to relate my original glimpse of unison way back in April, thus confirming her stimulus tonight that we should take our group soul involvement more seriously.

Not that we were careless about it. Both of us had read of group soul structure years before, in passing, and were acquainted with it as a concept. My study of its inception through the mineral, vegetable and animal kingdoms, again in passing, had soon moved to her scan of the human stage from books like Testimony of Light and Road to Immortality. But neither of us had given it any special attention or even discussed it. There was no desire in us to belong to anything. Strangely enough, throughout my studies I never once thought in terms of myself being part of a group soul. For all I know Valerie didn't either. Now, out of the blue, we found ourselves not only in working collaboration with our own group but addressed prima facie by its Nucleus and wrapped in an integral experience of "Us". The transfer from book to life was almost from native of earth to astral missionary in our outpost here.

Agreeing to let it sink in, we had started on the matter of two unknown absentees when the back door opened and Peter was hovering there solicitous:

"Hey did Gran come through?"

A momentary standstill, which recalled his motive for channelling, saw Valerie first off the mark. In motherly fashion she explained the slim chance of his relative being yet ready after her convalescence to communicate short notice at the precise time he chose. Hadn't he often picked up the phone to find a person engaged or away? Even if she were free it was David who had promised to arrange it and he had been away with the others outside their normal sphere. But as soon as Betty's help was secured for writing contact we would make a firmer arrangement via Orlando.

The complexity took Peter unawares:

"Oh, well let me know when it's fixed okay?"

Her assent sped him back into the garden, and us back into discussing those absentees – two "original people" who were apparently meant to have joined us at the start and had never turned up. There should have been five of us at rescue, according to Brian, which seemed rather a squeeze physically and awkward personally if the two did come – unless one of us left. Then again, why must we expect them to come all of a sudden simply because The Seven had realised their absence? Two missing from the start however would explain an incongruous team thus far. What baffled us most was how we could "restart the group" without a complete come-back by Peter, let alone how "in the next few days" he would become "informed" and disposed to channel for anyone except Grandma.

★ ★ ★ ★ ★

Our doubt had underrated a seminal aspect of Peter's world: the shop. This creative fulfillment of his was serious stuff. It enabled him to support his family, buy the children presents, take them on outings, and keep himself in fashionable clothes. It also provided his access to relationships beyond Ashdene, meaningful for such an outgoing character as he. In particular it gained him entrance to society functions which called upon his floral skill, a much relished chance to mix with the rich and well-to-do. Through its business he was able to connect with his valued secular reality and make his unique impact on it. Any person or thing therefore seen to affect the shop's welfare, almost his raison d'être, affected his regard of that person or thing in direct ratio.

Several weeks ago he had played at asking favours of The Seven, occasionally with mild result it appeared. He had asked for a specific rare flora and got something near it, which whetted his appetite. Not all favours were shop-related, though lately they had become so in his ambitious drive to increase business. His appeals had piled up for the rarest of flora and unlikeliest of business connections, whose lack of result had made him shrug off the whole idea. That is, until a turn of tide.

Remarkably they now began to trickle in, one by one, "as ordered", he said with fascination. By what he termed extraordinary coincidences, chance meetings and the like, he was coming into receipt of the exact rare plants and the two commercial opportunities sought. His business was booming it seemed, with even dealers "amazed" at his "luck",

To attribute this bounty to The Seven, I felt, was altogether rash. In my opinion a more feasible cause was either those "self-planned" fruits for enjoyment, or his sheer drive and desire-power bringing it to him spontaneously. But attribute it to the Seven he did. Valerie rung me the newsflash once it had stood the test of time. She said he was "absolutely over the moon", and I came to see for myself. Without doubt he was somewhat changed, a new lightness in his step and voice. One could tell that for him there was no doubt of their being responsible. He had ordered and they had supplied. Simple as that. They had done a "more real" thing, also affecting the welfare of his shop.

Naturally the cause mattered less to us than his turning-point of belief, and as the success stories died down our sanguine faces became obvious to him. He threw us the knowing look of capitulation. "Fair's fair," said his euphoria, "a deal is a deal", and he agreed to continue channelling provisionally. With the relief it gave us, we took his proviso of the shop's future welfare on faith. We could see that he meant it. We had got through our valley of the shadow. Our way was clear again.

Valerie was then the artful dealer. Would he offer a session right now to show his bona fides? An obvious unreadiness in him balked slightly. We recognized of old his cast-about for a reason why not, she watching him with tongue-in-cheek discernment, both of them breaking into grins.

"Get out of that one darl'!" she teased, at which he put on a mock grimace to plea that conditions were probably frightful.

"No they couldn't be better Pete, brilliant in fact!"

He chuckled with the fun of drawing her, and gave in freely. My sole reserve, as we moved upstairs, was David having said "the channel will be informed" when next they could speak, though he must have meant on an inner cue which the ego would make its own. Perhaps Valerie had been so informed too. At any rate he was attaching no strings and she had already prepared the Sanctuary.

We took our usual seats, Peter resigning himself into his. The routine felt habit-worn and yet housing a rebirth this time into the new. Whatever change The Seven had in mind after their higher vision was still largely inscrutable, but we remembered being told that they would assimilate all they had seen and be able to share "something of it" with us. Looking back over the stoppage meanwhile, both Valerie and I had the sensation of underpinning support from them of a spiritual kind, and the tape she put in play was somewhat appropriate near its end where, with her voice's warmth, the prayer ran:

"For Thy help with the problems of our daily lives, for the blessing of this knowledge, and for the service we receive from Thy loving spiritual messengers, we thank Thee. May we have a purer and gentler understanding of our human companions, and may the glory of the Presence bless and fill our service with joy and thanks to Thee."

She wanted us to strive for such an understanding of Peter. There and then however the only understanding in me was that he had gone, so palpable to sentience was his character. Even before my eyes opened I knew he had left the body, and sure enough it had become a mere ghost.

We anticipated David, who after all was the deputy-in-charge having said "we must restart" and promising to share their news. But on its way into the channel was a Brian-like aura, if less corporeal – as he had felt last week. Offhand I did a check:

"Is that you Brian?"

"You don't recognise me any more?" he spoke up, by then growing more distinct and in control. Valerie's excuse was down to earth:

"Well we do really, but it's so long since we've been in contact apart from that day you returned."

"Yes I'm really sorry, but you know what we have been doing. It'll be hard for David tonight. We're all here now though."

Puzzled by the David mention I bid him on.

"What can you tell us Brian?"

"We're going to tell you some of the plan for us all. You see, inwardly we're all together. And just as you and Valerie interact with each other and us on your plane, so it will be forever in an inward sense, whatever happens there. Time, on the other hand, is not short for any one individual but for us as a group, because even though the work that we do is important we need to uplift ourselves as a group in order to progress."

"Do you mean there's a time limit?" asked Valerie.

"There isn't an overall time limit of course, but we have much to do in the short time that you have on earth. David is going to leave us and return to your plane shortly. It is imperative that he does this. He has elected to do it for the good of the Whole. You will find your communications with us more frequent, although we shall have more trouble coming through because we are now further from your plane."

"You've moved up in consciousness?" she inferred.

"That's hard for me to answer in those terms. The point we wish to emphasise is that the team you have formed to work with us in rescue must be more stable."

"Yes, you said we'd know who would be best for it because we are not separate from you."

"That is why your team must be made up of members who have been picked by both of you. We cannot do anything but guide you in your choice."

Here she erased from the tape her complaint about Robert being out of step with us during rescue, also his absence twice, and got the reply:

"Robert should remain. However he will not do so. He will move away from you."

"In that case," said she, "it's no good him sitting with us even till then is it? Because there must be people who will definitely stay mustn't there?"

"It is of course much better for your work if you have people who will be with you permanently."

I was more interested in the two meant to join us.

"Brian, when you spoke of two people missing, did you know because they're part of Us?"

"Yes."

"And they'll just come into our surroundings?"

"Yes but you will know them inwardly."

"Do we already know them outwardly?"

"One of them, yes."

355

"So we have to wait and they'll become obvious?"

"Yes. It is not permitted for us to tell you their names, only to guide you in your choice, because as I have said, the team must be made up of people chosen by both of you."

"Do you think it's wise for young J.M to operate here as well as in the new proposal for my Broadwater class?"

"He must stay until your team is complete. I know that you have people in mind for it. Jules, you can help me to become stronger."

I did so and he went on:

"But do be careful that you do not play with those who are in the circle of dark forces."

Valerie perked up immediately.

"Are you thinking of anybody in particular?"

"You know to whom I refer."

I was unsure whether we did, unless he meant the Baha'is whom we hadn't seen in that context. Another tape erasure here might indicate his having given us some hint, though one since forgotten. At the time I was evidently satisfied with it, promising him we would be careful, and Valerie changed subject to that person of the "two" whom we were said to know already in an outward sense. She had a candidate up front.

"It's rather awkward because Betty has always very much wanted to join us in the work, and although we were told in the beginning that this was not advisable, when I asked again it sounded as if David would have the final word."

"David will be with Us for a while. Do remember that it is of utmost importance to have unity, not just for your team's sake but for our development as a Whole. If you feel this member is necessary then you must invite her, but she will not stay for many evenings."

His sterner message, taken by me to warn her that in rescue Betty would pose a vulnerable security risk and pretty soon feel the pinch, at last made Valerie drop the issue for good.

"Oh I see. Now, don't you think we should have more than one rescue session per week? I mean it seems so little when there are so many in need of help."

"We are going to continue with one, but we hope to have at least two other evenings devoted to what we call Illumination. This will also be developed as an idea amongst yourselves."

"We can ask people to listen to you can we?"

"You must wait and see. It is better for us all if you come to the idea in your own way."

"So next Friday," I advanced, "will have the usual rescue team and from there we'll see what happens. As David is going, will you be the main control or will someone be joining you?"

"One will be joining us."

This possible sixth of The Seven I put aside.

"And will John and Orlando stay in place? They're here now I think."

"Yes, John is beside you. I'll move over for him."

"Okay Brian, thanks for explaining."

John was not the eager incomer we used to know. Although identifiable he was mellowish, and his "Good evening friends" carried a certain sadness. Valerie's notice of it switched to the time gap.

"We haven't spoken to you properly for ages John!"

"No it does seem a long time doesn't it? Do you want to talk about your young friend?"

"Oh yes, J.M.," I said. "Alright, how's it going?"

Under review of course was their attempt, backed by the Golden Ones, to speak through J.M. direct to the earthbound like David had done through Peter, also to generate further channels and supportive teams for that purpose. But the launch was held up.

"Frankly," said John, "I don't know if we can use much more time waiting for this one to develop. It may be that we shall send a medium to you whom we can work with easily, and then we could get that project going in a matter of weeks."

I accepted the solution, Valerie showing interest.

"Would this mean that Peter will be able to talk to you at last through a channel?"

"Yes. Anyway you've both heard the news?"

"We have," I replied, not quite catching his drift.

"Good. There is so much ahead for us, but we shall miss David. It's more difficult coming through tonight because we have many present with us to guide him, and our vibrations are higher. I want you to listen to him now. God bless."

All at once the bare fact hit us that David was about to leave our scene altogether and return to earth. We had been so hooked into our own corner that its import had passed us by. As it took effect there came to mind a rush collage of this large-bodied, fair-haired, gentle and endearing man who, nearest to Philip in rank, had originally broached their request that we do rescue with them. Thereafter he had been master of ceremonies, the mainstay and provider of our work. He had counselled us and become an invisible friend, offering succour with much patience. A former watercolour painter from Bristol, he had tried to help Valerie break new ground in her art, and had shared with pride a verbal picture of his work tending the community children. Above these things, and behind his attributes of courtesy and shy reserve there lay, we felt, a particular integrity of purpose which formed the unseen structure, his very keystone.

Such was Valerie's mental arrest over his actually going that she forgot to turn up the recording level for him as he moved in with deliberation and began softly to speak. Little I believe is lost however of what were now his farewell words to us. Step by step they grew more choked, uneven, with a difficult pause here and there.

"… My decision to return is taken sadly, as all decisions that take one away from one's friends must be. But as the Channel made his decision for the eventual benefit and uplift of us all, so I have been advised and helped to make mine. I already have my parentage. This will be the last time for a good many years that I shall be able to speak with you. I will spend many years on your plane, so I will not be home until you are already here."

"That," I said, "will be a momentous hour."

"Yes. Perhaps for the first time I realise the wisdom of not knowing one's previous lives on your plane. It would be awfully hard to bear I should think. The relative ease of making such a decision, not only for my sake but for all our sakes, rather surprised me at first, for I had not given it much thought. Now I find it hurries forward," he quavered, a sob rising. "I shall miss you both very much my dear friends … the conversations we've had. Leaving you for such a long … period is hard enough for me to grasp let alone bear. May you always walk in the light, and may we all … through our work and sacrifice attain the evolvement we aspire to. Remember we are all built from love … and although groups are all equal under Our Father, I always like to feel that ours is very special to each of us. God be with you Jules, in your work. God be with you Valerie … "

"May our every blessing," she said, "be yours too David. We'll think of you always with love."

"Goodbye my dear friends … "

With that, and tears streaming down the channel's face, he slipped out. The silence between us was like a sacrament. As we sat there gaping, amid the hushed sounds of the summer night, any comment would have seemed almost a profanation.

At once this had deepened our sense of involvement with The Seven. If outwardly they were more ethereal, inwardly they were somehow more substantial. It was a feeling from which we could better understand Brian's claim that we knew or had been "told" already of their group event. Perhaps to a small degree we were "drawn in among them", Valerie put to me, our leaven having come from the "collective consciousness".

Peter's waking face was blankly confounded to find the tears of human sentiment down it, knowing they were not self-made. Told the reason he thought it so beyond his paradigm that an extra measure was added to his new belief in them. He also reported "release" in allowing us the session, release from an untraced "nagging hunch off and on" these past days that he had made some oversight. His association of it with business, a client's order not written out maybe, was startled at my quote from David about his being "informed as to when" they would like him to channel. Now believing The Seven responsible instead of any failure toward the shop, his mind made it "really them".

We let these bonuses reinforce a brighter outlook, though across that future with him the warning shadow had fallen. His fickleness would need to be handled with care. In terms of the work it seemed we were to expect a streamlining of attitude and personnel. People would go, people would come, they said. There was little we could say to each other, or do. We knew too little and too much. Hopes and fears shuttled to and fro; except that is, about one thing which we knew very well. Indeed, Valerie's promise to David would bear out through the years. We were to think of him always with love. Dear David: patient, caring, earnest, quiet as a pool in a wood.

ACKNOWLEDGEMENTS

My heartfelt gratitude goes to Linda McVan for her editorial suggestions, crucial work in preparation of this volume, and her patient support.

Acknowledgements also go to Paul Beard for his advice and encouragement, and to Keith Ellis for permission to quote from Paul's book, Living On.

COMING IN VOLUME TWO

Brian takes over control of rescue work with brisk educational talks ★ Also explains their journey to the record ★ Takes team to hellish regions ★ Tussles and attacks ★ Intruders try seizing channel ★ Thorny debate with Brian ★ Valerie & Robert clash ★ Rajneesh issue flares up ★ Philip's answer ★ Brian opens Peter to hear him ★ More confusion at the rescue ★ Peter's astral self intervenes ★ His ego shocked to see earthbound ★ Brian talks on group soul, reincarnation, soul path, and drugs ★ 6th member of Seven enters work powerfully ★ Robert has to leave, joins Rajneesh ★ Team become celebrities in astral church ★ Peter's shop in trouble, his suicide attempt, hospital ★ J.M. leaves for India ★ The Seven move higher ★ Jules goes to India for Valerie ★ The Seven speak as one about ongoing plan ★ Group's "Guardian Lord" gives Peter stern warning ★ Jules returns ★ Valerie grows ill.....

Does the second Channel appear as predicted and remember her role? ★ Do those many workers who stood behind The Seven set a model for the plan's final phase? ★ Can T.E. Lawrence and Col. "H" Jones really be fostering it? And will members on earth recognise their own role?

WARNING
IT MUST BE EMPHASISED THAT RESCUE WORK OF ANY KIND IS DANGEROUS AND DEFINITELY INADVISABLE FOR MOST PEOPLE